A Pictorial History
of American Mining

A Pictorial History of American Mining

The Adventure and Drama of Finding
and Extracting Nature's Wealth from
the Earth, from Pre-Columbian Times
to the Present

by Howard N. and Lucille L. Sloane

CROWN PUBLISHERS, INC.   NEW YORK

To Amy, Gary, Jeffrey, Karen, and Wendy

Acknowledgments

The authors gratefully acknowledge the following individuals and organizations for assisting us with photographs and information: A. J. Industries, Alabama Geological Survey, Alaska Travel Service, University of Alaska Museum, American Metal Climax, Inc., American Smelting and Refining Company, American Zinc Company of Tennessee, American Zinc Institute, Anaconda Copper Company, Arizona Department of Library and Archives, Arizona Pioneers Historical Society, E. W. Arndt, Ayrshire Collieries Corporation, Bell and Zoller Coal Company, Bethlehem Steel Company, Alfred E. Birdsey, Bituminous Coal Institute, Don Bloch, William Browning, Bucyrus Erie Company, Bunker Hill Company, Preston H. Burnett, C. F. & I. Steel Corporation, California Department of Parks and Recreation, California Division of Mines and Geology, California State Library, Calumet and Hecla, Carey Salt Company, Carlin Gold Mine, Carnegie-Illinois Steel Corporation, Caterpillar Tractor Company, Central Nevada Newspapers, Chesapeake and Ohio Railway, Chester County (Pa.) Historical Society, Collectors' Center (Denver, Colorado), Colorado Bureau of Mines, Colorado Department of Public Relations, Colorado Division of State Archives and Public Records, Colorado School of Mines, State Historical Society of Colorado, Columbus (Ohio) *Daily News,* Consolidated Coal Company, Cooley Gravel Company, Dahlonega (Ga.) Courthouse Gold Museum, William Culp Darrah Stereo Collection, Deadwood (S.D.) Chamber of Commerce, Dr. Robert Delany, Denver Equipment Company, Denver Public Library Western Collection, Detroit *News,* Diamond Crystal Salt Company, Dow Chemical Company, E. E. Dowell, Rev. Ed J. Dowling, S.J., Dr. Roy W. Drier, E. I. duPont de Nemours Photo Library, Duval Corporation, Eagle-Picher Industries, Inc., Guy L. V. Emerson, Florida Development Commission, Florida Division of Geology Library, Florida Phosphate Council, Florida Publishing Company Historical Archives, Foote Mineral Company, Free Library of Philadelphia Print and Picture Department, Freeport Sulphur Company, Alys Freeze, F. M. Genty, Georgia Geological Survey, Georgia Historical Commission, A. D. Gill, Gilpin County (Col.) Chamber of Commerce, William R. Graham, Grants (N.M.) Chamber of Commerce, Grass Valley (Cal.) Chamber of Commerce, Grass Valley (Cal.) Mining Exhibit, Greenlee County (Ariz.) Chamber of Commerce, Marvin and Ruth Gregory Historical Collection, Gulf Oil Company, *Harper's,* Phil Harris, Brooks Hawley, Homestake Mining Company, Homestake-Sapin Partners, Hopewell Village National Historic Site, Don Howe, Frank Hrabley, Idaho Bureau of Mines and Geology, Idaho State Historical Society, Idarado Mining Company, Illinois Division of Parks, Illinois State Historical Library, Indiana Coal Producers Association, Indiana Geological Survey, Indiana Historical Bureau (State Library), Indiana Limestone Institute, Inland Steel Company, Inspiration Consolidated Copper Company, International Minerals and Chemical Corporation, International Salt Company, Iowa Department of Mines and Minerals, George Jackson, H. M. Jacob, Jeffrey Manufacturing Company, Jerome (Ariz.) Historical Society, Jerome (Ariz.) State Historical Park, Johns-Manville Corporation, Joy Manufacturing Company, Kansas Department of Economic Development, Kansas State Historical Society, K. E. Kefauver, Kennecott Copper Company, Kentucky Historical Society Library, Kerr-McGee Corporation, Koppers Company, Inc. – Hardinge Division, Lake Carriers Association, Rex Lauck, Leslie's Miscellaneous Editions, Library of Congress, Duncan MacDonald, Machinery Center, Inc., Mackay School of Mines University of Nevada, J. N. Macomb, Jr., Magma Copper Company, Maine Historical Society, J. H. Maize, Harriet Malloy, Marquette County (Mich.) Historical Society, Fred and Jo Mazulla, Michigan Bell Telephone Company, Michigan Conservation Department, Michigan Historical Commission, Earl D. Miller, Milwaukee Public Museum, Missouri Division of Geological Survey and Water Resources, Missouri State Historical Society, Charles E. Mohr, Montana Bureau of Mines and Geology, Montana Chamber of Commerce, Montana Highway Commission, Montana Historical Society, Morton Salt Company, Clarice Mullins, Museum of the American Indian Heye Foundation, NASA, National Coal Association, National Lead Company, National Mine Service Company, National Park Concessions, Inc., National Park Service, Nevada Historical Society, University of Nevada Mackay School of Mines, New Jersey Historical Society, New Mexico Bureau of Mines and Minerals, Museum of New Mexico, New Mexico Tourist Bureau, New York *Herald Tribune,* New York Public Library, New York State Museum and Science Service Geological Survey, Newmont Mining Company, North Carolina Department of Archives and History, Oakland (Cal.) Public Library, Buck O'Donnell, Ohio Historical Society, Oklahoma Geological Survey, Oklahoma Industrial Development and Park Department, University of Oklahoma, Old Ben Coal Company, Oregon Historical Society, Oregon State Department of Geology and Mineral Industries, Robert S. Palmer, Park City (Utah) Chamber of Commerce, Donald A. Parks, Peabody Coal Company, Miriam Peacock, Felix A. Peckham, Pennsylvania Historical and Museum Commission, Perlite Institute, Mrs. Mary Perry, Phelps Dodge Corporation, John T. Pierce, Placer County (Cal.) Museum, Public Service of Indiana, E. C. K. Read, Republic Steel Corporation, Reynolds Metals Company, Laverne B. Rollin, John D. Rompel, Ruggles Mining Company, Salt Institute, San Manuel Copper Corporation, George Schafer, Schuylkill County (Pa.) Historical Society, Shaft and Development Machines Company, J. R. Simplot Company, J. E. Smith Collection Courtesy of Heirs, C. Owen Smithers, Smithsonian Institution, Smithsonian Office of Anthropology Bureau of American Ethnology, South Dakota State Historical Society, John Spence, William Spora, Standard Oil Company (N.J.), William J. Stephenson, Suburban Photo Service (Phila.), Tennessee State Library and Archives, Texas Gulf Sulphur Company, Union Carbide Company (Union Carbide Nuclear), *United Mine Workers Journal,* United Park City Mines, U.S. Borax and Chemical Corporation, U.S. Bureau of Land Management, U.S. Bureau of Mines, U.S. Forest Service, U.S. Gypsum Company, U.S. Steel Corporation, Utah State Historical Society, Utah Travel Council, William Varnedoe, Jr., Virginia Chamber of Commerce, W. P. Visick, Washington Department of Natural Resources, University of Washington Libraries, University of Washington Press, H. C. Weed, Wells Fargo Bank, West Virginia Department of Archives and History, Western Nuclear Corporation, Western Ways Features, Westinghouse Air Brake Company, White Pass and Yukon Route, White Pine Copper Company, Brian Wilson, Frank Winebrenner, Hamilton Winslow, World Wide Photos, Wyoming State Archives and Historical Department (and Stimson Collection), University of Wyoming.

Many of the Alaskan pictures that appear in this book were taken by Eric A. Hegg, a professional photographer who rushed north in 1897 to make a remarkable photographic record. His pictures were sent to the authors from different sources, principally from the University of Washington (Audio-Visual Services) and the University of Washington Press, which published a collection of Hegg's pictures in their fine book, *One Man's Gold Rush,* with text by Murray Morgan. Wherever possible, proper credit has been given, and any omissions are either inadvertent or the result of ambiguity.

Because of their special efforts we particularly would like to thank the following individuals: Mrs. J. D. Anthony who supplied photos and history of Dahlonega, Georgia; William Culp Darrah who sent hundreds of his valuable stereos for our selection; Mrs. Marvin (Ruth) Gregory who supplied information and valuable personal photos from her collection; Dr. John N. Hoffman, Smithsonian Institution, who selected many interesting and useful photos from his files; Ray Koernschild, Suburban Photo Service, Philadelphia, Pa., who developed many of the rephotographed pictures with great attention to detail and clarity; John La Font who supplied unusual photographs and offbeat history of Creede, Colorado; Robert F. Looney, Free Library of Philadelphia, who researched many old photographs and provided facilities for photographing old prints; Carrie McLain who sent us an unusual collection of her Nome, Alaska, pictures; Robert W. Morse, University of Washington, who supplied many of the Hegg Alaskan pictures; Bluford W. Muir, Chief Photo Section, U.S. Forest Service, who opened his files for our selection and procured many special pictures that we requested; H. W. C. Prommel who sent photos and information on Colorado mining and persuaded many of his friends to do the same; Irene Simpson, Wells Fargo Bank, who generously provided many mining pictures of the old West; R. O. Swenarton, Chief, Office of Mineral Information, U.S. Bureau of Mines, who secured Bureau photos from many sections of the U.S. and provided the Appalachian coal pictures; and Jerry Vineyard who supplied the Missouri and Tri-State photos and wrote many of the captions. Barbara Paliscak deserves our thanks for many tedious hours of typing and retyping; as does Bruce C. Sloane who reviewed the geology; and Herbert Michelman of Crown Publishers, Inc., who suggested that we convert our idea of a biographical history of mining to a pictorial one, for which we are grateful. Paul Nadan, also of Crown Publishers, Inc., deserves our special thanks for his editing of the text and photo captions, for his suggestions in the arrangement of this volume, and for his painstaking attention to detail.

HOWARD N. SLOANE
LUCILLE L. SLOANE

Contents

Preface

In compiling this volume, we have excluded those minerals that are so minimally mined as to offer no historical or economic background, those derived as a processing by-product, and those mined outside the United States. Also excluded are gem stones, precious and semiprecious, because of their interest principally to geologists and rock hunters. However, we have attempted to include in one book what obviously could be the history of many industries. Thousands of books have been published on mining; ours is intended as a representative word-and-picture history of mining in the United States in its many aspects, from the beginning to the present.

Blood of the Hills

The veins of the hills are deep and old,
The blood of the hills is colored gold.
The blood of the hills has seeped and spread,
Through shifting gully and riverbed.
Till, over the face of the old terrain,
The blood of the hills has left its stain.

Heavy with gold the rivers moved
Through bottomland that they gouged and grooved.
And, everywhere that a river ran,
Men have followed with sluice and pan.
Men have gambled and won and lost
On every sandbar a river crossed.
But in the struggle have somehow learned
That blood of the hills is dearly earned,

The blood of the hills is deep and old
But deeper yet is man's love for gold
And on men searching the old terrains
The blood of the hills has left its stains.

—HELEN HOWLAND PROMMEL

Pre-Columbian Mining

"Mining" is the *extraction* of mineral-, chemical-, or metallic-bearing material from rock, soil, or water, below ground, on the surface, or from fresh- or salt-water bodies.

In considering pre-Columbian mining, with a few important exceptions, we have ignored the stone implements of the "Old Stone Industries," and the artifacts of these cultures found profusely throughout the United States. These points, pendants, arrowheads, tools, etc., in general, were not quarried but formed from material lying on the surface of the earth.

THE "OLD COPPER CULTURE"

Our ancestral American inhabitants mined salt in typical underground tunnels; dug copper in open pits; quarried flint, turquoise, and other hard rock substances from rock on the surface of the ground, on cliffs, in exposed strata, and in caves.

Archeologists cannot agree positively on the antiquity of American mining, but evidence suggests that it dates from the "Old Copper Culture" of the upper Great Lakes, particularly around Michigan

and Wisconsin. Large spear or lance points, knives, gouges, axes, adzes, chisels, harpoon heads, fishhooks, awls, and various ornaments made from copper nuggets have been found here. These nuggets were probably quarried from the Michigan traprocks of Isle Royale and Keweenaw Peninsula or from masses of copper along the shore and in the bedrock. Among the thousands of copper pits here, many were fifteen to twenty feet deep. Since we have no evidence to indicate that the inhabitants had any knowledge of smelting processes, we are fairly certain that the artifacts were made by hammering the copper nuggets, possibly after heating them in an open fire to increase their malleability.

Samples of wood from Wisconsin's Oconto Site tested at the University of Chicago for radiocarbon dating revealed an age of $5,600 \pm 600$ years. Samples from other locations produced an age of $7,150 \pm 600$ years. In a 1962 paper, James B. Griffin of the University of Michigan's Museum of Anthropology, claims that between 2500 and 1200 B.C. the Oconto Site was covered by the lake waters of the Michigan Basin, which would therefore have contaminated the results of the radiocarbon dating. He believes that the University of Chicago dates are too early and that Oconto should be dated at about 1000 B.C. According to Griffin, most copper specimens from the Great Lakes area were made between 2000 and 1000 B.C., none before 3000 B.C. On the other hand, both Professor Roy Ward Drier and Octave Joseph Du Temple believe that samples of charcoal from the bottom of two Isle Royale pits indicate an age of approximately 3,500 to 4,000 years ago. From whatever evidence we have, whatever their ages, these specimens represent one of the earliest forms of mining in the United States. According to Griffin, the copper was mined by means of hammerstones, wedges, and fire. The fire heated the surrounding rock, which was then abruptly fractured by the application of cold water. Copper implements commonly found in eastern Wisconsin were traded by aborigines from the Northern Plain states and Canada and subsequently found

J. C. Tidball's 1855 engraving of an ancient Indian working his copper mine on Lake Superior. *Library of Congress*

1

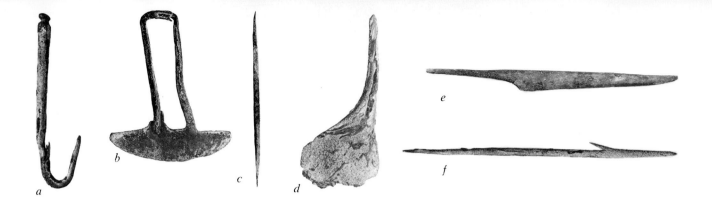

Ancient copper tools found in Wisconsin: (*a*) fishhook (note the groove at top for attaching a sinew line); (*b*) rare crescent used for chopping; a repair is visible at the base of the left side of the prong; (*c*) possible surgical instrument for abscesses or for puncturing holes in hides; (*d*) spatula, though probably a "knife" for cutting skins for clothes or even for cutting ornaments; (*e*) one of the largest of the knife implements found— 17½ inches. The tank, or handle, end was probably wound with rawhide; (*f*) this harpoon was used for spearing sturgeon, muskellunge, and other large fish. *Milwaukee Public Museum*

their way into New York and New England as well as into central Ohio, Illinois, and southeast of Lake Superior's shores.

THE MOUND BUILDERS

Our search for copper takes us to the many Ohio and Illinois sites where Indian burial mounds have revealed much information about the life of the mound builders. The Hopewell Indians occupied the area between 300 B.C. and A.D. 600, and the Fort Ancient Indians were there between A.D. 1200 and 1630. The Hopewells built huge "forts," digging earth and carrying limestone slabs to construct walls four to twenty-three feet high. They buried their dead within these walls beneath mounds, and erected crescent-shaped earth walls and laid stone pavements to form settings for religious and social ceremonies. Since 1893 archeological explorations have been un-

covering pottery, tools, and ornaments, revealing an interesting agricultural society. Corn, squash, and beans were grown, and tobacco, smoked in bird- or animal-shaped pipes. The Hopewells were traders. Bear teeth and claws, obsidian from the Rocky Mountains, shark teeth from the Atlantic Coast, shells from the Gulf of Mexico, copper from the Lake Superior region, and mica from the Carolinas have all been found in mounds in such shapes as ear spools, breastplates, bracelets, headdresses, and other ceremonial objects. Indian mounds are common throughout the Midwest.

One of the most important group of mounds was excavated near Cartersville, Georgia, beginning in 1953. Known as the Etowah Mounds, the area occupies about forty acres surrounded by a large moat that runs into the Etowah River. The site was a village ceremonial center from about A.D. 800 to 1550. Burial pits opened here often contained several skeletons, each usually accompanied by a copper celt. Accompanying several of the bodies, the skulls of which were usually covered with a rectangular

Pieces of copper carefully pieced together to reform a copper decoration from Etowah Mounds. *Georgia Historical Commission*

These ancient Indian ceremonial mounds were a valuable source of artifacts that provided clues to the history of their time. This one is known as Serpent Mound, in Adams County, Ohio. *Ohio Historical Society*

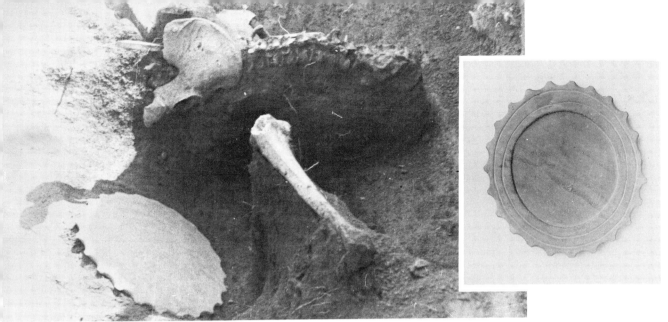

Inset: This sophisticated slate palette was uncovered at the Etowah Mounds burial site together with iron and lead ores that the natives used as pigments for ceremonial body painting. It is possible that the palette was used to hold the pigments. In the central photograph it is seen as it was found lying overturned in the site. The bone on the right may well have participated in the original fashioning of the piece. *Georgia Historical Commission*

sheet of copper, were polished stone disks with scalloped edges. Lumps of graphite and lead ore (galena) found on one of the disks indicate that these disks may have been used for the preparation of face or body paint. Each skull had its elaborate headdress of embossed copper cutouts. In addition, the mounds disclosed copper-covered beads, seed pearls, various tools, figured copper plates, and copper axes. A number of Georgia marble statues were excavated along with copper flints and knives, mica and copper ornaments, copper-covered rattles, and a copper headdress with horns.

A detailed study of nine Etowah copper specimens was made by Vernon J. Hurst and Lewis H. Larson, Jr., in 1957. Physical, chemical, and spectrographic analyses revealed that four of the specimens were, more or less, from local Georgia native copper deposits, one from a North Carolina deposit, three from Michigan, and one a native copper nugget from Santa Rita, New Mexico. Similar artifact-containing mounds have been found in other southern states, especially Alabama.

MISSOURI IRON MINERS

One of the most remarkable discoveries of underground mining by pre-Columbian aborigines

The Great Circle and Octagon, prehistoric Indian earth-works, Newark. *Ohio Historical Society*

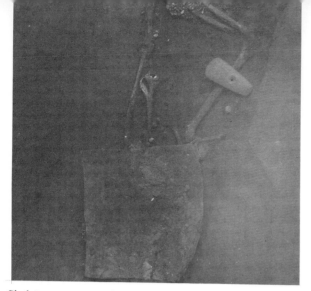

Skeleton uncovered at the cult burials at Etowah Mounds. A rectangular sheet of copper covers the skull. *Georgia Historical Commission*

Figured copper plate of a human figure from Mound C at Etowah Mounds. *Smithsonian Office of Anthropology, Bureau of American Ethnology Collection*

occurred in 1903 in an iron mine near Leslie, Franklin County, Missouri. The early inhabitants had removed the iron ore from a space about 100 feet wide, 100 feet long, and between fifteen and twenty feet deep. These ancients had honeycombed the ore body with passageways and partially filled galleries, many large enough to accommodate standing workmen. In the debris of the old excavations, more than 1,000 stone implements were found, consisting mainly of stone masses weighing from one to five pounds, all roughly grooved or notched for attaching handles. The large number of these implements in-

Figure carved from Georgia marble found in the Etowah Mounds. When unearthed, this male and a female figure were covered with paint—ears red, eyes white, other portions black, red, or white. *Georgia Historical Commission*

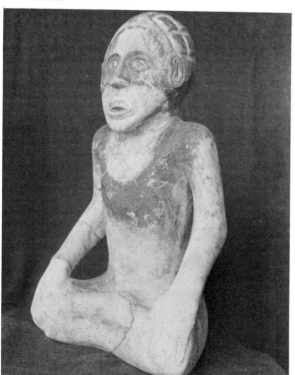

dicated the extent of the operations. Investigators discovered the exposed ore surfaces to be a brilliant red, and those handling the material soon became smeared with red oxide that required a number of washings to remove. Very probably the red and yellow oxides were mined for paints rather than for their metallic value.

THE PUEBLO INDIANS

Mining was not unknown to the Pueblo inhabitants of the Southwest who mined salt, coal, and turquoise, the latter a favorite of both ancient and modern Indians, and found only in the southwestern United States. This highly desirable stone, used as a medium of trade, was made into mosaic inlays for bone, stone, shell, and wood objects, as well as fabricated into beads and pendants. Ancient turquoise mines have been found in Colorado following the New Mexico borderline, New Mexico, Arizona, California (near the Nevada line), and Nevada. Most of these deposits were quarries, with the turquoise appearing in fissures and joint planes in hard crystalline rock, which the Indians mined with crudely shaped deerhorn mauls and picks. Like copper, the turquoise was first heated by fire, the sudden pouring of cold water over the heated rock caused it to crack, releasing, though often damaging, the turquoise. Los Cerrillos, New Mexico, was the largest turquoise area, where one mine was excavated to a pit 200 feet deep and more than 300 feet wide. Tunnels were sometimes dug twenty or thirty feet into the rock.

THE HOPI INDIANS

As for coal, the only prehistoric coal mines known in the United States were in the sandstones of Arizona, where the Hopi Indians around A.D. 1300 learned to burn the black rock they found in beds of various thicknesses. The Hopis used coal for baking pottery. Evidence of their coal mines is so extensive it would seem each family had its own coal deposit. Almost four centuries later, in 1697, Fray Agustin de Vetancurt wrote about the mission at Awatobi, Arizona, noting that the Hopis had "stones which served for coal but the smoke is noxious in its strength." Some of these mines are still worked today.

Footprint of an ancient Indian miner embedded in the dirt at Mammoth Cave National Park. *National Park Service*

MAMMOTH CAVE

A striking example of ancient mining was discovered in 1935 by two Mammoth Cave guides, Grover Campbell and Lyman Cutliff, while crawling on a high ledge two miles in. Odd scratch marks along a section of gypsum-covered wall had aroused their curiosity. Squeezing through a narrow passageway between the large rocks, Campbell's hand, to his amazement, had suddenly come to rest on the head of a mummy, its body partly hidden beneath a huge slab of rock. Recognizing the importance of their discovery, they left it undisturbed, and Dr. Alonzo W. Pond was rushed to the scene. Dr. Pond's impressions were recorded in *Natural History* in 1937:

Many years of archaeological exploration on four continents had given me more than my share of "firsts," but nothing gave me the thrill I experienced as I sat on that narrow ledge in Mammoth Cave with the discoverers and saw with my own eyes the perfectly preserved body of that prehistoric miner trapped at his work centuries ago.

Nothing had been disturbed. The ledge was covered with loose, dry sand over which had settled fine, black soot from the torches of ancient and modern "cavers." In the tragic tableau before us, time had stopped centuries ago. With the event of death and the subsequent drying of the man's body the scene had remained unchanged. Here was preserved one of the most complete chapters in the life of prehistoric peoples. . . .

It seems that the ancient explorer had been trapped, face down, under a block of limestone weighing between six and seven tons, but that part of his body was exposed, indicating that perhaps the victim had not been killed instantly by the rock fall but had died a lingering death. Careful examination of the surrounding sand disclosed two bundles of oak sticks tied with grass, a small piece of a gourd, a hickory nut, a bundle of reed, and some excreta.

Dr. Pond was puzzled by the scarring and scratching of the gypsum-covered walls wherever they could be reached on ledges, crevices, and crawlways. He was puzzled by the blunt-edged sticks and the worn-down pieces of stone, and the mussel shells. It was evident that the miner had come to gather the gypsum, possibly for medicinal value, or as a love potion, or to make white paint. When the six-ton rock was raised, "Lost John's" complete story was revealed.

Dr. Pond concludes:

For two miles he had wandered through the majestic passages of the great cavern, a puny soul wandering in eternity, his footsteps guided by the fitful, yellow glare of a reed torch. Through tortuous rock falls he had clambered where even his precious bundle of torches was a burden. His faith in the sacredness of the tribal need for gypsum, precious ceremonial paint of the ancestors, had driven him on through the silence.

At last he was ready. He adjusted the folds of his fiber blanket across his hips, knotted it in front and drew a large part of it over his chest, biblike. Cautiously he crawled under a great block of limestone that had lain for centuries on the steep ledge. He knelt on the loose sand of the ledge. With a large chunk of limestone he started to chip away the gypsum. His position was cramped, awkward. He moved his left foot for greater comfort; it dislodged a small key stone beneath that huge block of limestone!

An agonized scream of terror shattered the cavern's stillness! A few pebbles rattled down over the ledge to the cave floor. The reed fire flared up and flickered out. Silence and the blackness of eternity descended again on the great cave. Death had posed a tableau of prehistoric man's intimate daily life. The strange chemistry of the cave began the process of preservation. A rat gnawed a little of the body, then left its job unfinished. Other gypsum miners worked on a higher ledge. Sand from their diggings trickled down with hour-glass

Mummy of Lost John, the Indian gypsum miner discovered in Mammoth Cave under a 6-ton block of limestone, which the National Park Service lifted with a crane. *National Park Service*

slowness to bury the ledge of tragedy. Eternal minutes in the cavern grew to years. Decades lengthened into centuries.

THE FIRST SALT MINES

Also in great demand was salt. Along the seacoast, natives knew that the sun would evaporate the water, leaving behind the ocean's salt. But inland salt wells, lakes, and mines were their greatest sources of supply. Ancient Indians often discovered salt by watching the wild animals, whose instinct would lead them to the salt springs and salt-imbedded rock for their salt licks. Georgia is only one of many places where a number of ancient salt springs have been found and salt was extracted from inland salt lakes such as Great Salt Lake and Zuni Salt Lake in Nevada. Rock salt, when it could be found, was considered a luxury. Underground salt mines in Arizona and Nevada have been studied extensively. The Arizona mine, tunneled on at least four different levels by the ancient Indians, was worked with conical stones used as picks. For lighting, the pre-Columbian salt miners used cedar-bark torches, as they often did in their caves. At St. Thomas, Nevada, the old

Descendants of the early Indians demonstrate salt mining by using stone hammers in Salt Cave Number 1, St. Thomas, Nevada, an ancient site. *Museum of the American Indian, Heye Foundation*

salt caverns extended for 100 yards or more into the sides of the mountain. When discovered, the floors were covered with debris, torches, and other refuse. Without roof supports, these tunnels often had collapsed. The mines were known to have been worked between A.D. 900 and 1200, possibly even hundreds of years earlier.

PIPESTONE

The Sioux Indians along the Mississippi quarried a stone known as catlinite—named for George Catlin, the American artist who painted Indians from 1829 to 1838. Actually, these quarries were controlled by the Dakota and Sioux since early historic times, but ancestors of the Iowa and Oto Indians may have even worked them, on a large scale, several hundred years before. Catlinite was used by the Indians to manufacture pipes, an important commodity in their rituals, symbolizing peace and war, distinguishing the pipes by the color of the feathers adorning them, red for war and white for peace. Today, the quarry area, in Minnesota, is known as Pipestone National Monument, about one mile north of the city of Pipestone.

EARLY URANIUM

The Navajo and Ute Indians who roamed the Colorado Plateau hundreds of years ago were the first to recognize the value of uranium. But their use was far different from the use of uranium today; they decorated their bodies with brilliant red and yellow war paint made from the ores that they found on the Plateau. This ore was powdery carnotite, from which uranium is obtained today.

FLINT

Of all the nonmetallics used for tools and implements, flint was the most important. Sometimes it was found loose on the ground, but more often in one- to six-inch seams in caves or cliffsides, where pieces were chipped off for arrow- or spearheads.

MERCURY

Still another metal ore was mined by the Santa Clara Indians, long before the white man arrived in California. This was mercury (quicksilver), found near the site of the yet undiscovered New Almaden Mine, the nation's most important mercury producer. The brilliant red cinnabar, the ore from which mercury is obtained, was used by the Indians as a ceremonial body paint.

The First 300 Years

THE SPANISH

In 1493 Christopher Columbus returned to Spain with more than gold ornaments—he was fired with visions of great wealth lying to the west. Though Columbus' four trips to the New World were confined to the West Indies, the natives spoke of unlimited gold and silver and other treasures to be had on the mainland. Such tales lured the Spanish conquerors to the Americas, North, South, and Central, as well as to the United States' Pacific Coast. Soon the fabulous gold and silver of the Aztecs and Incas filled the Madrid coffers of Isabella and Ferdinand. As for their quest north of New Spain (Mexico), they were doomed to disappointment. Juan Ponce de León on his trips to the mainland found neither gold nor the fountain of youth. Hernando de Soto in his exploration of much of the southeastern United States found no precious metals; his parties prospected in North Carolina, South Carolina, and Georgia. Cabeza de Vaca visited New Mexico and was told of copper deposits at Santa Rita, where a fort was established.

It is probable that they mined some copper but the Spaniards were really interested in gold. In the 1530s the lure of gold (and silver) was no less intense than it was for the California Forty-niners. As Spanish explorations spread farther west, rumors of the Seven Cities of Cibola (its streets reported to be "paved with gold and silver") prompted Nuño de Guzmán, president of the Governing Board of New Spain, to send out an expedition. It left in 1536, following reports by Cabeza de Vaca and his Negro, Esteván.

An old sketch of Santa Rita as it looked soon after the first visitor to New Mexico, Cabeza de Vaca, arrived in 1535. The fort in the lower center went up first. Note the stone towers, called "torreons," in front and behind the fort. *Museum of New Mexico*

In 1539, on orders of Francisco Vasques de Coronado, Esteván, accompanied by Friar Marcos de Niza, took his own expedition out. Niza thus became the first European to enter Arizona. But the expedition was a failure. Esteván was slain by Zuñi Pueblo (western New Mexico) Indians; Niza escaped, later to report even more imaginative tales of gold and silver utensils. It immediately provoked a full-scale expedition by Coronado himself. He started off with 250 horsemen, seventy Spanish footmen, and several hundred friendly Indians, plus baggage animals and herds of cattle. On discovering the Seven Cities of Cibola, Coronado found seven Indian villages without metallic riches of any kind, and he turned west into the Grand Canyon and the Rio Grande, where he wintered. Here he was re-inspired by tales of "Quivira," a land of gold. Looking for Quivira, Coronado entered Texas in the spring of 1541 and, with part of his force, penetrated central Kansas. But in 1542, he no longer believed in the fabulous streets of gold and silver, and returned to Mexico. All the time, the gold and silver (and copper) were beneath his feet—in the ground. Coronado's reports were so pessimistic as to discourage all others until forty years later, when Antonio de Espejo, upon rumors of silver, traveled up the Rio Grande River, past the San Francisco peaks, and down portions of the Colorado plateau to the Verde River. There he almost came upon the fabulously rich United Verde copper deposit—as close as Verde's overlying silver deposits.

Very likely Espejo, and Farfan, after him, while passing through Arizona were taken by Hopi Indians to see the diggings in the Verde Valley, now occupied by the city of Jerome. Original reports of metal in the valley made no mention of copper, unquestionably because ground water would bring to the surface copper's comparatively small silver content, distributing it in a thin icing on top. This may account for the many original silver mines that turned into copper bonanzas.

Spanish hopes were kept alive by the trickle of gold coming into Florida around 1565; Indians would load their canoes with gold-bearing sands collected from Appalachian Mountain streams and paddle in from the Carolinas to sell it.

We now turn to Padre Eusebio Francisco Kino, who in 1691 came to Arizona and spent twenty-five

7

Indians in the sixteenth century digging ditches in an Appalachian Mountain stream. The sand runs into the ditches, and is then collected and sifted for gold and silver. Later the ore was transported by canoe to Florida for sale to the Spaniards. *New York Public Library Picture Collection*

years exploring the country, but found no minerals. In 1705 he referred to rich silver ores being mined, probably in the Santa Rita Mountains area. In 1737 the first important strike was made. At Arizonac, near Nogales, lumps of pure native silver were found lying on the ground. Because the Spanish Crown did not characterize these workings as mines requiring the traditional one-fifth "royalty," it regarded the loosely found silver as treasure, meaning that it belonged entirely to the Spanish Crown. The early Arizonans, not relishing this, skimmed off the silver and disappeared. But Arizona mining did not amount to much until a century later.

THE BRITISH AND FRENCH

While the Spaniards were exploring and developing the southern United States, the British and French were making equal progress in the northern two-thirds. Like the Spaniards, the British were anxious to discover precious metals, but these included copper. King James had issued a charter to the London and Plymouth companies to explore and settle the new continent. It provided for the crown to receive one-fifth of the gold and silver and one-fifteenth of any copper that might be discovered. In the meantime, Captain John Smith, while exploring the Chickahominy River in his search for a waterway to the Pacific, found what he thought was gold and sent an entire shipload of mica and pyrite—"fool's gold"—to London. Nevertheless his "discovery" started a minor stampede. The British made good use of their find. A first iron-ore shipment left James-

town for England in the second year of James's charter. This—probably the first pig iron made from American ore—proved to be of a high quality after it was smelted. In 1620, 150 skilled workmen were sent to Jamestown to build an iron works, which lasted two years before it was destroyed in an Indian massacre. But the British interest would make itself known later. In 1719 the British House of Parliament would pass a resolution whose intent, because "the erection of manufactories in the colonies tended to lessen their dependency on Great Britain," would be to prohibit the construction of iron-manufacturing plants. Heavy American protest, however, was to prevent the resolution from becoming law. (In 1750 another attempt by the British Parliament was made to prohibit the erection of fabricating plants in the United States. It was among the grievances cited in the Declaration of Independence.)

All iron ore used in colonial days consisted of bog iron, or bog ore, a variety of limonite formed by decayed vegetable matter in streams or swamps acting upon iron salts in the water. A high organic content in sluggish water often provides an environment that permits a chemical reaction to pick up the iron in solution and carry it to the water surface, where it oxidizes or rusts. Such iron oxide is deposited on the banks of the streams or swamps and often accumulates in large chunks on the bases of trees or exposed rock. This material once was "mined," and often was found in chunks too large for one man to lift.

If the conditions of vegetation and sluggish waters have not been disturbed, bog iron can renew itself in about twenty years. In the 1700s it was used by most forges and furnaces which were built near bog-iron deposits surrounded by an ample wood supply to provide charcoal.

Meanwhile, though the British were eager to control the market, the French competed right from the beginning. It was a Frenchman, Pierre Le Sueur, who discovered lead mines on the Upper Mississippi in 1690, and Missouri's first lead mine was discovered when the territory belonged to France under a license granted to the Mississippi Company. One of its first discoveries was the Mine la Motte, which remained in operation over a hundred years.

The Franciscan and Jesuit missionaries were the first whites to explore the upper Great Lakes region. These men were as anxious to enhance the power of the French throne in the New World as they were to advance religion. Beginning in 1660, they constantly reported to the French throne stories of copper deposits they had heard about from friendly Indians. Probably the first white to see copper in this area was Father Claude Allouez, who actually found copper nuggets on the shores of Lake Superior in 1667. The Upper Peninsula of Lake Superior was explored by Jesuit Father Marquette, who reported an abundance of copper. However, actual mining would await Alexander Henry's operations in 1771 near the Forks of the Ontonagon.

By 1763 the British had taken over the territory. A mining company was organized in London and a group of English miners was sent to Michigan to begin mining operations. The men drove an adit into a clay bank and found a number of nuggets, called "float," a term applied to loose pieces of copper found on beaches and riverbeds, or in the soil. They began work in winter, and as spring warmed the earth, the frozen clay collapsed and operations were discontinued. A year later the miners tried drilling into the solid rock, following a vein of copper, but after progressing for about thirty feet this played out and it, too, was abandoned. No further mine work was ever attempted by the British. In 1783 the territory, along with Isle Royale, was ceded to the United States. Copper mining on the Keweenaw Peninsula would await Douglass Houghton's 1830 arrival in Detroit to join the Schoolcraft expedition.

But before the British had vacated the Great Lakes area, lead mines had commenced operations in 1765 at Southampton, Massachusetts, (as they did in Columbia and Dutchess counties, New York). These were discontinued during the Revolutionary War. During this time, Benedict Arnold, in his campaigns through Lake Champlain into Canada, was in command of the Crown Point Fort. From here he sent a group of Negroes to dig iron ore at the Cheever Mine, near Port Henry, which had begun operations in 1766. The Cheever was operated by Major Philip Skene who shipped boatloads of ore to his forges at Skenesboro. The mine supplied Arnold with ore for warships and bateaux constructed at Whitehall, New York, including armor for the *Monitor,* and assorted cannon balls. The first naval battle of the Revolution supposedly utilized Cheever iron, which continued to flow for United States forces in 1812, 1845, and in the 1860s. (The hull of one of Arnold's boats, the *Philadelphia,* is in the Smithsonian Institution.)

ROCK SALT

One of the first industries established in the new world was rock-salt mining. The first post-Columbian mention of salt is credited to Father LeMoyne, a French Jesuit who obtained some in 1653 from New York's Indian salt springs.

Later, Daniel Boone's sons, Daniel M. and Nathan, operated a brine-boiling installation employing about eight men operating forty kettles near Boonesboro, Missouri. They produced about thirty bushels of salt a day, and shipped them down the Missouri River to St. Louis where they were sold for $2.00 to $2.50 each. Their business grew and they enlarged the operation to 120 kettles, keeping about twenty men busy making 100 bushels of salt a day. In 1811 the Boones sold their salt works, which remained in business some sixty-five years.

SALTPETER

It is a far cry from salt to saltpeter. About the only thing they have in common is the approximate date of their first use in the United States. The following is from an 1861 document:

The process of making Saltpetre from the earth of the limestone caves in the Southern Confederacy is so simple that any one residing in the neighborhood of a cave in a limestone rock—and nearly all the caves are in such rock—can without any expense make at least a few pounds of the salt every day, and with assistance could make it a very profitable business at a price which Government is now paying. To furnish the practical information required, in plain language, to such persons, so as to enable each one to add to the production of an article so indispensable to the military operations of our country, now struggling for its free existence, induces the writer to publish these notes; he would earnestly appeal to his countrymen who may live near any cave, to put themselves, if need be, to some inconvenience, in order to aid in the invaluable production.

. . . But the nitre is still in the earth, and it behooves us to extract it in time, before we commence to feel a pressure in this direction. It is true we are receiving daily from a few caves what would be considered a very large amount in ordinary times, but the times are extraordinary, and hence require extraordinary supplies; thus the individual who makes a pound of saltpetre each day, contributes in fact more to the ultimate success of his country, than if he shouldered his musket and marched with all his sons to the tented field.

Gunpowder is made of over three-fourth parts of nitre (purified saltpetre,) fourteen parts of charcoal and ten parts of sulphur, all by weight; hence the niter is much the largest portion of gunpowder material, requiring consequently the largest daily supply.

The above was extracted from a pamphlet published in 1861, entitled *Notes on Making Saltpetre from the Earth of the Caves* by Major George Washington Rains, Corps of Artillery and Ordnance, in charge of the Gunpowder Department, C.S.A. Major Rains details the processes for manufacturing saltpeter or niter even to the exact quantities and costs, including a section on refining saltpeter.

But Rains's story of saltpeter began in the United States about 140 years earlier. At about 1720, the pioneers had manufactured gunpowder from saltpeter, particularly around Virginia. Before he was inaugurated president, Thomas Jefferson published his *Notes on the State of Virginia,* describing the use of cave saltpeter for the manufacture of gunpowder during the Revolutionary War. During the war a great many caves were activated but the recovery and processing of saltpeter peaked during the War of 1812 when about 1,000 caves were mined as a result of the American supply being cut off by the British.

Prior to 1800, nitrate deposits were discovered in Mammoth Cave, Kentucky, derived from the droppings of hordes of bats that once lived there. Slaves and oxen removed the saltpeter, which was then shipped to New Orleans to be manufactured into gunpowder. Some 200 tons are estimated to have come out of the cave. When Henry Schoolcraft explored the Ozarks, he found many such saltpeter workings.

Sauta Cave, near the Georgia-Alabama border, is credited with arming *Old Ironsides* (the *U.S.S. Constitution*) with its saltpeter. Texas' Frio Cave

Old wooden tracks at saltpeter workings at Big Bone Cave, Tennessee. *William J. Stephenson*

A large saltpeter leaching vat from Big Bone Cave, Tennessee. *William J. Stephenson*

Mammoth Cave supplied United States troops with much of its saltpeter during the War of 1812. Note the wooden vats and pipelines. *Photo by W. Ray Scott, National Park Concessions, Inc.*

Mammoth Cave's wooden pipes carried water to saltpeter leaching vats. Note how they were connected by sharpening one end, not unlike a pencil. *Photo by W. Ray Scott, National Park Concessions, Inc.*

Oxcart tracks at Head of Millpond Cave, West Virginia.
C. E. Mohr

produced saltpeter for the Civil War and later the residue of guano was bagged for fertilizer. Halfway between the cave and San Antonio is Ney Cave, on the Ney brothers' ranch, whose family carried on saltpeter operations for generations. Relics of the old saltpeter workings abound in many of the caves, whose nitrates today also go into fertilizer, the coloring of fireworks, signal lights, and medicine.

PRECIOUS AND BASE METALS

Preceding the salt industry by some thirty years, Virginia mined lead as early as 1621, and in 1651 Governor John Winthrop received a license to work any mines of "lead, copper, or tin or any minerals at antimony, vitriol, black lead, alum, salt, saltspring, or any other of the like . . . to enjoy forever said mines, with the lands, woods, timber, and water within two or three miles of said mines." That was in addition to a special grant of mines or minerals found near Middletown, Connecticut, and it is possible that he opened the old Middletown Silver-Lead Mine; the exact date is unknown. Winthrop was also believed to have been involved in nickel and cobalt mines near Chester, Connecticut.

COLONIAL AND AMERICAN IRON

And in Delaware before 1661 there was an area named Iron Hill, where throughout the Colonial period, iron ore was mined in small quantities, occasionally more extensively. The Abbington Iron Works (1675) alone encompassed over 1,000 acres. By 1734 the iron works's forge and furnace were sold by the sheriff (the first true iron furnace is believed to be the one at Pennbrook, Massachusetts, built in 1702). The plant is mentioned in a deed of 1768; its ore pits became the property of an Abel Davis, who later bequeathed them to his heirs. About

a hundred years after its sale, meaningful mining operations resumed, which continued for fifty years.

Iron mining in New York began in the 1760s in the eastern section of the Adirondack Mountains, where, for the next forty years, many small iron works flourished. The flow of iron ore increased and larger plants were built; the first Catalan forge was operated in 1798 on the Saranac River, near Plattsburg.

Eighteenth-century Pennsylvania was not idle, as it had many small, locally owned iron enterprises utilizing hand methods. A number of these plants were furnaces, the beginning of Pennsylvania's successful steel industry. "Miners villages," generally self-contained communities, grew up around the plants, which often were remote from miners' sources of supply. The so-called "iron plantation" communities mined the ore, quarried the limestone, cut wood for charcoal, and prepared all the material required for smelting.

It had all begun in the 1730s when Peter Grubb mined these banks and acquired land along Furnace Creek. He built his furnace in 1742 and named it Cornwall after the English county of his ancestors. It remained in operation until 1883. After Grubb's death in 1754, the property passed to his sons but

Lead miner's bucket, from an old lead mine at Dubuque, Iowa, now in the Columbia Museum, Dubuque. The date is unknown, but it is undoubtedly from the late 1700s or very early 1800s. *Annals of Iowa*

A unique, well-preserved Colonial-Revolutionary iron furnace (1742–1883), open to the public at Cornwall, Lebanon County, Pennsylvania. Typical of the period, it was built into the side of a hill for ease in charging. The weighing room and charging platform, where the ingredients were fed into the furnace, were on the upper level. The casting room, the engines and machinery, and the air tanks for blowing air blasts into the furnace were at the base. The furnace was remodeled and enlarged in 1856–1857 when the present building was constructed. At the same time a new steam-driven blasting arrangement was installed, so loud in operation that it could be heard over the countryside for miles. The furnace worked ore from the nearby Cornwall Ore Banks, a rich early source. The Cornwall Furnace, which helped make Pennsylvania the leading American iron smelter, produced quantities of war material—from 1775 to the war's end. Most old furnaces have since disappeared, but Cornwall Furnace (Furnace Creek, Cornwall) remains intact as an important historic site. It was worked by Hessian prisoners-of-war, manufacturing forty-two cannon, among other munitions, for service during the Revolution. Washington and Lafayette are believed to have visited Cornwall during their encampment at Valley Forge. The Cornwall Ore Banks are now owned by the Bethlehem Steel Company. *Pennsylvania Historical and Museum Commission*

In 1880 these men were employed at the Cornwall Mine. The ore was simply shoveled into the carts by hand and pulled to the ironworks by horses. *Bethlehem Steel Corporation*

The Cornwall Ore Banks, one of the first iron deposits discovered in the United States. It was converted to open-pit mining by Bethlehem Steel. *Bethlehem Steel Corporation*

was eventually acquired by Robert Coleman who also owned the Hopewell and Coalbrook forges and the Elizabeth Furnace. Cornwall Furnace remained in the Coleman family until 1932 when a great-granddaughter gave it to the State of Pennsylvania.

But in 1838 the hot-blast method of smelting iron began, ending the use of charcoal-burning furnaces by mid-century. Only twelve of hundreds of charcoal furnaces remained, including the Hopewell, which would operate until 1883.

By the late 1700s Pennsylvania also had introduced strip mining, as did northern New Jersey when their iron pits were opened up in order to follow the ore veins. New Jersey started mining iron ore almost as soon as the settlers arrived. Forges already were being worked in 1713, securing iron ore locally, probably limonite (bog iron). Many furnaces were built in the 1750s and 1760s, and by 1784 eight blast furnaces and seventy-nine forges were in operation. Some forty years later one of the earliest iron mines in the United States was opened, the Schuyler Mine near Belleville. Its iron ore went into the first steam engine ever built in the United States, in 1793.

As for iron-ore outcroppings, these were principally magnetite, worked more extensively in New Jersey after 1800. As surface ores were removed, deposits were mined in open cuts, leaving trenches sometimes 100 feet deep, making it more practical for shaft mining. The Mount Hope mines near Rockaway, New Jersey, were such examples; in the Mount Hope Blue Mine, in operation from about 1771, the ore was reached from two inclined planes that descended about 100 feet. The workings were extended underground only sometime before 1855, and the mine remained in operation well into the twentieth century.

In the meantime, iron mining developed and new plants were built in New Jersey's northwest,

Typical of the old ironworks once operated in Delaware is this undated illustration of the Tasker Iron Works at New Castle. Just about every type of vessel is depicted among the river traffic. *Free Library of Philadelphia*

13

This is how Hopewell Village appeared in 1887, four years after the last blast of the furnace. *Hopewell Village National Historic Site*

The Warwick Furnace, in 1789 the largest furnace in Pennsylvania, with a capacity of 1,200 tons. The Hopewell was second with a capacity of 700 tons. It was from "mine holes" such as this that the early mines obtained ore that did not come from bog iron. This is a mine hole near Warwick, Pennsylvania, that supplied the Warwick and Hopewell furnaces. The early mines were usually small open pits with rich veins of ore lying near the surface. Shaft mining developed from these holes at a later date. *Hopewell Village National Historic Site and Chester County, Pennsylvania, Historical Society*

The ruins of the Hopewell Furnace and its blast machinery about 1925, before restoration. Following Mark Bird's failure, the Hopewell passed into the hands of James Old and Cadwalader Morris, but in 1800 it was acquired by Matthew Brooke and his brother Thomas and their brother-in-law, Daniel Buckley. Under the administration of the Brookes, Hopewell reached its greatest prosperity. *Hopewell Village National Historic Site*

Hibernia Mine, near Rockaway, New Jersey (circa 1855). It furnished iron for Lord Stirling's forge during the Revolutionary War. The mine is still in existence, although no longer producing. The entranceway remains just as it was. The Hibernia was a Mount Hope mine, one of the most important and largest producers in New Jersey. It is not clear how far its adit extended in the 1860s, but it now covers nearly a mile and a half underground, stretching with only one curve along its entire length. Vestiges of railroad tracks still remain. At regular intervals along the adit, shafts had been constructed to the hilltop several hundred feet above. The shafts are partially caved in today, with funnel-like entrances that fill with ice in winter. They are extremely dangerous.

Howard N. Sloane, son Bruce (left), and photographer's assistant exploring Hibernia Mine adit. Note the floor ridges caused by the old railroad bed. *New York Herald Tribune. Photo by Nat Fein*

The Dickerson Mine, Succasunna, New Jersey. It was one of the first operating mines in New Jersey. The mine was bought originally by Joseph Kirkbride in 1713, but prior to its purchase the ore was free for anyone who cared to remove it. The mine worked bog iron, which was carried in leather or canvas bags on the backs of horses. In 1807 the Honorable Mahlon Dickerson, a former governor of New Jersey, purchased it. After his death it was owned by the Suckasunny Mining Company, and in the 1860s it was developed for underground mining. Around 1865 a shaft struck a vein about fifty feet belowground, and followed it to the floor of the mine, where later the mined ore was loaded into cars pulled by mules or horses. At that time an engine, pump, shaft, and an opening to a portion of the outcropping of the vein comprised the surface workings. The building at extreme right was probably a combination office and mine superintendent's living quarters. The lower center could be a pile of tailings.

More than thirty mines in the vicinity of Dover, New Jersey, were in operation in the late 1700s and during the 1800s. The Byram Mine was one of these, and the artist's sketch shows the surface workings. Notice the arrastra at extreme left. This mine was the first in the state to use a steam engine, installed in 1844. Because the ore vein was offset, it required stoping at different levels. In 1860 the ore was removed by a horsewhim (the steam engine supplying power for pumps and surface workings), but within a few years a 40-horsepower engine for underground workings was erected. The ore cars were pulled by chains, which frequently broke, crashing cars that sometimes hit the bottom with tremendous force.

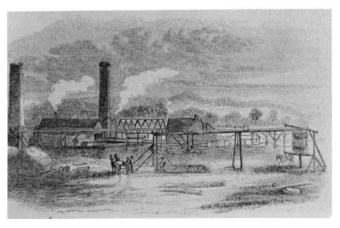

15

A gallery or large room in the Byram Mine. The miner riding the ore car seems to be enjoying himself.

Emerging from the mouth of the adit at Swedes Mine, as drawn by an 1860 artist. Apparently it was owners' visiting day.

though most of the bog iron still came from the southeast. In late Colonial days some iron ore was still being recovered from ore-bearing strata found in outcroppings. Throughout the eighteenth century, shaft mining remained rare in the colonies, and ore from outcroppings continued to be removed with picks, axes, and crowbars.

Exceptions occurred in eastern Pennsylvania, particularly along the Delaware River where some shaft mining was practiced before 1775. The Durham Mine, which supplied the Durham Furnace near Reigelsville, Pennsylvania, almost on the banks of the Delaware, was one example. During the Revolutionary War the Durham Furnace was an important source of iron products, and the mine reputedly was manned by slaves who carried out the ore on their backs. Durham has an estimated vertical depth of over 300 feet and five or six entrances atop a hill, only one practical for entering. The mine descends sharply to about the level of the Delaware River, indicated by deep shafts partially filled with water; undoubtedly an adit once was in use here for the removal of the ore.

For many years speleologists Charles E. Mohr and Howard N. Sloane had banded bats together in this mine. One bat that Mohr had banded was found at about the same location nineteen years later—a new record for bat longevity! Asked to lead a crew for a national magazine to photograph the hibernating bats, they suggested that the photographers, with an accompanying reporter, be physically fit—and agile. A female reporter and two male photographers were sent. About halfway into the

A driverless mule-drawn railcar in the adit of Swedes Mine, another iron mine near Dover, New Jersey. In the 1860s the Morris Canal was in operation, and was used extensively to transport ore from the northwestern New Jersey mines. Swedes Mine was directly on the canal, and was equipped with two adits and two shafts; driverless mules were trained to pull the ore cars from the adits. Morris Canal served a great many

mines that opened at that time, but by 1900 most were closed. Some, however, continued well into the century. Hundreds of iron mines were in operation in New Jersey and eastern Pennsylvania in colonial days, and some huge iron-ore deposits still remain. In the event of failure of the Great Lake ores, which today are mined more economically, these deposits could be utilized again.

Stereograph of a furnace at Hackettstown, New Jersey, circa 1880. *New Jersey Historical Society*

The Warren Furnace near Hackettstown, New Jersey, circa 1880. *New Jersey Historical Society*

mine, at a 105-foot near-vertical drop, the reporter panicked and had to be removed, screaming and shaking. Following the photography expedition, to which Mohr and Sloane had returned without her, she was found writing her imagined story in the back seat of a parked car!

But the mine is perhaps best known for the Durham boats that were used to haul the bog iron; George Washington impounded them to cross the Delaware. In the famous painting—"Washington Crossing the Delaware"—Washington is standing in a Durham ore boat.

Connecticut claims an early copper-mining company—Simsbury Mines, in Granby. The mines, which began operation in 1705, were chartered in 1709. They were abandoned about 1770 and acquired by the state for use as a prison, which endured for sixty years. Mining was resumed around 1830 but again was abandoned after a few years.

Pennsylvania's first copper mine is believed to have been the Gap Mine in Lancaster County, opened in 1732. (As early as 1708, William Penn had written to a Joshua Logan regarding some secret mines, but unfortunately, they remain a secret.)

In 1799, North Carolina provided the first authentic discovery of gold in the United States, which was doubted at first. It was later confirmed by a Hessian who had fought against the Americans in the Revolutionary War.

GYPSUM

In 1792 gypsum was discovered in New York but it had been introduced into the United States earlier by Benjamin Franklin when, as the American Commissioner to France in 1776, he became interested in gypsum plaster as a finish for walls. France and Nova Scotia provided the first gypsum used in this country. It is generally mined in an open pit, although

some underground mining is practiced if the quality is high or the material is close to the consuming market. An example is the underground gypsum mine system of Saltville, Virginia, originally famous for salt-brine deposits. Saltville's huge gypsum deposit was created millions of years ago as an evaporite deposit in a shallow sea. Later, a fracture, or fault, was formed in the earth's crust; Saltville's fault lifted the rock 14,000 feet, the mass movement of which broke up the once flat bed of gypsum into large pieces, or boulders, scattering them haphazardly throughout the fault zone. The boulders, from fifteen to twenty feet wide and fifty to one hundred feet high, are mined by the "open stope" method.

To find an underground boulder, test holes 100 to 400 feet deep are drilled along the drifts; some boulders extend through several mine levels. Then a new drift is driven into the boulder, from which slots are blasted. When the stope, or underground excavation, depletes the gypsum in the boulder, the operation is repeated in a new location.

Saltville's Plasterco Plant. First used as a fertilizer, gypsum went into use as a domestic plaster about 1835, in New York, and gained in popularity in the middle 1880s when methods were developed to retard the setting of the plaster. *U.S. Gypsum Company*

Alabaster Caverns State Park is the site of the world's largest known gypsum cave, almost 200 million years old. The uses of gypsum (alabaster is a translucent variety of gypsum) have expanded, although construction still consumes the largest quantities. It is employed as a soil conditioner, for making industrial models and patterns, crayons and chalk, coverings for pipes and boilers, insulation lining in the walls of safes and filing cabinets, in surgery for bandages and plaster casts, and other minor uses. *Oklahoma Industrial Development and Park Department*

OTHER SIGNIFICANT HISTORICAL EVENTS

The 300 Years

New York
1798: Levi Highboy and George Throop built an iron works at Hillsboro Falls, near Lake Champlain. Liberty Newman opened an iron works in Ticonderoga near the upper falls of the outlet to Lake George.

New Jersey
1685: Robert Morris owned a mine works at Tinton Falls in Monmouth County.

1751: A copper mine had been opened near New Brunswick, and at Somerville the nearby Bridgewater Mine was in operation before the Revolution.

Early Mining Techniques

Mining is accomplished through a variety of methods that depend not only on the nature of the mineral but its depth below the ground surface. Most minerals are mined by several methods, some from the ground surface and some through underground shafts and tunnels. Ground-surface methods are placer, hydraulic, dredge, strip, and open-pit mining. Underground methods may be by shaft, stope, and room-and-pillar, among others.

This chapter will demonstrate, by illustration, all of these methods in their earliest usages, plus the beginnings of mechanization in mining. Obviously, there were many variations in all of these operations but the principles were consistent.

Panning was the most popular mining method when water was handy. Tools were cheap and simple—pick, shovel, and pan. Miners without gold pans often used baskets or bowls made of twigs, preferably willow, agitating the material in the basket so that the smaller pieces would fall through the cracks. The most popular panning vessel was the washing pan or Spanish *batea*, requiring only one person. This illustration depicts panning at a placer deposit near Carsons, California, circa 1850. The term "placer" is probably derived from the Spanish for *plazo de oro* or "place of gold," and simply defined a surface working. Placer workings often were worked to surprising depths, removing the gravel pan by pan. Note the use of the pick in the background.

The pan was partially (and hopefully) filled with gold-bearing dirt, and water added, while the operator merely held the pan by the rim, rotating the entire conglomeration. By gradually removing any large stones that seemed to contain no gold, the rotary movement would wash the lighter material over the edges, leaving pebbles and pieces or flakes of the heavier gold in the center. In this way the mass slowly was reduced to fine sand. *Montana Historical Society*

When prospectors found gold-bearing dirt in dry territory, without available water, and consequently could not "pan" their gold, their best hope of success, initially, was in "winnowing" or "dry washing," the simple method of spreading a sheet or blanket partially filled with the dirt. The blanket was then held by two men who tossed the material into the air, allowing the wind to carry off the dust and light matter while the residue fell back onto the blanket. This left only the heavier pieces to be culled for gold. This old winnowing scene occurred near Chinese Camp, California around 1850.

An improvement over the pan was the rocker. Its first known use in California was at Coloma in 1848 by Isaac Humphrey, a Georgia miner. Its advantages were self-evident, and it caught on rapidly. One of the earliest photos of California gold mining was this 1849 picture of the Celestial Diggings at Mongolian Flat. Notice the use of a rocker by this placer miner with his inevitable pan in the foreground. *Wells Fargo Bank History Room*

If the sand were dry it could be blown off by breath, wind, or bellows, leaving the heavier gold as a residue. This old bellows, found at the Brighton Mine in Colorado, was probably used to blow out the dust after panning and to light this test forge. *John Spence*

Various rocker models were devised, the commonest a box three to four feet long, about two feet or less wide, and about eighteen inches deep. Set upon it, at the rear, was a smaller box, preferably with a perforated metal base to allow small pebbles to wash through. Underneath the entire structure was a wood or metal base curved like a child's cradle to assist the rocking motion. The gold-bearing earth was thrown into the upper box, and added water carried the smaller particles through the lower box, where it was washed out into the stream. A fine example of an old cradle that probably processed many pounds of gold dust in its day is shown. *Wells Fargo Bank History Room*

Though in operation the rocker, or cradle, differed little from the pan, it required considerably less effort and washed far more gravel. The Stanislaus River in California was "mined" by this crude "cradle-rocking" method. Note the gun stuck through the miner's belt.

Some miners used a jig, a modified rocker, around the 1870s. As the photograph shows, material was placed in the upper tray, which was then rocked on the rolling pipe. The tray was made of a type of chicken wire, allowing the material to fall into different trays with varying sizes of mesh, the finest material falling into the bottom tray. *United States Geological Survey Photo, Montana Historical Society*

Cleats or baffles nailed about halfway up the exit across the lower box would salvage any heavy material that got through. Such cleats were called "riffles," and many different riffle arrangements were used (circa 1850). *Montana Historical Society*

It became practical, and popular, to divert entire stream beds into watercourses so that the remaining dry stream beds and river bottoms could be placered. A group of miners are engaged at the Gold Queen placers in digging a channel for this purpose. *Denver Public Library Western Collection*

By a lengthy extension of the cradle, miners developed the "long tom," first called a "Mexican trough" because of its origin. Usually from ten to twenty feet long, the iron "mouth" end was slightly upturned and, like the sieve of the cradle, perforated. Beneath the sieve was a box lined with riffles, or baffles, often called Hungarian riffles, performing the same function as in the rocker.

Placed on an inclined ground with the sieve end lower than its counterpart, when available a stream of water was directed to the elevated end. Running a ditch from a nearby stream provided a continuous flow. If a stream was not handy, water was poured by hand. The scene of this long tom is near Murphys, California, circa 1850.

To secure a gravity flow, ingenious methods of raising water were devised. A rare device was the flutter wheel (circa 1855) that filled the flumes at a high level.

Murderer's Bar was the site of a large-scale gold operation in the 1850s. The water from this stream has already been diverted into the channel at the right.

Full-scale mining operations are taking place in the old stream bed. *Free Library of Philadelphia*

In the early 1850s the use of flumes to carry water to the sluices from canyons or across valleys was a laborious task, but it paid off in the long run. Sometimes flumes were constructed to permit riverbed mining, and such flumes had to be of sufficient capacity to carry all the water of the river. This permitted gathering the gold that remained in the riverbed. Water wheels were erected across the flumes to help pump out the water left in the former bed of the stream. This sketch shows a flume with waterwheels on the Yuba River in California, and appeared in *Three Years in California*, 1857. *New York Public Library Picture Collection*

Usually a box containing quicksilver was attached to the end of the riffles thus fine particles of gold were saved by amalgamation with the mercury. A tapered end permitted a number of toms to be connected, and sometimes the mercury (quicksilver) was placed along several riffle bars to amalgamate greater quantities of small gold pieces (circa 1850).

An 1867 miner is "panning out" while waiting for the long tom to accumulate more material. *William Culp Darrah Stereo Collection*

Long toms were successful only if sufficient water could be supplied to operate them. If the water and the terrain were ideally situated, "ground sluicing," or "coyoting," was a popular and easy method of gold recovery, since the natural terrain itself acted as a long tom. One advantage of coyoting was that the large volume of water enabled prospectors to get deep beneath the surface, often to the rock level where gold was more likely to be found. This type of "drifting" led to the first tunneling in the California district; if gold occurred at a depth of thirty or forty feet, it was often easier to try to follow the vein or lead by tunneling than by washing away all the excess material.

In some instances, coyoting led to myriad tunnels, running under the claims of others fifteen to forty feet below the ground surface. It was not unusual for miners from different tunnels, working by candlelight, to meet underground. Because the coyote diggings often caved in without warning, the miners sometimes placed supports for safety (circa 1850).

Pressure boxes were often constructed along the flumes by water companies to contain large quantities of water that were used to increase the pressure when the water was released. *Denver Public Library Western Collection*

Properly graded "flumes" made it possible to carry water long distances. No more than a pitched channel, the flume sometimes ran one hundred or more feet above ground level. High flumes such as this one near Smartsville, Yuba County, California (circa 1866), were not uncommon. *William Culp Darrah Stereo Collection*

Iron ore for some years had been broken by other means. One of the earliest, a levered sledge developed in Mexico, was simply an extremely enlarged rock hammer lifted by a lever and dropped on the piece of ore to be broken so as to extract the metal. But this, too, was slow, although it occasionally was used in the United States to break up gold-quartz rock. *Free Library of Philadelphia*

24

The next improvement was the "bastra," or "rastra," commonly known as the *arrastra*, extensively employed by the Spanish in Mexico. This early sketch (circa 1850) shows the details of construction for a two-mule ore-crushing arrastra. *Montana Historical Society*

The arrastra was a circular depression half filled with hard rock, such as granite. The depression was surrounded by a coping wall to hold the ore material to be broken and ground up. The miners broke large pieces into smaller to throw into the arrastra. A supported center pole was set in the middle of the circular trough. Fastened to the pole was a bar extending beyond the coping. The bar, which could be rotated about the pole, was attached at one end to a horse or mule that walked around the circle. Attached to the opposite end of the bar, which extended only up to the outer rim of the circle, were one or two large, heavy stones to drag on the dumped rock within the trough as the animal revolved about (circa 1850).

A modified one-horse arrastra in use in Montana in the late 1870s or early 1880s. *Montana Historical Society*

Instead of, or in addition to, arrastras, crushing wheels occasionally were used to grind the material. This crushing wheel, built by Chilean miners in the 1840s, was found in Sequoia National Forest, California. *United States Forest Service*

The finer the ore was crushed in the arrastra, the more easily and completely could the gold be extracted. Retorts were used, generally cylindrically shaped iron vessels in which the amalgam was heated. A tube emanating from the top of the retort permitted the separation, or distillation, of the mercury from the gold. This process was accomplished in the following manner: The amalgam either from a stamping mill or an arrastra was placed in a spread cloth together with the mercury. The ends of the cloths were gathered together and twisted to form a bag. Some of the mercury would thus pass through the meshes of the cloth, but a mass of gold, still amalgamated with mercury, remained. These remains, in the cloth, were placed into the retort. When heated, the mercury would be expelled through a tube passing out at the top. The other end of the tube remained underwater to cool the quicksilver and to prevent it from splashing. The object was to heat the mass sufficiently to expel the mercury but not enough to melt the gold completely. After the mercury was expelled, the gold would be removed almost in the form of a casting, marked with the texture and impression of the cloth. These "castings" were placed in pails or metal boxes, and during transportation abrasion would rub off the small pieces we know as gold dust. The pictured retort, published around 1855, was an elementary model; later retorts were far more elaborate.

As improvements were made, horse and mule power for arrastras was replaced by waterpower, and in hundreds of mining operations throughout the West the waterwheel became a common sight. In this early Oregon photo the arrastra was turned by means of a waterwheel. *Oregon State Department of Geology and Mineral Industries*

Oxen were used to move big, heavy loads. They seemed to thrive underground, many gaining weight. *Jeffrey Manufacturing Company*

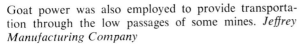

Goat power was also employed to provide transportation through the low passages of some mines. *Jeffrey Manufacturing Company*

An excellent example of an arrastra, powered by water, that crushed quartz ore near Pierce, Idaho, in 1895. It was common to dismantle the arrastra after the ore played out so as to recover any gold that seeped through. Some arrastras were leased out at fixed rates, most at a percentage of the gold recovered. Some claims had 50 or 60 arrastras working at once. This leasing system made cheating easy, and required careful supervision if the claim owner was to collect. For larger operations, stamping mills powered by water, later by steam, were often used. *Idaho Historical Society*

The first stamping mills were waterpowered, and consisted of a series of wood stampers, each covered with iron, that fitted into iron boxes into which the gold quartz was placed. Before being placed into the boxes, the quartz was broken into egg-sized pieces. By utilizing cogs or cams, the stampers fell into the boxes with a pile-driver action, ultimately finely crushing the ore to an arrastra consistency.

These iron stamps at the Empire Mine, California (circa 1900), show the cam and boss. *Grass Valley, California, Mining Exhibit*

Multiple stampers took much less time and produced a much greater quantity, and the larger the operation, the more stampers were required. This picture shows the stamp process at Sensenderfer's Mill, Colorado, by J.

Bien from Alfred E. Mathews' "Pencil Sketches of Colorado," 1866. *Library, State Historical Society of Colorado*

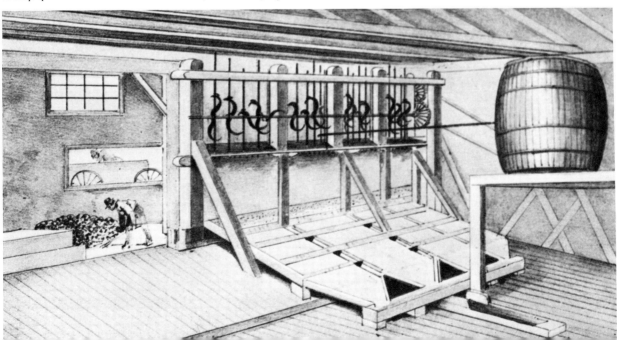

By 1851 most of the placer surface workings were depleted. If further quantities of gold were to be recovered, larger operations would be necessary. Cooperative efforts were the answer, and miners banded together to form co-ops for hydraulic mining, a method of washing large quantities of auriferous earth. This sketch from the 1850s depicts the entire hydraulic process. A flume can be seen at the top right at the edge of the embankment, permitting a head of water to flow down the pipe to the "monitor." From there the washed gravel ran into sluiceways, and the tailings were carted away to the opposite bank.

The entire wash was then channeled into a carefully screened sluice system. Hydraulic washings were extensive, and often devastated large acreages, to this day leaving the land barren and strewn with rock. Hydraulic mining continued well into the twentieth century. These high-pressure hydraulics were operated in La Grange Placer Mine in the Trinity National Forest in 1923. *United States Forest Service*

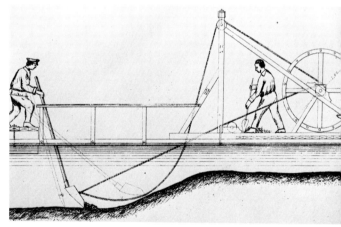

The hydraulic operation was similar to using a fire hose. Special nozzles, called "monitors," increased the water pressure, making it possible to wash out tons of sand and gravel an hour. The volume of water and the force by which it could be ejected depended to a great extent on the height from which the water came. This picture from the 1850s gives a good idea of the huge volume of water that could be made available for hydraulic mining. *Wells Fargo Bank History Room*

A logical mechanical extension of placer mining was the dredge, developed in the 1870s and designed to dig its way through gold-bearing sands and to separate the small quantity of gold from the mounds of worthless sand. Basically, a dredge is a many storied, flat-bottomed, shallow hull with excavation machinery for digging, a steam engine, and placer equipment for separating the gold. The dredge's forward end consisted of an endless conveyor belt with scoops or shovels to carry the material to the top, where the separation began. Earlier dredge types had scoops that merely brought the gold-bearing ore material to the deck of the hull where it was treated as normal placer sand. The dredges operated on the same principle as placer mining, permitting gravity to wash the material through riffle boxes, which caught the gold, and dumped the unwanted tailings into the stream bed or along the shore. *Jeffrey Manufacturing Company*

Because in most areas dredges operated in nonnavigable waters, they had to be constructed on the spot. The cables, hoist, pump, and other machinery were added during the construction. This gold dredge was being worked in the 1880s along Stanley Creek in what is now Challis National Forest. *United States Forest Service*

These Indiana strip banks, sometimes called "earthworms," have been reforested, and new growths of trees are easily visible over the entire area. *Indiana Coal Producers Association*

Since it was costly to dismantle and remove a dredge after mining was completed, it was simply stripped of its machinery, and the hulk and structures were abandoned. It is for this reason that the remains of so many dredges are still found in mining areas throughout the West. This is an abandoned gold dredge at Elizabethtown, New Mexico. This type of dredge was land-based, operating into the stream bed, with the workings onshore. Its simple construction enabled it to be moved up and down the stream as needed. *United States Forest Service*

Open-pit mines are in effect strip mines, but these usually remain in operation for many years, sometimes more than fifty, and most excavations of this type are at stone quarries and excavations opened to produce iron and copper. The open-pit copper mine of the Phelps Dodge Corporation at Ajo, Arizona, is more than a mile in length and nearly a mile in width. The bottom level of the pit is about 900 feet below the topmost level. Note model housing in foreground. *Phelps Dodge Corporation*

Wherever metals or minerals are close to the surface, it is more economical to remove the topsoil, or overburden, and dig out the material from the surface. This is called "strip mining." One of the first attempts at mechanization of strip mining occurred in 1877 when an Otis-type steam shovel was used in Pittsburg, Kansas, in place of horse-drawn plows and scrapers. Actually, the shovel proved to be too short effectively to handle the twelve-foot-thick overburden beneath which was three feet of coal. The shovel was later remodeled. *Bucyrus-Erie Company*

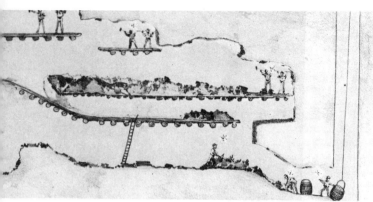

The interior of Number 1 of the Gregory at the Black Hawk Company's mine, Black Hawk, Colorado. From a lithograph by J. Bien that appeared in Alfred E. Mathews' "Pencil Sketches of Colorado," 1866. After placer deposits came the quartz-rock deposits occurring in veins that often went deep into the ground. The veins, called "lodes," had to be followed no matter how deep they went or how tortuous their paths, and the ideal situation was to find the "mother lode" from which branches could be followed. This led to several kinds of underground mining, in this case shaft or lode mining. *Library, State Historical Society of Colorado*

Glory-hole mining utilizes a funnel-shaped opening, connected by a vertical passage driven from below. The passage, called a "raise," acts as a chute through which the ore slides to an underground level to be removed through a tunnel or adit. Here (circa 1850) a shaft intersects the Hibernia Mine adit. Ultimately the adit was developed for nearly 1½ miles into the hillside. The timbers were used as shoring to prevent collapse of the side walls.

Underground mines generally have vertical shafts with horizontal levels opening out of the shaft. Vertical passages, called "winzes," often connect the different levels. Branching off from these levels are openings called "stopes" through which the ore is extracted. Sketches of New Jersey mines about 1860: "driving a breast" (left), which is a method of stoping, and a turntable by the same artist. The turntable enabled cars to be shunted into a stoping at any level, while cars above or below were free to pass.

This unidentified mine interior in the Virginia City area shows the early use of the square set. *Nevada Historical Society*

Hand drilling was "single-jack" or "double-jack," depending on the number of available miners. The lone miner (single-jack) held and turned the drill steel with one hand and struck it with the other, using a four-pound hammer. Note candlelight. Blasting followed drilling. Thousands of Cornishmen, popularly known as "Cousin Jacks," were imported for hard-rock or lode mines. *Buck O'Donnell, Shaft and Development Machines Company*

Underground mines are supported by timbers, where practical, in the form of "square sets." The square set here shows the timbering of the mine. The square-set system of timbering was developed by Philip Deidesheimer. Sometimes concrete and steel or brick supports are used. A common form of underground mining is the "room-and-pillar" method. In such mines huge pillars, comprising about one third of the ore, remain as columns to support the entire roof surface. These pillars are sometimes mined out when the workings are about to be depleted. *From De Quille's* History of the Big Bonanza, *1877*

Double-jacking was accomplished with two or three men, one man holding and turning, while the others pounded the drill. The large hammer was swung by one miner while his partner(s) held the drill steel. In drilling upper holes, the job was slow and arduous. The drills were quickly dulled, and blacksmith shops were set up in the mine for resharpening and tempering the steel. *Buck O'Donnell, Shaft and Development Machines Company*

By the end of the 1870s, though steam drilling was used extensively, it was unpopular because the boilers had to be erected outside the mine, and the steam lost a great deal of energy in the long transportation to the working face. In addition it was difficult to make connections under steam pressure, and the exhausted steam filled the mine with a heavy wet heat. All this changed with the development of compressed-air drills. These proved so satisfactory that 75 percent of the drill teams could be laid off without affecting the production of the mine. Big compressors were required to build up a supply of compressed air for the new tools. These compressors were in use at lead-zinc mining operations in the Tri-State District (Missouri, Arkansas, Oklahoma) around 1907. *Eagle-Picher Industries, Inc.*

An early steam pump developed entirely for mining in Cornwall, England, from an engraving dated 1717. Hundreds of these pumps were in operation throughout Cornwall in the 1700s and 1800s to keep water out of the coal mines. They were introduced into the United States in 1850. *From* A Student's History of England *by F. R. Gardner, Free Library of Philadelphia*

The Cornish pump or beam engine was first used in Cornwall, England, and was brought to California in 1850. By 1855 the Gold Hill Mines at Grass Valley were successfully using Cornish pumps, which remained the principal method of dewatering difficult mines of all types until around 1908. These pumps were highly successful despite breakdowns, and the larger ones or combinations were able to lift from 3,000 to 15,000 gallons of water per hour. Some of these pumps had rods extending thousands of feet, and were operated by a piston. In general the pump consisted of a steam plant on the surface. The engine was connected to the pump, deep in the sump pit of the mine. If the mine was extremely deep, a series of pumps lifted the water from one pumping level to another. The pump consisted of the piston with check valves that lifted the water on top of the piston rather than by suction. The original piston levers were later replaced by huge flywheels, one of the largest being a 100-inch cylinder used at the Comstock-lode mines. This Cornish pump at the old Chapin Mine at Iron Mountain, Michigan, stood 50 feet high and could pump 3,000 gallons of water per minute. *Michigan Historical Commission*

Before electric power became generally available for hoisting machines and elevator cages for getting men and material in and out of the vertical shafts, the easiest way to remove ore from a shaft was with an ordinary hand hoist, a simple winch similar to raising a bucket of water from a well. This winch removed gold ore in Montana in the 1860s. Note in the background the pile of tailings, or discarded ore-bearing dirt, and, beyond, the miners' cabins. *Montana Historical Society*

As soon as it became necessary to remove larger loads of ore, horse winches or horsewhims were used. This old-fashioned horse hoist was in use in Missouri for lead and zinc mining. As the horse walked around the turntable, the ore was hauled from the bottom of the shaft on the pulley. *State Historical Society of Missouri*

This type of cage was used primarily to bring men up from the mines rather than for hauling supplies. It was in use around 1870. *Montana Historical Society*

By the end of the 1800s electricity was used to wind up the cables that pulled the ore cars along the mine tracks. Note in the upper left the gong attached by a wire running into the adit. The operator of the hoist would receive his signals by these gongs. This scene is believed to have been at the Kelly Mine, New Mexico, circa 1887–1888. *The J. E. Smith Collection, courtesy of the heirs*

Electric drills soon came into use. This electric coal drill was worked in 1908. Notice that the softness of the coal permits a more conventional type of drill to be used rather than a boring type of tool. Electric cables were carefully wound on reels to prevent accidents. *Jeffrey Manufacturing Company*

Power mills had entered the scene. Here a conical mill is being delivered to the Mint Hill Gold Mining Company, Matthew, North Carolina, in 1915. These cone crushers were set upright, with the point down and slightly off center to create a wobbling motion as they revolved. Inside the cone a second central cone was usually set on center, so that the space between the inner and outer cones would vary. The ore, dumped in from the top, was ground between the walls of the cones. The egg-size pieces were then passed through steel rollers that crushed the ore into finer particles. Jaw crushers that broke the ore into egg-size pieces were sometimes used instead of cones. The material was finally screened. *Koppers Company, Inc.*

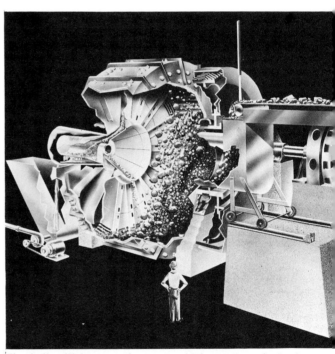

Coal mines were simpler in structure, and most of the operations were housed in a tipple building. Here, assisted by gravity, coal was washed, graded to size, and finally loaded into cars. Modern coal tipples are marvels of efficiency. This drawing of a coal tipple or coal-washing plant was typical of those built in the 1890s. Coal passed through washers that permitted the waste materials to be washed away in the form of sludge, and screening separated the coal into various sizes before loading. *Jeffrey Manufacturing Company*

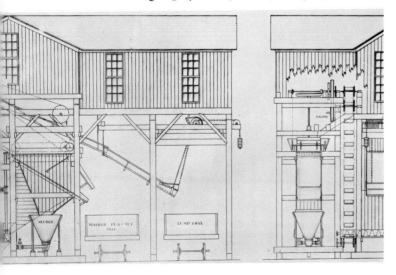

The ball mill became the most widely used method of ore crushing. Such a mill consisted merely of a large hopper in which steel balls were used to crush the ore as the hopper rotated. An artist's conception of a cutaway view of the Hardinge Cascade Mill showing the cascading action of the charge from which the mill takes its name. It was known that oil or grease attracted metallic sulfides. By putting the proper amount of oil and water in the ball mill, plus a small amount of acid and sodium cyanide, a rich foam was formed that attracted the metallic contents, which could then be "floated" away, retaining most of the metals in the "float." The process was not commonly used until around 1910, when chemical leaching processes were developed that utilized a weak solution of sulfuric acid. The highly technical flotation and cyanidation methods proved very successful in reducing copper as well as gold. *Koppers Company, Inc.*

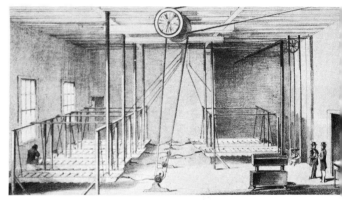

The Keith Process of amalgamating ore. The upper left-hand photograph is the ore-breaking room, a process in which the Blakes Ore Breaker was used, but almost any of the described crushers would have served the purpose. The ore was then placed in the furnace for calcination, as shown in the upper right-hand picture. The lower left-hand picture shows an endless chain that picked up the roasted ore, and dumped it into an in-cline tray that scattered it as it fell into the bin, thereby drying it out. The lower right-hand corner shows the amalgamating room, in which the sludgy material was amalgamated with quicksilver. Lithographs by J. Bien of the Keith Process at the Hope Gold Company's works from Alfred E. Mathews' "Pencil Sketches of Colorado," 1866. *Colorado State Historical Society Library*

This material was then put into the ore-dressing room, where it was mixed and amalgamated before being put into the reverberatory furnace. From the furnace it was put into the cupulos or cupel furnace, and then into the Scotch hearths, which melted the gold or silver and formed it into bullion. Lithographs by J. Bien of the smelting process at the James E. Lyon and Company's smelting works from Alfred E. Mathews' "Pencil Sketches of Colorado," 1866. *Colorado State Historical Society Library*

The Pre-Boom Years

GOLD

Considering reports of gold production at the Oliver, Dunn, and Parker mines prior to 1775, there seems to be no question that gold mining was carried on in North Carolina before the Revolutionary War. However, in all of these reports, authentic references are lacking; even the earliest mint returns did not appear until 1793. Therefore, the generally accepted North Carolina gold discovery goes to a seventeen-pound nugget found on the Reed plantation in Cabarrus County, in 1799. John H. Wheeler's *Historical Sketches of North Carolina, 1584 to 1851,* recounts the event:

The first piece of gold found at this mine was in the year 1799, by Conrad Reed, a boy of about twelve years old, a son of John Reed, the proprietor. The discovery was made in an accidental manner. The boy above named, in company with a sister and younger brother, went to a small stream, called Meadow Creek, on a Sabbath day, while their parents were at church, for the purpose of shooting fish with bow and arrow, and while engaged along the bank of the creek, Conrad saw a yellow substance shining in the water. He went

Twelve-year-old Conrad Reed accidentally discovering gold in 1799 while shooting fish with a bow and arrow in a North Carolina stream. The nugget found by the boy was used as a doorstop for several years until its true nature was realized.

in and picked it up, and found it to be some kind of metal, and carried it home. Mr. Reed examined it, but as gold was unknown in this part of the country at that time, he did not know what kind of metal it was: the piece was about the size of a small smoothing iron.

Mr. Reed carried the piece of metal to Concord, and showed it to a William Atkinson, a silversmith, but he not thinking of gold, was unable to say what kind of metal it was.

Mr. Reed kept the piece for several years on his house floor, to lay against the door to keep it from shutting. In the year 1802, he went to market to Fayetteville, and carried the piece of metal with him, and on showing it to a jeweller, the jeweller immediately told him it was gold, and requested Mr. Reed to leave the metal with him and said he would flux it. Mr. Reed left it, and returned in a short time, and on his return the jeweller showed him a large bar of gold, six or eight inches long. The jeweller then asked Mr. Reed what he would take for the bar. Mr. Reed, not knowing the value of gold, thought he would ask a "big price" and so he asked three dollars and fifty cents ($3.50)! The jeweller paid him his price.

After returning home, Mr. Reed examined and found gold in the surface along the creek. He then associated Frederick Kisor, James Love, and Martin Phifer with himself, and in the year 1803, they found a piece of gold in the branch that weighed twenty-eight pounds. Numerous pieces were found at this mine weighing from sixteen pounds down to the smallest particles. The whole surface along the creek for nearly a mile was very rich in gold.

The veins of this mine were discovered in the year 1831. They yielded a large quantity of gold. The veins are flint or quartz.

I do certify that the foregoing is a true statement of the discovery and history of this mine, as given by John Reed and his son Conrad Reed, now both dead.
January, 1848   George Barnhardt

Some believe Reed learned the true value of the gold and returned to the jeweler, where he recovered about $3,000 (an unlikely story!). Other nuggets were soon discovered at the Reed plantation, and a systematic search for gold in North Carolina and other, adjacent, southern states was on.

Copper, of course, had preceded gold. The

The Gold Hill Mine (mid-1800s), which typified the lode mines of the day. The shaft, entered by ladders, descended 425 feet. Various galleries ran off this shaft, worked in a supervisory capacity by the Cornishmen among the 300 employees, because of their experience, and by Negroes who, without the benefit of mechanical devices, bored into the rock with sledges and augers. Most rock was blasted by powder, and the ore was removed in barrel-size copper vessels, drawn through the shaft by a windlass worked by a horsewhim. An empty bucket was lowered as a full one came up, rising about twelve feet beyond the surface landing. Occasionally the horses would forget to stop, causing the buckets to crash into the shaft. Once removed, the ore was ground to a powdery mass in the crushing mill and carried in wheelbarrows to the cradles. The pulverized ore was then carried by water to the open end of the cradle, amalgamating with the quicksilver in the grooves. The dross was generally washed into a blanket, which, when filled, was squeezed to form a solid lump of amalgam. The amalgam was then placed in a retort, which would separate the quicksilver while the gold remained. North Carolina is no longer a factor in the gold economy today, though small quantities of gold are still produced. In addition to the Reed Mine and Gold Hill Mine, there were the Phifer, Davis, and Pewter mines (Union County), the Hearne Mine (Stanly County), Long Creek and Reynolds mines (Montgomery County), the Kings Mountain Mine (Gaston County), the Phoenix and Barnhardt mines (Cabarrus County), the Reimer and Fisher Hills mines (Rowan County), the Rudisil Mine (Mecklenburg County), and the Conrad Hill and Silver Hill mines (Davidson County). All operated up to the beginning of the Civil War. The entrance to the Gold Hill Mine was by a series of twenty-foot ladders reaching to the bottom of the shaft. Running parallel to the ladders was a steam-operated Cornish pump that removed water from the base of the shaft. Though the Cornish pumps created a terrific racket, they were very efficient in getting water out of the mines, and without them work would have been impossible.

The unique cradles used for rocking the ground ore at the Gold Hill in North Carolina are clearly illustrated in this 1857 drawing. The cradles are closed at the upper end and open at the lower, and on the inside can be seen ridges or grooves to hold the quicksilver. The crushed ore is placed in the upper end of the cradles, and a small amount of water is turned on. Most cradles were rocked vigorously by machinery, but at the Gold Hill Mine and at other private mines, girls between twelve and fifteen years of age were used to rock the cradles.

Another view of the Gold Hill Mine. This drawing of the Gold Hill works from an 1857 *Harper's* is particularly interesting because it depicts the extensive employment of the multiple cradles. The cradles are eighteen or twenty feet long, and were formed from the trunks of trees, which were split in two and hollowed out, not unlike Indian canoes. This work is going on in the left center of the picture. The cradles were placed on parallel timbers at an angle and fastened together so that twelve or fifteen could be moved at one time, and were set up in the building in the extreme right center on the opposite side of the flume. *North Carolina Department of Archives and History*

These copper buckets were used to remove the gold ore from the Gold Hill's 425-foot shaft. Although most miners descended by ladder, some preferred to come up on the buckets rather than climb the long steps to the top of the shaft.

Cornish miners in an 1857 drawing—the best skilled help at the time. As lode mining developed, the Cornish workers, from Cornwall, England, were employed because of their vast experience in coal-mine shafts.

Prior to the discovery of lode mines in North Carolina, most placer workers were Negro slaves.

existence of copper in Santa Rita, New Mexico, dates to 1535 when Cabeza de Vaca was given a copper rattle by Indians who told him of copper deposits in the area; a hundred years later these deposits were well known. The oldest active mine in the southwestern part of the United States is the Santa Rita Copper Mine, actually one of the country's first. In 1798, the mine was "rediscovered" when Apache Indians led José Manuel Carrasco, the commander of a Spanish post, to the site. Carrasco worked it for about two years and sold the property to Francisco Manuel Elguea, a Mexican, who received a grant from the Spanish Crown to develop the mine. Using convict labor obtained from the Spanish government, Elguea built a smelting plant. Eventually, Elguea's widow leased the mine to Sylvester Patte, an American trapper, who continued to use Spanish labor. For over fifty years the mine continued in more or less active operation, and later it was purchased by a group of Denver financiers. Ample evidence exists that the mining of gold, possibly copper, too, was practiced in the Mexican settlement of Pinos Altos in 1837, eleven years before New Mexico became part of the United

Santa Rita Copper Pit, January, 1938. *United States Forest Service*

Remains of an early 1800 arrastra first used by Spaniards in the recovery of gold at Pinos Altos. *George Schafer*

Kennecott Copper Pit, Santa Rita. *Felix A. Peckham*

Relics from Santa Rita Spanish mines. Note ore-carrying bags among the amorphous materials and rockers. *Museum of New Mexico*

States; in fact, Mexican records reveal that during that same year a gold shipment was made to Chihuahua. Artifacts of the mine workings have been found.

In Pinos Altos, on May 18, 1860, Count Jacob Snively (or Shively), Henry Birch, and a party of Forty-Niners discovered gold on Bear Creek. Birch, while drinking from the stream, found it lying free in the water. While in Santa Rita ten miles away for supplies, the party told the Marston brothers of their discovery, and, within six months, 1,500 miners arrived. They renamed the camp Birchville in honor of Henry Birch, but following the Civil War it reverted to its original name. Within a year, 500 Indians under Mangas (Mangus) Coloradas, a Mimbreno Apache chief, attacked the town. Most of the miners fled, while a few with fortitude remained. One who remained was Virgil Mastin who in 1866 formed the Pinos Altos Mining Company. In January, 1863, the California Volunteers, led by Colonel West, captured Coloradas. Among a group that had apparently tricked him by offering a flag of truce was Jack Swilling, a gold prospector at Pinos Altos. Tortured by the troops who prodded

him with hot bayonet points, Coloradas was forced to the ground and slain when he attempted to rise. Supposedly, he was buried in the hills; later his remains were exhumed and sent to Washington where on examination his skull was reported to be larger and heavier than Daniel Webster's.

About $10 million in gold was taken from Birchville. But after some forty years most of the mines were controlled by the Hearst interests who managed to produce almost $5 million more.

In 1879, over twenty years before the Hearst interests were ogling Birchville, the first lode discovery in the area was being recorded at the foot of Baxter Mountain. Though a gold lode found by cowboys had been known to exist as early as 1850, no one had ever been able to find the mother lode. The Baxter find started a small rush and led to the creation of White Oaks a year later, one of the largest towns in the territory, with a population of 4,000. One old landmark was the Little Casino, operated by Madam Varnish who was known for her smooth, slick manners. For twenty years she dealt faro and poker and provided roulette, making and losing fortunes.

Pinos Altos mine personnel line up to have their picture taken before the mine entrance. Note the assortment of hats and divisions in dress. *George Schafer*

Photo labeled "Struck It Rich!" taken between 1880 and 1890 at the Coconino Silver Mine, near Socorro. *Museum of New Mexico*

Production of gold in Bland began in 1894, and by 1901 it was a thriving gold camp, shipping ore to the Albermarle Mill. Gold was mined in this area until after World War I. In 1914 a 20-stamp concentrating mill and a 100-ton cyanide plant were in operation here. *Museum of New Mexico*

Little remains of White Oaks, now a ghost town; a few brick and stone buildings stand, including the gambling hall, bank, and church, whereas the surrounding hills are filled with the wreckage of the old mines, and many abandoned shafts are visible. *United States Forest Service*

Placer mining in E-Town (circa 1880). Predating the Baxter Mountain discovery by a dozen years, a small rush began in the Sangre de Cristo Mountains in the streams that ran off Baldy Mountain, and two years later E-Town was laid out. That same year the forty-one-mile Big Ditch was started, running from Red River to E-Town. It was to furnish water for the placers and hydraulic mining, which by then had become extensive. *Museum of New Mexico*

Elizabethtown (E-Town) showing the Froelich store, where the horses are standing (right center); and above, on the corner, the John Pierson store; and the corner still to the left of that, the Remsberg store; in the extreme background is the Maxwell Land Grant, E-Town headquarters. By 1870 E-Town had 7,000 inhabitants, but five years later it appeared that the placers were being played out. Despite new discoveries in 1880, this, plus continuing Indian troubles, slowed down activity tremendously. However, some dredging had begun during the late 1880s to early 1890s, and in 1901 the Oro Dredging Company built an enormous dredge and the settlement began to prosper again. The dredge had a daily capacity of 4,000 cubic yards, and operated for about four years. A stamp mill and a cyanide plant were built in 1914, but the armistice reduced E-Town to ghost status. *Museum of New Mexico*

The coming of the telegraph (circa 1891) in Baldy, which boomed before E-Town. *Museum of New Mexico*

A prospecting party in Los Cerrillos where in the Cerrillos Mountains metal deposits were known in 1583. They were discovered by Don Antonio Espejo and Fray Bernardino Beltran, and in 1697 a man called Vetancurt noted various deposits in Los Cerrillos, including copper, gypsum, lodestone, salt, turquoise, and veins of lead and silver. However, the first record of actual mining in the Cerrillos district credits the Mina de la Tierra; gold was mined there in 1722, but not until 1879 was the district heavily prospected when a small smelter was established, which soon shut down despite discoveries of lead and zinc. Another smelter was built at Cerrillos, in 1902, but mining ceased shortly thereafter. *Museum of New Mexico*

Scene from Socorro, probably at the Billings Smelter. Slag cars with a crucible in the background. *The J. E. Smith Collection, courtesy of the heirs*

Smelter town near Hot Springs, deserted at the time this picture was taken, probably in the 1880s. *The J. E. Smith Collection, courtesy of the heirs*

Billings Smelter and surface workings west of Socorro, once the largest in the state. It was built in 1881, but only traces of the foundation remain. *The J. E. Smith Collection, courtesy of the heirs*

Posed street scene in Kelly. *The J. E. Smith Collection, courtesy of the heirs*

Street scene in Kingston, typical of New Mexico's many mining towns. *The J. E. Smith Collection, courtesy of the heirs*

COLONIAL COAL

While metal prospecting was moving west, the scarcity of firewood back east, in Pennsylvania, was to expand a different kind of mining—coal.

Records for 1755 indicate that Pennsylvania gunsmiths had been accustomed to using coal, and that by 1770 their bellows were feeding oxygen to burn it in their forges. Coal might even have been mined earlier had firewood not been so plentiful and inexpensive. But now forests near industrial areas were nearing depletion. In the search for substitutes for charcoal (coal had been discovered in Carbondale coinciding with the War of 1812, and it was soon in extreme demand), by about 1817 a number of small coal mines had been opened, but it took another dozen years before all known coal deposits were worked.

Coal became the impetus that built the transportation industry, and beginning in 1818, development of an inland canal system to handle bulk shipments got under way.

A Scranton operation. Scranton was the largest city in the anthracite region, though in the 1770s it consisted of only a few settlers' homes. It did not become the city of Scranton until 1851, but was originally known as Dark Hollow, Slocum Hollow, Harrison, the Lackawaxen Iron Works, Scrantonia, and, finally, Scranton. Actually, settlers were attracted to the area not by coal but by iron ore. *Pennsylvania Historical and Museum Commission*

Engraving showing early method of working coal by descending levels. Of the two kinds mined in the United States, anthracite and bituminous, about 95 percent of the anthracite is found in ten counties of northeastern Pennsylvania, with the balance coming from Arkansas, Colorado, New Mexico, Virginia, and Washington. Anthracite, or hard coal, is compact, difficult to ignite, and long-burning with a clean blue, smokeless flame. Bituminous, or soft coal, which includes lignite, is soft and crumbly, and easily ignited. It has a duller luster and a nonuniform texture. Anthracite is used principally as an energy fuel and secondarily as a source of industrial carbon. Bituminous coal and lignite are consumed for heat and power production, and are carbonized to produce metallurgical coke. When coked it produces a good heating-quality gas. Bituminous is widely used to generate electric power, for lighting, manufacturing, transportation, communications systems, air conditioners, domestic appliances, and so forth. The second largest outlet for bituminous is the steel industry, which consumes about 20 percent of the total mined. It is also widely used as a basic raw material for manufacturing chemicals and synthetic rubber, detergents, plastics, perfumes, explosives, medicinals, wood preservatives, disinfectants, and a host of other things. *Free Library of Philadelphia*

Old cut showing miners' descent into a mine. Visible over the door is a 200-foot marker indicating the level of the workings. Anthracite is mined not only underground but also in strip pits and from culm banks, and limited amounts are also recovered by dredging. Culm banks are comparable to the tailings of other types of mining, residues from former mining. Dredging operations consist of recovering anthracite that was dropped into streams from boats and barges, or in the process of manufacturing. While bituminous coal is removed by strip mining and underground mining, auger mining has recently been developed, a system of drilling into exposed coal seams where strip mining is no longer practical. *Free Library of Philadelphia*

Pennsylvania coal miners leaving mine via entrance drift, around 1928. *Free Library of Philadelphia*

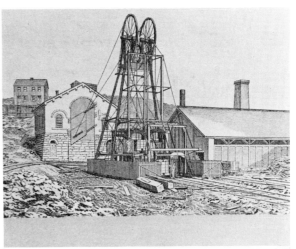

Farther south, Pottsville coal veins were discovered in 1870 by Nicho Allen. Pottsville's Necho [*sic*] Allen Hotel was named for him. *Free Library of Philadelphia*

43

This is not a hotel, but the Derringer Breaker at Cross Creek Coal. *Pennsylvania Historical and Museum Commission*

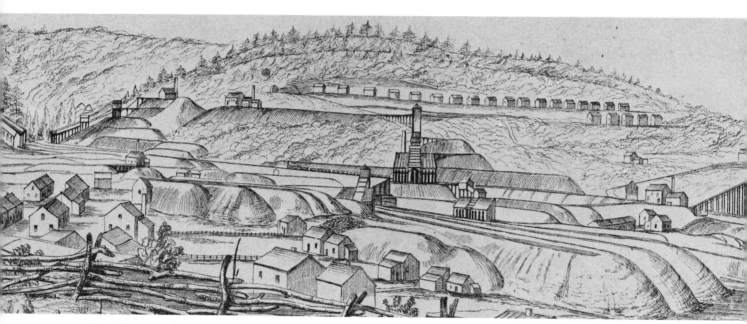

The Silver Creek Collieries, 1853, seem to blend with the countryside, though not in reality. *Smithsonian Institution*

Moving day in Pennsylvania mining country. Usually only one trip was necessary.

After being graded in the breaker, coal is being loaded out of barges and into railroad cars.

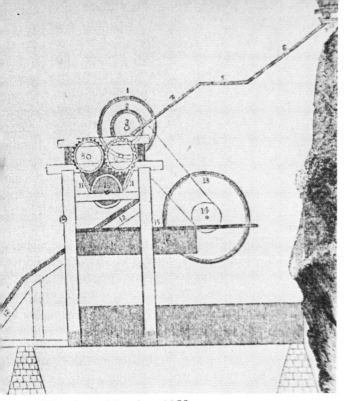

Side view of breaker, 1855.

Front view of breaker, 1855.

The Philadelphia and Reading Coal and Iron Company engineers conformed to the rules of their trade—the wearing of lantern hats and the smoking of pipes. *Smithsonian Institution*

An early Pennsylvania colliery. Although coal-production statistics were not kept until 1807, and then incompletely, the best records available show that about 5,700,000,000 tons of anthracite coal have been mined in Pennsylvania since 1807, a staggering figure, representing about 115 million carloads. Pennsylvania has also produced about 8,750,000,000 tons of bituminous coal and lignite, an estimated 175 million carloads. The record output of Pennsylvania anthracite was 100 million tons in 1917, but as heating oil and natural gas began to compete, the output dropped to less than half this amount by 1938. During World War II, there was an increase to about 65 million tons a year, but since then production has declined to about 18 million tons a year, produced by more than 800 underground mines, 200 strip mines, about 110 culm banks, and 15 or so dredging operations. Pennsylvania is no longer the leading coal-producing state, although it has, in total, produced more than any other. West Virginia, Kentucky, Pennsylvania, and Illinois are the four leading states in that order.

"Bootleg" coal mining in Pennsylvania. During the 1940s and 1950s bootleg mines were operated on the hillsides of the anthracite region. Most of these mines were worked by a single miner and his family, and were on the property of the regular hard-coal mine lands, hence the name "bootleg." Apparently the owners, while not condoning the practice, did little to stop the bootleggers, who sold their coal at lower prices. Bootleg mining was dangerous, and in 1953 came under the jurisdiction of the State Mines Department, which applied regulations for use of such mines. *Free Library of Philadelphia*

MICA

Almost every youngster sometime or other has discovered a small piece of mica and tried to separate its thin semitransparent sheets. But despite its wide occurrence, in small pieces, mining is confined to the few mica regions where sufficient quantities warrant working the deposits.

It all began back in the days of the whale-oil lamp, when Sam Ruggles, of New Hampshire, not only discovered mica on his land but knew just what to do about it. The demand for mica was keen, for use in lamp chimneys and stove windows.

A shrewd, hardworking farmer, he set his large family to working it out and hauled it to Portsmouth by ox team along with his farm products. There it was consigned and shipped to relatives in England to be sold. (Ruggles was too sharp to sell to American buyers lest they learn the secret of his mine.) Soon, however, the demand for his fine product became so great that special trips to the port were necessary. These were made in the dead of night by horse and buggy, or sleigh in winter. This continued over several years, and as volume increased, relatives and other trusted employees were added, including a mine boss, said to be "a ferocious driving man who directed operations with abundant profanity." The Ruggles Mine is still operated for mica, but mainly for feldspar.

Because of the nature of mica, most modern mining operations are small. Though about 600 companies produce the material, ten account for 40 percent of total output, a large portion of which ends as sheet mica and scrap mica, a by-product. Usually scrap mica is ground for use as a filler and surface coating in roofing materials, wallboards,

Ruggles Mine, Grafton, New Hampshire

cements, paints, rubber, plastics, and drilling mud. Sheet mica is widely used in the electronic and electrical industries, particularly in the miniaturization of electronic components.

INDIANS GET THE LEAD OUT

Even before Pierre Le Sueur's lead mine over a century before in the Mississippi Valley, rich lead discoveries were made in the Galena, Illinois, area by the Indians who traded off their lead to the French for food, guns, and trinkets. The French were in urgent need of lead for their bullets, and encouraged the Indians to conceal their production from the English and the Americans whom they resented equally. The Indians, for trading purposes, smelted lead into roughly seventy-pound "plats," which they sometimes shipped as far as St. Louis in payment for their purchases.

As late as 1817, Indians refused to permit Americans into their territory in fear that discovery of their huge lead deposits would result in their being driven from their land. Congress, however, recognized the value of the Mississippi Valley lead deposits. In 1807 it had passed legislation ordering that the lead-bearing lands be reserved from sale and leased for mining by the War Department. At first, government leases were for three-mile-square tracts, which were later reduced to one mile, and leasees were required to return 10 percent of the value of the ore to the government. In about 1825 this was reduced to 6 percent.

It took until 1822 for the first lease to be granted; it went to Colonel James Johnson, surviving brother of Richard M. Johnson, former vice-presi-

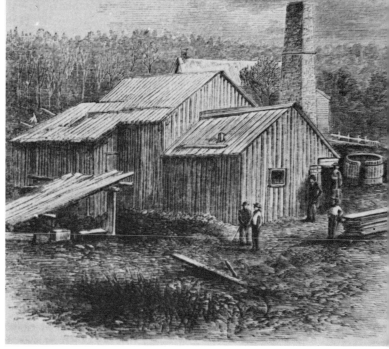

The Marsden Diggings on the Mississippi River, circa 1866, which soon became a leading lead producer of the area. Discoveries also were made at New Diggings, Hamilton's Settlement, Mineral Point, Dodgeville, and, six miles south, below Galena, at Marsden's Diggings among other places. The mines at Hamilton's Settlement were first worked by William S. Hamilton, a son of Alexander Hamilton.

The Kipp Mine, a lead and zinc operation near Galena, Illinois, probably in the late 1870s. Note that all lighting is by candlelight. This must have been visiting day for the youngster and mother in rear. Mining at Galena was accomplished by sinking shafts, which usually encountered the first strata of lead at ten to twenty feet below the surface. At this point, drifts were extended to follow the veins. Because of the low melting temperature of lead, furnaces usually were constructed near the mines to enable reclaiming the ore on the property. *Illinois State Historical Library*

Hughlett's Furnace around 1890, one of the first non-Indian furnaces built in the Galena area. Galena remained a prosperous center for lead and zinc until post–Civil War days; its importance diminished as the railroads superseded river transportation. Galena later became famous as the home of Ulysses S. Grant, who lived there for many years. His house is now a state museum. *Illinois State Historical Library*

dent of the United States. That year only five leases were granted; nine were leased the following year. By 1834 a fair number of leases had been signed, but strife, litigation, and a reluctance by the smelters and miners to pay the fee marked the beginning of the end of the federal leasing system. In general, federal income from leases equalled about one-quarter of the collection costs; in 1846, Congress authorized that the reserved mineral lands in Illinois, Arkansas, Wisconsin, and Iowa be put on the market.

All mining prior to Colonel Johnson's lease had been primitive; where Indian squaws had formerly provided most of the hard labor, Colonel Johnson imported workmen and tools necessary to modernize the mining at the French and Indian settlement known as Galena.

Thanks to the colonel, people from the Missouri Territory, Kentucky, Tennessee, and other places immigrated into the area. During the summer months thousands prospected for lead ore; they left during the winter, when there was no way of bringing in supplies. The first house had been built as early as 1819, within the present limits of Galena. The entire village was laid out by 1827, and two years later Galena's first post office was established. Its first newspaper, appropriately called *The Miner's Journal,* began in 1828.

MINEVILLE IRON AND TITANIUM

During an 1810 compass survey (the Kellogg Survey) at Mineville, New York, large quantities of iron ore were discovered that would one day help rank New York fourth in production. Fine iron-ore specimens were found but the opening of any mines awaited Harry Sherman and Elijah Bishop. They bought a quarter interest in some ore property from D. E. Sandford for $100. That was fourteen years later. The ore, principally magnetite, differed from the hematite ore of the Lake Superior region. Hematite ore is a red-colored mineral while magnetite, sometimes called lodestone, is a black mineral with magnetic qualities. About 10 percent of the ore mined in the United States is magnetite, mostly produced in northern New York.

Mineville is something of an underground city. Through a tunnel eight feet high and twenty feet wide blasted through the rock, a cable car descends at a thirty-three-degree angle to a depth of 8,000 feet.

Two years after the founding of Mineville, Archibald MacIntyre and Duncan MacMartin were oper-

A road had to be built fifty miles through the wilderness to connect the Adirondac Mine with Lake Champlain. The enterprise grew rapidly, adding forges and smelters, a puddling furnace, and a blast furnace around the town of Adirondac. Eleven years and four hundred inhabitants later, Adirondac boasted, in addition to sixteen dwellings, a boardinghouse, schoolhouse, general store, carpenter and blacksmith shops, a gristmill, sawmill, cupola, blast and puddling furnaces, a forge, and a stamping mill. In 1854 a second village was built, Tahawus, ten miles down the river. Here a dock and a crane for handling ore, a warehouse, blacksmith shop, sawmill, boardinghouse, three dwellings, and a school were constructed to supplement the Adirondac operations. *From Benson J. Lossing's* The Hudson: From the Wilderness to the Sea

ating a furnace at North Elba, on the Ausable River. The poor quality of the available ore made the operation unprofitable, so the men explored the region for silver deposits. Instead they found a ledge of solid iron ore and purchased 105,000 acres of land—which included the iron deposits—from the State of New York for ten cents an acre. They then organized the Adirondac Iron Works, later incorporated as the Adirondac Iron and Steel Company.

In its tenth year, Adirondac's ore was running 10 percent titanium, which at the time was in small demand. Within a few years, high refining costs and transportation difficulties, combined with the financial panic of 1857, caused an abrupt cessation of operations, and Adirondac became a ghost town. The mining property remained more or less dormant, except for its use by a succession of fish and game clubs. A new organization, incorporated as The Tahawus Club, acquired the property from the MacIntyre Iron Company, and 7,000 additional acres. Again attempts were made to refine the ore but the high percentage of titanium still rendered it unworkable.

During its period of occupation by fish and game clubs, in 1870 a young French chemist, Dr. A. J. Rossi, had arrived in the United States to experiment with a blast furnace in Boonton, New Jersey, where some titanium ores were successfully smelted into pig iron. Dr. Rossi was engaged by

Loading a car from a raise at Mineville. Most New York State mines ceased operation after the discovery of the Mesabi deposits in Minnesota. But Mineville's workings were an exception. In 1900 Mineville and nearby Lyon Mountain produced 23 percent of the total American output. Mineville's big development year was 1938, when Republic Steel took over, sinking new shafts, opening additional drifts, installing modern equipment, introducing wet drilling, and a wet concentrator to eliminate hazards of silicosis, a disease of the lungs. Today, however, of all the iron ore mined in the United States, open-pit mining accounts for about 75 percent. Nevertheless, Republic's shaft mines at Mineville are still important iron producers, shipping about 1,300,000 tons of ore annually. *Republic Steel Corporation*

James MacNaughton, who was responsible for finding a means of utilizing the ore from the MacIntyre Development. They formed a new company (with a blast furnace at Buffalo) for the purpose of smelting titanium ore and manufacturing titanium alloys. It quickly developed into an important industry. Actually, titanium was first discovered in 1791 by a William Gregor and rediscovered in 1795 by a German chemist, Martin H. Klaproth, who gave it its name.

Fluorite mine. Most early mines, in an area along the Ohio River in southern Illinois and in western Kentucky, were simple shaft affairs, and material was hoisted by winches to the surface, where it was processed for use in fluxing in the manufacture of iron, steel, castings, and other metals. Later, production increased substantially with the introduction of the open-hearth furnace in the steel industry, and larger mines resulted. Even with present demand, however, fewer than thirty native mines operate; and though the United States remains the world's largest producer, more than half of all fluorite consumed in this country is imported. *Kentucky Historical Society Library*

FLUORITE

In about 1820 the United States began mining a mineral called fluorite, which for centuries had been used for carving ornaments. (Its usefulness as a flux was already known around the sixteenth century, but it just was not mined here.)

Although metal fluxing remains fluorite's principal use, it also finds important applications in the glass and enamel industries and, in its acid form, hydrofluoric acid, is used in the manufacture of aerosols, refrigerants, and plastics. In other forms, among varied metallurgical uses, it is used as a fluxing material for such metals as aluminum and magnesium.

MERCURY

Soon after the United States had gone into fluorite mining, Antonio Surol, a Mexican, had come to search for silver, in 1824. He had been led by Indians to mercury deposits at New Almadén, California. But it was not until 1845 that Andreas Castillero, a Mexican army officer, proved that mercury also could be found in the cinnabar ore at New Almadén. The Mexican government had offered a $100,000 reward for a quicksilver discovery. But a British company, realizing the importance of the

An 1866 view of the New Almaden Quicksilver furnaces, with the adobe yard in the foreground. Though the United States consumes around 80,000 flasks annually, only about 20,000 flasks, mostly from nine mines, are produced domestically each year, about 70 percent from California, 25 percent from Nevada, and the balance from small deposits in Alaska, Arizona, Idaho, and Oregon. By far the largest United States producer is the New Almaden Mine, opened at about the time of the California gold discoveries. *William Culp Darrah Stereo Collection*

This cinnabar mine is in the Ochoco National Forest in Oregon. (The ore of mercury is cinnabar.) Mercury is an important commodity used principally by plants that produce chlorine and caustic soda, electrical apparatus, industrial and control instruments, and in chemicals for agriculture and industry. Smaller amounts are used for castings, dental preparations, laboratory applications, and for mildew-proofing paint. In 1968 a few discoveries were made that might become important: one is in Pershing County and the other in Humboldt County, Nevada, both in the Winnemucca area. It is also possible that new deposits might be uncovered in Alaska. The largest producer is still the New Almaden Mine, with the Cordero Mine the Number Two producer. Another large producer is the Cahill Mine. *United States Forest Service. Photo by Bluford W. Muir*

deposit, bought the mine from Castillero and developed it, removing the cinnabar and naming the mine after the famous Almadén Mine in Spain, which was then the world's greatest mercury producer. In 1848 the new mine was refining small amounts of mercury.

Perhaps nothing could have been more timely: James Marshall's discovery of gold the year before was creating a tremendous demand for mercury (popularly known as quicksilver), essential for the amalgamation processes used to separate the gold from the ore. The growth of the New Almadén Quicksilver Mine was immediate and fabulous. The quicksilver was (and still is) shipped in seventy-six-pound flasks, totaling 7,000 flasks in 1850 and 30,000 in 1851; by 1881, the mine had produced nearly 55 million pounds—worth over $70 million. (Mercury today sells at about $500 a flask.) And the British had sold out to the United States Quicksilver Mining Company in 1864 for nearly $2 million.

New Almadén curtailed operations after World War II but many remnants of the old quicksilver mine remain, particularly the mine superintendent's residence, constructed in 1854. About thirty buildings erected in town in the 1850s still exist, most used as private residences. Although the mine is still worked occasionally, visitors can take guided trips to portions of it.

The mine was once owned by T. J. and Allan Hoover, brother and son of the late President Hoover. It is now owned by the Idria Mining and Chemical Company, which operates a quicksilver mine near Hollister, California. The company plans to activate and expand the New Almadén Mine.

FELDSPAR

In sharp contrast to the scarcity of mercury, is feldspar, one of the few native minerals mined for export long before its adaption for local consumption. It is one of the commonest components of the earth's crust. But its use is confined to a few industries. The glass industry accounts for over half the output, pottery approximately a third. A small percentage is used for enamel and the balance is consumed by the ceramic, soap, and powder industries. Originally, feldspar had wider uses as poultry grit and granules in roofing, but these are relatively unimportant today. The first feldspar mine operated in North Carolina in 1744, and its entire output was shipped to England. It was not until 1825 that a Connecticut deposit became the first feldspar used domestically and yet it took twenty-five years more before the first feldspar mill was built. It stood at the Toll Gate Mine, near Middletown.

Feldspar commonly is found associated with quartz and mica; some of the earliest feldspar mines were mica mines, the Ruggles Mine (New Hampshire) in 1803 being among the first and best known. Modern feldspar generally is mined by open-pit methods, although a few mines are underground.

Three leading feldspar companies contribute two thirds of the entire domestic production, operating plants principally, in order of production, in North Carolina, California, Connecticut, Georgia, South Carolina, South Dakota, New Hampshire, Virginia, Arizona, and Maine.

COAL EXPANDS

Almost immediately following Connecticut's first domestic use of feldspar, Pennsylvania had most of its main canals in operation, and feeder lines to carry coal from its mines to the canals were under construction. These feeders generally used gravity cars that ran downhill to the canals. The empty cars were brought back by horses or mules. Ironically, it was anthracite that replaced these animals because the coal they transported was responsible for the development of the first railroad. The famous "Stourbridge Lion" was one of the first steam locomotives put to use in this country, carrying coal between Honesdale and Seeleyville. Its first trip was on August 8, 1829. Before long a network of railroads covered the anthracite fields, rendering obsolete many of the newly built coal-hauling canals, some even before completion.

In Scranton, the first important miners were the Wurtz brothers, William and Maurice, who bought up coal land and began marketing extensively around 1855. Transportation costs to New York City were high and so in 1828 the brothers helped develop the Delaware and Hudson Canal connecting the Delaware and Hudson rivers. From then until the 1850s, Scranton's coal industry grew phenomenally; companies engaged in removing the "black gold" were numerous. But for size, other coal towns varied little from Scranton. Welsh prospectors, in 1813, discovered coal near Hazleton when it was called Hazel [sic] Swamp. Wilkes-Barre was named earlier, in 1806, but it was not

As the demand increased, canals were built connecting the East Coast waterways with the Midwest, and transportation of coal and other materials by barge through an intricate system of canals became an important business. Here is an artist's sketch of a barge canal looking east from Pottsville to Port Carbon in Schuylkill County. *Smithsonian Institution (from Schuylkill County, Pennsylvania, Historical Society)*

In the 1700s and early 1800s coal was carried by colliers to discharge points, where it was transferred into barges such as the one depicted in this 1828 sketch. *Free Library of Philadelphia*

An 1869 sketch of a horse being lowered into a mine shaft. *New York Public Library Picture Collection*

Powerful teams of mules were used in the old coal mines, such as this team working in the Morley Mine, in Colorado. *C. F. & I. Steel Corporation*

Getting material in and out of a mine, circa 1855, was often a problem; at times there was not sufficient head room even for a dog, which meant that the miners had to supplant the animals and do the work themselves.

At Wheelwright, Kentucky, a coal town, seekers after the truth are baptized in a local pond formed by partially blocking off a tiny stream. *Inland Steel Company*

Company housing in Connorsville, Ohio, provided a number of unattractive two-family houses in early coal-mining days. *Ohio Historical Society*

This is typical of the worst of the company-owned dwellings. Six families lived in a single room in each of these boxcar homes set on stilts in a gully adjacent to the mine waste dumps. A single outhouse served the six families. One can be seen at the extreme left center. *Bureau of Mines, Department of the Interior*

The cleanliness and happy appearance of these children is a direct contrast to the conditions under which they live. *Bureau of Mines, Department of the Interior*

Regardless of living conditions, a good deal of the miner's health and happy family life depends upon housekeeping habits. Some Appalachia wives managed to keep their families clean. *Bureau of Mines, Department of the Interior*

Eva Hibbert, age ten years, received worldwide publicity in 1929 when her picture was published throughout the world. The child was the daughter of a British miner who gave the Prince of Wales a vivid account of her suffering and the poverty that was a national calamity in the coal-mining districts of England. *World Wide Photo*

In the gold and silver mining days, mining communities often took pride in their school facilities. This is a school near Creede, Colorado, in the late 1800s, attended mostly by miners' children. Note that the hills in the background have been completely denuded of timber, some used for the construction of the school-house and other buildings, but most going into construction in the mines. *John La Font*

"Red Row" was an ultramodern miners' apartment complex for 1910, and offered hot water and electric lights. The community also had its own church, bakery, school, and general store. These apartments were torn down shortly after the mines closed, and not a trace is left. History of Portsmouth, R.I. *Illustrated by John T. Pierce*

Too young to go to school, and no recreational facilities. The broom near the child's foot might have been used to chase the chickens out, but apparently it received little floor-cleaning use. *Bureau of Mines, Department of the Interior*

In 1946 these homes were considered medium-quality company housing. The small building at the right was the school building for this little community. *Bureau of Mines, Department of the Interior*

55

An old-fashioned company store at a coal mine in Buxton, Iowa. *Iowa Department of Mines and Minerals*

An 1895 store in California. Old-fashioned company stores were not things of beauty, and often became hangouts for miners in their idle times. *United States Forest Service*

The slops being eaten by the animal on the floor of a miner's home is evidence of the frustration of the hard life of an Appalachian coal miner. Note the miner's shirt and helmet hanging on the wall. *Bureau of Mines, Department of the Interior*

By the mid-1940s, state laws often required adequate washhouses at the mines for the use of the workers. After changing their clothes, the miners hung their garments high in the air, where they were shaken and aired so that they could be dried in time for the next day's work. *Bureau of Mines, Department of the Interior*

A 1947 kitchen in a Kentucky miner's home that exemplifies poor housekeeping, no doubt in a poorly furnished, inadequately maintained house rented from a real-estate company. *Bureau of Mines, Department of the Interior*

The 1947 kitchen of a Kentucky miner and his family in a house rented from his employer. Good housekeeping and company maintenance made the difference. *Bureau of Mines, Department of the Interior*

These West Virginia miners' bedrooms in duplicate, adjoining houses indicate that the fault was not always

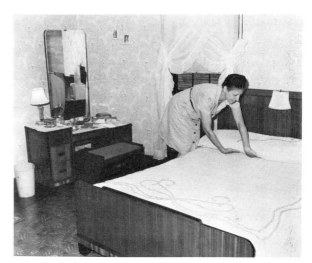

with the mining company. *Bureau of Mines, Department of the Interior*

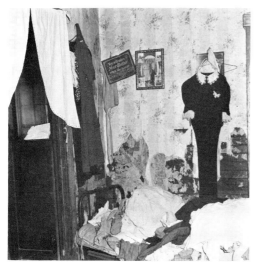

A well-kept miner's bedroom, and one that undoubtedly reflects the frustrations of a miner's life. In the disreputable-looking bedroom the one item that is well

cared for is the dress hanging on the wall. *Bureau of Mines, Department of the Interior*

incorporated until 1871. Coal mining in Wilkes-Barre was fairly active in the early 1800s when Wilkes-Barre judge Jesse Fell discovered that anthracite coal would burn in a grate. But Abijah and John Smith, who were shipping coal before Judge Fell's discovery, are the real pioneers of the anthracite industry. It was Abijah who in 1818 first tried to break down coal in the mines with blasting powder. His black powder blasting methods were later carried over into western gold and silver mining, until powder was replaced by dynamite.

GOLD IN THEM THAR HILLS

Authorities may differ on the date the white man first found gold in the United States. But it is undisputed, however, that as early as the 1500s Indians offered to sell gold to the Spaniards in Florida; De Soto, from the reports of Indians, suspected there was gold in present Georgia but was unable to find it. About twenty-five years after the Reed boy's gold discovery in North Carolina, the rapidly spreading gold-placer workings had extended southwest, reaching into Georgia. Actually, the first records of gold fever of major proportions began in 1828 when Ben Parks found gold in Georgia while deer hunting on Cherokee land, and that year a man named Wilpero found gold in Habersham County.

As prospectors encroached upon Cherokee territory, federal and state troops moved to prevent their "intrusion" into the Indian lands. But this did not deter the white man from settling along the Chestatee, Etowah, and Yahoola rivers and building huts and cabins. The state government therefore decided, in 1830, that the Cherokee Reservation would become a county and the Indians sent west, beyond the Mississippi River, thus opening the Georgia lands to prospectors. Though this action became official only with the treaty of 1835, it did not hinder the state from quickly dividing the mineral lands into forty-acre lots for public-domain settlement, to be determined by lottery.

AURARIA

By 1832 most of the productive area lay between the Chestatee and the Etowah rivers, where two squatters, William Dean and Nathaniel Nuckolls, settled. Dean built a cabin; Nuckolls set up a tavern, which was the beginning of the town of Nuckollsville. The name later was changed to Knuckellsville and again to Auraria, meaning a gold region or a gold mine.

A pocket produces a nugget. One of these, found on Alfred B. Holt's lot near the Auraria-Dahlonega area, was said to weigh twenty-eight pounds.

Old sluice box with "Hungarian" riffles used in Georgia to collect gold from washed sands. *Georgia Geological Survey*

As the lotteries awarded increasingly more land to the prospectors, trading in real estate became as profitable as gold mining itself, with some forty-acre lots selling for $30,000. And as the Auraria ores continued to produce greater quantities of high-quality gold, prices for lots increased.

New types of gold-washing machinery were developed to supplant the old rocking cradles and sluice boxes, and several were patented. According to the *Western Herald,* a local newspaper, one such device to be used by eight people was guaranteed "to wash more grit in a given time than any five machines now in use, and to lose less gold than any one."

By 1833 rock mining began. In the summer of 1834 one such mine had been tunneled 100 feet deep, and its owners built a stamping mill. Pigeon-Roost Mining Company, a consolidation of several lots that offered a public issue of stock, was the first big mining company. The Belfast Mining Company also authorized a stock issue of half a million dollars. Work in the vein mines, where large numbers of Negro slaves were employed, absorbed more and more miners as the gold-panning areas thinned out.

For the first eight years, most of the gold was shipped to Philadelphia for conversion, estimated to equal several million dollars. Auraria continued to grow until there were over 100 homes on its original forty acres, as well as twenty stores, a number of taverns and saloons, and a population of about 1,000 people. Over 10,000 were living in the county, and since Auraria was the only established town, it did a thriving business. Gold remained the medium of exchange; as early as 1830, two years before Auraria was founded, private mints had been established. Roads were built and stage lines were opened between North Carolina, South Carolina, Georgia, and Tennessee.

SLAVES IN THE MINES

Unlike the western mining towns that were to follow within twenty years, Auraria was relatively free of crime. Only one murder was committed during its mining existence. However, slavery was practiced widely, and slaves were bought and sold for work in the mines; tracking down runaway slaves was a major problem for mine operators.

Meanwhile, placer mining in North Carolina had reached its peak about 1833, with much of the labor provided by slaves working from early morning to darkness. They were required to deposit the gold in quart jars, which the slave owners were said to demand at the rate of one jar daily for every four to eight slaves. The South Mountains District at the headwaters of the First and Second Broad rivers, Muddy Creek, and Silver Creek held the most lucrative deposits.

Contemporary geological reports had as many as 3,000 slaves working along a single stream at the height of activity, especially at Silver Creek. At that rate, if an average of six slaves filled a quart jar daily, the placers would be producing over a million dollars a day. Sheer fantasy! They did remove enough gold to deplete the rich deposits

and cause the work to spread up the hillsides to gold-bearing bench gravels and into the upper decomposed layer of the rock.

MINTING THE GOLD

Converting the gold into a circulating medium was a separate problem. As with Georgia, the only available mint was at Philadelphia. Consequently in 1831, Christian Bechtler, a German jeweler, arranged to coin the miner's gold, at a 2½ percent fee, minting various denominations—$1, $2.50, and $5 gold pieces, each bearing his name. When Bechtler died, in 1843, his nephew, C. Bechtler, Jr., continued the business, which lasted until June, 1857. For some ten years, between $4,000 and $5,000 a week was coined. Many of Bechtler's coins are still in existence and command premium prices.

During this time, North Carolina's successful placer mining had spurred constant searches for vein and lode deposits, and by 1850 many important mines were opened. And as the California gold rush developed, many miners from North Carolina and Georgia joined the stampede, leaving the South bereft of manpower. Widespread propaganda urged Georgians to remain in the state. Publicity stressed the difficulties of working the California goldfields, and emphasized that the reports of the strikes were exaggerated, that hundreds en route to California, via Panama, had died, and that many more had been murdered by Indians. Only the most profitable mines were financially able to continue, but only until the start of the Civil War. After the war, during Reconstruction days, many of the old mines reopened. The search for gold was renewed; a few new mines were discovered, and many North Carolina mines continued production, spasmodically, until 1915.

DAHLONEGA

Meanwhile Dahlonega, Georgia, became important. Panning occurred as early as 1830 at Cave Creek, and a rivalry between Dahlonega and Auraria reached a climax in 1838 with the building of the first United States Mint in Dahlonega.

The exodus from Georgia carried along William, Levi, and Oliver Russell, known collectively as the Russell Boys, from Auraria, who joined the "Pike's Peak or Bust" stampede to discover the gold-bearing sands at Cherry Creek. They named their Colorado settlement Auraria, which was the beginning of Denver. However, from about 1850, Auraria, Georgia, declined, and in a few years the Civil War tolled its final death knell.

Harper's Magazine of August 29, 1879, carried

Dahlonega in the 1840s. The shifting of the county seat to Dahlonega, as well as the 1838 construction of the United States Mint, ended the importance of Auraria as the gold center of the United States.

John C. Calhoun, before becoming Vice President of the United States, struck it rich at this exact spot. Photographed by S. W. McCallie at the Calhoun Mine. *Georgia Geological Survey*

A stamp mill in Dahlonega utilizing the waterpower provided by the Yahoola River dam.

a detailed description of mining in Georgia, describing among other things the work of the Yahoola Ditch, which supplied water to the mines. But it did not convey the bitterness and dissent over the Ditch, best expressed in a letter that appeared in the *Dahlonega Signal,* August 29, 1879, entitled "Gold Mining in Georgia." The letter, signed "Native," is worth reproducing for its vituperous language.

Messrs. Editors: Under the above caption (Gold Mining in Georgia) a lineal descendant of a jackass pays a hurried and false notice to the people of this section, and publishes, with accompanying caricatures in that disreputable periodical, *Harper's Monthly.* As the editor and proprietors of that unfair and unjust New York institution live, ghoul like, upon such airy filth, generally gotten up by those whose minds are incapable of "strad-

dling even the frontier of a thought," doubtless that correspondence was a feast to the aforesaid eds. and prop'rs. Said descendant and correspondent frequently alludes to the civilization of this section. He is not accustomed to it. We are happy to confess that our civilization has not yet assumed such gigantic proportions as is seen every day in boasted Northern civilization, a fair sample of which is now being discussed by the papers, and in which a boasted New York statesman figured in his usual grand style. A yellow dog in this section acting with no more manhood than this kind of Northern civilization would have been sent to the bottom of one of our played-out shafts.

It is these silly flings at the South, Mr. Editor, as well as the out and out slanders upon our people, and which the Harpers delight in publishing that has a tendency to keep burning the fires of hatred and distrust between the two sections.

This old cut shows a view of the Yahoola River, a principal site for placer mining in Georgia. Note the cabins, not all of which belonged to the early miners.

The Yahoola Ditch. It became an important factor in supplying water to the Dahlonega mining area, running in part through ditches and in part through pipe, sometimes soaring as high as 250 feet, especially at a point where it crossed the Yahoola River. Many of its trestles ranged from 100 feet to 150 feet in height. Ultimately, iron pipes replaced much of the original wooden flumework.

This correspondent has not stated facts and I will call attention to only one of his statements. In speaking of the Yahoola Ditch he says it is "the work of Col. Hand to whom more than anyone else, no doubt belongs the credit of this splendid development of the industry during late years, and the glowing prospects it now holds out." When the truth is the credit should belong to Dr. M. H. Van Dyke who superintended those operations and accomplished the completion of the Yahoola Ditch very nearly to town before Col. Hand ever came to this country. I hardly think Col. Hand has the brazen effontry to claim a credit that rightly belongs to Dr. Van Dyke. The Harpers had better send their man to Narragansett Pier.

Some gold mining is still done in the Auraria-Dahlonega area. The old mint is still standing and many relics of the historic mining days can be seen at the Dahlonega Gold Museum, housed in the old courthouse. An old gold mine can be visited at Blackburn State Park, seven and one-half miles south of Dahlonega, one mile from Auraria.

Marble works at Tate, Georgia. Georgia is noted for its marble industry, and by 1888, when this sketch appeared in *Leslie's Weekly*, quarrying was well industrialized.

This picture appeared in *Leslie's* in 1889, and depicts different aspects of the iron mine at Galton Hill near Cartersville, Georgia. In the late 1800s, Georgia iron mining was extensive.

VIRGINIA MAKES ITS BID

Had the California forty-niners read Volume XXXII, Number 187 of *Harper's New Monthly Magazine,* appearing shortly after the Civil War, they would have dropped their shovels, abandoned their arrastras, and rushed to the Virginia and North Carolina goldfields. Whether straight reporting or a campaign to help revive the South's depleted financial resources, the article described the Virginia mineral resources in such glowing terms that it could well have started an east coast gold rush. For example:

> To give any adequate description of the mineral wealth which Virginia contains would be not only to minutely describe every rod of her entire length, embracing hundreds of miles, but to enumerate almost every mineral of value hitherto known among mankind. It is not in gold alone that she abounds, but, scattered in profusion over almost her entire surface, are to be found—iron, copper, silver, tin, tellurium, lead, platinum, cinnabar, plumbago, manganese, asbestos, kaolin (porcelain clay), slate clay (fire clay), coal, roofing slate of the greatest durability, marble of the rarest beauty, soap-stone, sulphur, hone-stone equal to the best turkey, gypsum, lime, copperas (sulphate of iron), blue-stone (sulphate of copper), grindstones, cobalt, emery, and a variety of other materials that we have hitherto been compelled to import or to do without. Indeed it may be said, without exaggeration, that in the single State of Virginia, in the most singular juxtaposition of what might be considered geologically incongruous materials, is to be found an almost exhaustless fund of God-given treasures, more than enough to pay off our whole national debt, and only waiting the magic touch of capital and enterprise to drag them to light for the benefit of man.

The Marks Gold Mine, one of the first in Virginia, was started in 1830 by George Fisher, and remained in operation until after the Civil War. It was near Columbia, fifty miles from Richmond, on a 250-acre farm. It contrasts sharply with its bucolic surroundings. These two men could well be farmers or miners. Three other mines were adjacent to the Marks property: the Eades, Big-Bird, and Belzoro, the latter bought by Fisher.

The Belzoro, started in 1832 by William Southworth who operated surface washings until its sale. At its height a stamping mill with six stamps and a crushing machine were in operation, and $300 in gold was extracted daily. Crucibles were found on the property, and are believed to have been used by Indians for melting lead or gold.

Found a year before the discovery of the Belzoro was the Waller Mine, located in Goochland County. Nearby were the Lowry, Nicholas, Hughes, and Collins mines. The Waller was the most developed; veins were discovered within a year, ending surface washing and converting the mine to shaft operation. Sold several times, the mine fell to a British company, which failed after two years. It was one of the first mines in the area with shafts sunk to a depth of about seventy-five feet. Most of the labor was performed by Negro slaves, a practice that then prevailed in all Virginia mines.

Near Columbia was the Snead Gold Mine, first worked in 1837. The Snead contained deposits of lead, silver, and copper, and although it was worked until 1850, it yielded only $35 worth of silver a ton; mid-1800 technology had not progressed sufficiently to smelt these metals profitably in the process of obtaining the gold. Nearby was the Tellerium Mine. This 1865 woodcut is characteristic of the serene countryside.

Buckingham County provided several gold mines, the oldest being the Lightfoot Mine, about six miles from New Canton. From its discovery in 1832, it was worked only for gold, until the 1850s, when copper was extracted and shipped to smelters in Baltimore. By then gold had become merely a by-product. Mining ended with the outbreak of the Civil War.

FIRST AMERICAN MINE DISASTER

Harper's Magazine, incidentally, did not mention the first officially recorded mine accident—at the Black Heath Coal Mine, near Richmond, Virginia, on March 18, 1839. Reports indicated that fifty-four men were in the mine, and that only two, near the mouth of the shaft, escaped. The pit had exploded with a sudden force, so powerful that a descending basket containing three men was blown about 100 feet into the air. Two of the men fell out of the basket and were killed, and the third was thrown about eighty feet from the shaft, breaking his arms and legs.

In this 1874 sketch by Alfred J. Eames, miners flee the smoke of a burning coal mine at Wilkes-Barre, Pennsylvania. *New York Public Library Picture Collection*

Firedamp, or methane gas, was, and still is, a principal cause of coal-mine explosions. Cave-ins often accompanied fire or explosion as wall or ceiling structures were weakened. *Free Library of Philadelphia*

Fire extinguishers were not always very effective in fighting a mine fire. *Free Library of Philadelphia*

Disaster by flood. *Free Library of Philadelphia (from* Underground *by Thomas W. Knox, 1874)*

Going down a mine shaft. The miner at the bottom lost his footing. *Free Library of Philadelphia*

The first Indiana blast furnace was similar to this Catalan forge, and was built on Indian Creek near Bloomington in southwestern Monroe County in 1839. Called the Randolph Ross & Sons Virginia Iron Works, for about five years the furnace successfully produced iron both for local use and for export to New Albany. In this view an oxteam is making its way to the furnace with a load of iron, while the mules are about to carry off the finished product. *Indiana Geological Survey. Drawing by R. Judah*

INDIANA IRON ORE

Three prominent Indiana blast furnaces—the Lafayette, Brazil, and Vigo. During the 1830s, while gold was being discovered elsewhere, Indiana swelled with iron smelters and furnaces, raw materials coming mostly from bog iron from local swampy areas; but though some underground mines were still in operation around 1900, Indiana never became a major iron-ore-producing state. However, the early furnaces and smelters laid the foundation for the important steel mills now in operation; giant mills along the Great Lakes are served by iron ore shipped in by boat from neighboring states to the northwest. *Indiana Geological Survey*

A mid-nineteenth-century Indiana bog iron-ore deposit. Collected in the swamps, the iron was loaded into ore wagons pulled by oxen. *Indiana Geological Survey. Drawing by R. Judah*

MORE GOLD IN THE HILLS

It seems almost inconceivable that today only two major gold mines are operating in the United States —the Homestake Mining Company in South Dakota and the Carlin Gold Mining Company in Nevada; a third, Knob Hill, in Washington, produces about 15 percent of Homestake's output. Even so, much gold is obtained from the production of other metals where gold is a by-product.

Homestake and Carlin operations contrast greatly. Homestake was incorporated in 1877; Carlin started producing in 1966. Homestake's gold comes from over 200 miles of underground tunneling; Carlin's lies almost on the earth's surface, just beneath the overburden. Homestake's story begins in 1834 in the Black Hills of the Dakota Territory. No one actually knows when gold was first discovered in the Black Hills but Captain Seth Bullock, a frontiersman and first sheriff of Deadwood, South Dakota, wrote in his diary:

Shortly after the close of the Civil War, Father DeSmet, the heroic missionary, stated at a dinner party in the home of General Ewing at Columbus, Ohio, that he had repeatedly seen gold dust in the possession of the Sioux Indians. They told him that they got it in the Black Hills and that there was "heap plenty of it." Where and

how the Sioux got the gold which they had from time to time is a controversial matter. If it was from the Black Hills it is an almost assured fact that it came from the section now embraced in the county of Lawrence, as their trail through the Hills in going from their camps along the Belle Fourche River to their hunting grounds west of the Hills skirted Deadwood Gulch, crossed the Homestake Belt and the rich placer deposits in the gravels near Central City.

A sandstone tablet found in 1887 by Louis Thoen, near the town of Spearfish, revealed a scratching on one side that might well date the missionary's experience:

Came to these hills in 1833 seven of us DeLacompt, Ezra Kind, G. W. Wood, T. Brown, R. Kent, Wm. King, Indian Crow, all died but me Ezra Kind killed by Ind behind high hill got our gold dust June 1834.

And on the opposite side:

Got all the gold we could carry. Our ponies all got by the Indians. I have lost my gun and nothing to eat. The Indians hunting me.

There is good reason to believe that the stone is authentic: it was well hidden by grass and brush that had grown around it, and it was near a trail on Spring Creek that led from a fur-trading post at the mouth of the Redwater (Belle Fourche) to the Indian trail up Deadwood Gulch. But forty years of relative quiet would pass since that inscription.

In 1874, before General George A. Custer, on a military reconnaissance in the region, could forward his official report to Washington, the discovery of gold was rumored and a rush began that by 1876 became a stampede.

The earliest prospectors found evidence of prospecting along the tributaries of the Deadwood River that predated them by years. They nevertheless located placer claims on every creek in the Northern Black Hills, especially along Deadwood Creek, which runs through Central City and Deadwood. Many of the claims were highly profitable, especially the Wheeler claim; in one season in 1876 more than $100,000 worth of gold was panned.

The placer operations were quickly worked out, but by then enterprising prospectors were already searching for quartz lode claims. The Manuel brothers, Moses and Fred, prospecting in the vicinity of the Hills for a year, on April 9, 1876, discovered the Homestake Ledge, or Lead (pronounced *Leed*), from which the town was named. That spring they took out $5,000 in gold.

Oxen hauling supplies to the mines rest on Lead's Main Street, around 1880. Because at the time the nearest railroad, the Union Pacific, was at Sidney, Nebraska, it was necessary to haul all mine equipment the 270 miles by oxteam. Once the 80-stamp mill, boilers, heavy machinery, and other items arrived, the gold-bearing rock began to be mined in open cuts. Underground work was started through the use of shafts, and "square-set" stoping, developed for the Comstock Lode, which was discovered in 1859, was employed with good results. *Homestake Mining Company*

Lead and the Homestake gold mine, circa 1900, our largest gold mine. About 50 percent of United States gold production is produced from gold and silver mines. Over 35 percent comes as a by-product of base-metal ore production, and the rest from placer mining, including dredging. The major factors keeping down gold production in the United States are inflation carried over from World War II; the discontinuance of all gold mining during the war (War Production Board Order Number L-208); and the federally pegged price of $35 per ounce. Although ore bodies underlying our land still contain untold quantities of gold, the economics of mining make its removal unprofitable at the fixed $35-per-ounce price. *Homestake Mining Company*

In June, 1877, L. D. Kellogg, an experienced miner employed by a San Francisco syndicate, arrived in the Hills to investigate the gold discoveries. He optioned the Homestake and Gold Star claims for $70,000, which the syndicate quickly took up, purchasing other claims as well and rapidly undertaking their development.

In time, mill capacity increased, waterpower was developed, hoisting equipment was installed, and horses were replaced by motors. Eventually, as the depth of the mine increased, the square-set stoping of pillars was abandoned in favor of open cut and fill stoping.

One principal difficulty encountered by Homestake was the toughness of its ore, even more resistant than the nearby Mount Rushmore granite; so solid it could hardly be dented by a pick. Special tools and equipment had to be developed, including air compressors and drills, power shovels, power draglines or slushers, air and water hoses, and miles of compressed air and water lines. Now huge quantities of explosives are employed for breaking down the ore, and the company has a tremendous investment in machinery and technical staff.

Stoping operations by candlelight, around 1900. *Homestake Mining Company*

Homestake, 1887. The company was incorporated in California on November 5, 1877, and production began in 1878. Of the 6,000 acres of mining claims owned by Homestake today, the first two comprised only about ten acres. *Homestake Mining Company*

Piston drills were mounted on a column that was held in place by jackscrews. A forged drill steel and bit reciprocates with each stroke of the piston. The air hose is armored, and water was not used in the drilling operations until later. *Homestake Mining Company*

These air drills are set up to drill holes about twelve feet deep into the ore. But this follows an earlier task—the first job every morning of testing the overlying back, or roof, after the previous day's blasting. The idea is to pry down the loose rock that remains, called "barring down," which is an important safety precaution. *Homestake Mining Company*

Six days every week about 6,600 tons of ore are hauled to the shafts and hoisted to the surface on an intricate 18-inch-gauge underground railway system employing more than 100 miles of track. About 650 3-ton automatic side-dump ore cars and over 500 1½-ton rocker dump cars support the operation. They are powered by electric storage batteries or compressed air locomotives, and are further assisted by 20 8-ton bottom-dump cars moved by electric trolley. *Homestake Mining Company*

After the holes are drilled, explosives are blown into the holes by air pressure. The final operation is the actual blasting, after which timbers are set up to brace and support the roof and walls. *Homestake Mining Company*

A view of the power gates on the chutes. The ore is drawn from the stope chutes into the cars, hauled to the shaft ore bins, into which it is dumped, and later drawn off into the ore skips. The ore finally is hoisted to the surface and moved to the crushing plant. *Homestake Mining Company*

A slusher hoist and a scraper removing broken ore from a mine floor. *Homestake Mining Company*

After the broken ore is drawn from the stope, the resulting opening is filled with sand tailings (discharged from the treatment plants where the gold is removed). This is known as capping a "fill," which supports the walls and prevents rock movement. By the addition of dry cement, a smooth, solid six-inch cap is formed on the top of each ten-foot fill. *Homestake Mining Company*

Exploring with the use of a modern diamond drill.
Homestake Mining Company

Homestake's surface plant at Lead, Lawrence County,
1969. Major plant units are Yates shaft (upper left);
mechanical department's machine shops, foundry, pat-
tern shop, and warehouse (below and to right of Yates
shaft headframe); south mill (left center); east and
west cyanide plants (flat-roofed structure at lower left
and building at lower right); refinery (immediately
above west cyanide plant and to right of south mill).
Mining operations are conducted on 34 levels, from
1,700 to 6,800 feet. Approximately 200 miles of workings, drifts, and crosscuts have been installed to provide
access between the three shafts and the various ore
bodies at the different levels. Despite all the difficulties
encountered along the way, Homestake is one of the
most modern operations in the world, and is the largest
gold producer in the Western Hemisphere. *Homestake
Mining Company*

FROM BLACK HILLS TO BLACK COAL

Only six years after Homestake's beginnings, in
1840, in Farmington, Iowa, Samuel Knight was
mining coal. Mostly, there were local drifts and
small operations. Miners here were getting five cents
a bushel, while coal sold for $2 to $2.50 a ton.
Since most of these mines were not served by railroads, wagons were the principal method of shipment. But then the railroads had developed and so
did the demand for locomotive fuel.

George Williams formed the Iowa Coal Company in 1872, and employed about 100 men who
produced about 400 tons of coal a day. In its
second year the demand for coal fell during the
spring, and a number of miners were laid off. Those
who gave the least patronage to the company store
were the first to go. In defiance, a general strike
was called, which was broken when imported labor
was brought in.

The old Pioneer Coal Mine near Angus, Iowa, around
1875. Wesley Redhead and his associates organized it as
the Des Moines Coal Company, Iowa's first major coal
mine. Redhead changed the outdated weighing of coal
by the bushel to weighing it by the ton. By 1873 important new discoveries were made at the 125-foot level
of Redhead's mine, rechristened the Black Diamond,
and later changed to the Pioneer. The Pioneer was one
of the first to be equipped with such modern machinery
as steam hoists and ventilating fans. Three years later
the Pioneer employed 150 men, and was producing
over 200 tons of coal daily. *Iowa Department of Mines
and Minerals*

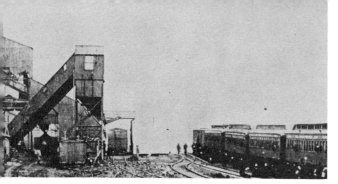

In 1875 many mines reorganized into the Consolidation Coal Company, including the Black Diamond, the Iowa Central Coal Company, and the Southern Coal Company among others. And two years later they bought out the Mahaska County Coal Company, making Consolidation the largest mining company in the area. In 1881 Consolidation was bought by the North Western Railroad, which over the next forty years expanded into the largest of the Iowa mining companies, operating nineteen mines. *Iowa Department of Mines and Minerals*

On May 1, 1900, an explosion in the Scofield Mine at Scofield, Utah, claimed the lives of 200 men, and left 107 widows and 268 fatherless children. Here is a mass burial of 150 bodies from the explosion. The remainder of the other 50 were sent to other parts of the state. *Utah State Historical Society*

The Ottumwa (Iowa) Coal Palace. In 1890, a dozen or more coal-producing counties cooperated in its construction. It was a massive and remarkable structure, veneered with blocks of coal constructed like a castle, 230 feet long, 130 feet wide, and surmounted by a central tower 200 feet high. The coal building contained huge display rooms for exhibits and a 6,000-seat auditorium. The palace was the center of a two-year coal exposition in 1890 and 1891, and during its lifetime attracted hundreds of thousands of visitors. It was ultimately torn down and replaced by a park. *Iowa Department of Mines and Minerals*

DANGERS AND ACCIDENTS

Coal mining was not all a matter of production and profits. On September 6, 1869, 179 men died in a mine disaster at the Avondale Mine at Plymouth, Pennsylvania, when a breaker, built directly over the shaft entrance—the only mine exit—caught fire. The men were trapped below and suffocated. To avoid its recurrence, subsequent legislation required two exits at every mine and prohibited the placement of breakers over a shaft.

The scene at the entrance of a Monongah, West Virginia, coal mine following the worst mine disaster in American history on December 6, 1907, when at least 362 men were killed in an explosion. The entrance is wrecked almost beyond recognition by the furious blast. Spectators and officials swarm over splintered timbers and twisted rails, possibly looking for evidence that would solve the mystery of the cause of the explosion. United Mine Workers Journal

Removing the dead after the Monongah explosion on December 6, 1907. *Bureau of Mines, Department of the Interior*

Waiting at the Monongah mine entrance for news. *Bureau of Mines, Department of the Interior*

The Cherry Mine where 400 men were entombed on November 13, 1909. Two hundred fifty-six of these men died in this accident, when at 1:00 P.M. drops of burning oil from a torch had fallen on a load of hay en route to the mule stables at the mine bottom, spreading fire through both shafts and cutting off all chances of escape. Eleven would-be rescuers were also trapped and killed, and the flames, smoke, and poison gases prevented any further rescue attempts. For a week, women and children prayed in quiet groups around the shafts. On the last day, after dozens of scorched and blackened bodies had been removed and laid out for identification, twenty-one men emerged alive. Concrete caps placed on the shafts finally smothered the fire some five months later. *Illinois State Historical Library*

Monument to the memory of the 256 miners who lost their lives in the Cherry Mine disaster on November 13, 1909. *Illinois State Historical Library*

View of wrecked tipple and conveyor and the crowd at the pit mouth after a Pennsylvania coal mine explosion in May, 1929. From about 1910 until about 1940, miners were killed at an average rate of 2,000 a year, and the death of 276 miners in the last quarter of 1940 caused the passage of the Coal Mine Inspection and Investigation Act. *Bureau of Mines, Department of the Interior*

Bureau of Mines men about to lead first rescue teams down slope after the 1929 explosion. *Bureau of Mines, Department of the Interior*

A miner crawling through a timber squeeze at the Colby Mine in Pennsylvania. The collapse of the roof has shattered the timbers, which were nevertheless strong enough to prevent a complete cave-in. *Pennsylvania Historical and Museum Commission*

Miners' families find time interminable during an accident. Here they await news of a December, 1911, accident (top) and of an entombment from an explosion on April 28, 1914, in West Virginia (bottom). *Bureau of Mines, Department of the Interior*

John L. Lewis and James Westfield (Assistant Director, Coal Mine Safety) during recovery operations following the 1951 explosion that killed 119 men in the Orient No. 2 Mine, Chicago, Wilmington and Franklin Coal Company, West Frankfort, Illinois. Together with another disaster in southern Illinois, at Centralia No. 5 in 1947, an explosion that killed 111 miners, these were responsible for the passage of the Federal Coal Mine Safety Act of 1952. John L. Lewis, in a speech before the House Labor Committee, made this comment on the 1947 mine disaster: "They left ninety-eight widows; they left seventy-eight orphans; and six of these men left dependent mothers or fathers. The reason for the small number of orphans to the total number of men killed, as miners' families go, is due to the age of the men employed. The average age of the employees of this mine was 55." As a result of the hearings, 518 unsafe mines were closed. After the Orient No. 2 explosion, Lewis told Congress: "They left 301 dependents, 109 of them being widows, 175 children, and 17 other dependents." Later, before Congress, Lewis gave the "appalling record": 119 men (the number killed at West Frankfort) dying every 17 days from 1900 through 1950 in mine accidents; since mine deaths were first recorded in 1839, 114,025 miners killed; 571 major disasters, killing 13,131; 25 of these disasters each bringing death to more than 100 men. *Bureau of Mines, Department of the Interior*

Testing for carbon monoxide gas with a canary (an unreliable and obsolete method). The deadliest killer undoubtedly is methane gas liberated from virgin organic coal. The gas is volatile, odorless, and highly flammable, and many workers died breathing the gas itself, although most succumbed from explosions of this lethal killer. Following an explosion at a Tennessee coal mine in 1911, a number of men saved their lives by "barricading." Rescuers conducted fresh air to the barricade, and the men were rescued. One of the barricades is shown here after being torn down. Such barricades help seal the miners from the afterdamp (poisonous gas produced by the explosion), the cause for most of the deaths following mine explosions. *Bureau of Mines, Department of the Interior*

Bureau of Mine employees pose in front of a Bureau Rescue Car, 1915. Here they demonstrate the various types of protective apparatus worn and used by rescue crews following mine disasters. This type of rescue car, which was called to the scene of many explosions, went out of service about 1940. *Bureau of Mines, Department of the Interior*

A recent United States mine disaster occurred at the Consolidated Coal Company's No. 9 Mine at Mannington, West Virginia, a modern, relatively safe mine that utilized the best techniques to prevent any disaster by gas—giant fans constantly circulated air into the mine. (Methane gas is not supposed to ignite or explode unless the concentrations are greater than 5 percent, and the fans were intended to reduce the mine atmosphere to less than 1 percent of gas as required by law.) But giant electric mining machines tear up the face of a coal seam with their rotary bits and raise dangerous clouds of coal dust despite water spraying to hold the dust in check. The first explosion at Consolidated's No. 9 occurred between 5:00 A.M. and 6:00 A.M. on November 20, 1968. (November and December comprise the "explosion season," probably because the cold, dry air and low barometric pressure help create static electricity.) At the time of the explosion 78 miners were still working in No. 9, and all attempts to rescue them were futile. For nine days and nights more than 16 explosions occurred inside the mine, the initial one traveling through the ventilation shafts and destroying the ventilation circuits, and for days giant clouds of black smoke poured from the shafts. The mine was finally sealed to starve the fire. No miners were rescued. The continued use of carbide lamps that generate light from a one- to two-inch flame (from acetylene gas made from carbide and water in the lamp) and the use of black powder for blasting are frequent causes of accidents. Although the Bureau of Mines approves battery-powered electric lamps for the miner's caps, half of the coal miners still use the carbide lamps, since they are handy for lighting fuses and are also lighter in weight. However, from mid-1941 to mid-1952, 835 miners died from explosions caused by forbidden electric arcs from mine machinery.

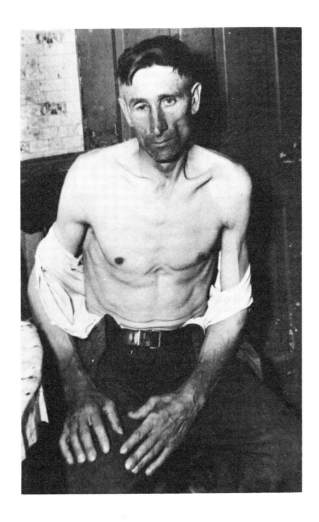

Miner preparing for examination for a lung disease caused by continual breathing of dust in mining operations. Chronic lung diseases—silicosis, caused by rock dust in underground quarries and limestone mines, and "black lung," or pneumoconiosis, caused by prolonged inhalation of coal dust—are constant hazards. A 1965 survey revealed that more than 100,000 coal miners, active or retired, suffered from black lung alone. *Free Library of Philadelphia*

James Williams, painfully burned on the face, is led from the Berwind No. 9 Mine, Havaco, West Virginia, through the doors of an escapeway after a dust explosion had snuffed out the lives of 15 men early on January 15, 1946. Williams was among 37 injured by the blast at the New River and Pocahontas Coal Company mine. The violent explosion, which demolished the mine tipple, left 53 widows and orphans. United Mine Workers Journal

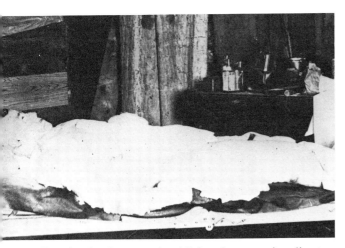

Despite the drama and publicity given to mine disasters that have killed large numbers of workers, probably half the deaths occurred among small groups of two. *University of Oklahoma Library, Division of Manuscripts*

A grieving widow and her children at the Great Valley Anthracite Coal Corporation mine at McCoy, Virginia. An explosion on April 18, 1946, killed twelve workers here. United Mine Workers Journal

During an anthracite coal strike in 1902, coal was so scarce that men and women stood in line to get their meager allotment of coal. By the time President Theodore Roosevelt forced a settlement of the strike, the price of coal had risen to $30 a ton, a very high price in those days. *Free Library of Philadelphia*

Soldiers at the mines during the 1902 strike. *Schuylkill County, Pennsylvania, Historical Society*

State mine inspectors, as well as supervisors and workers in mines, use an approved flame safety lamp, shown in the inspector's hand, to examine for gas. These examinations are conducted through the working shift as well as before workmen enter the mine. Authorities claim that all that is needed vastly to reduce the death toll and continued injuries is the expansion of just such existing government inspection facilities at every mine, with strict enforcement of the laws where violations are found. *Illinois Department of Mines and Minerals*

Measuring roof sag at rib-to-rib measuring station. *Bureau of Mines, Department of the Interior*

State mine inspectors take vacuum-bottle samples of mine air. These samples are analyzed at the State of Illinois Analytical Laboratory conducted under the direction of the Department of Mines and Minerals. Results of the samples are given to the state mine inspector and the management of coal mines. Illinois, like most states, limits the amount of methane and other gas content in all coal mines. *Illinois Department of Mines and Minerals*

A mine inspector using an anemometer measures the velocity and quantity of air passing through a face crosscut of a pair of panel entries at the Orient No. 3 Mine in Waltonville, Illinois. *Illinois Department of Mines and Minerals*

State mine inspectors examine top for dangerous conditions, and also instruct employees in the mine in the proper methods of examination for loose and dangerous top conditions. By placing the hand against the top and striking the top with a sounding rod, if the top is loose vibrations can be felt with the hand. State law forbids workmen working under loose or dangerous top. *Illinois Department of Mines and Minerals*

Another example of testing the roof, this time at the immediate face. The inspector is looking for slips or faults. *Illinois Department of Mines and Minerals*

In dry mines if combustible coal or other dust is found, finely ground rock dust is sprayed on the top, sides, and floor of the mine. Most state laws require that such combined dust be of at least 65 percent noncombustible content. *Illinois Department of Mines and Minerals*

Two views of fall of roof and coal. *Bureau of Mines, Department of the Interior*

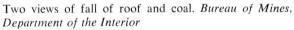

Roof "break line" behind cribs. Edge of fall taken from "gob" side of cribs. *Bureau of Mines, Department of the Interior*

In response to a need for a machine that would cut at various levels in the coal seam, this track-mounted unit was introduced in 1915. *Westinghouse Air Brake Company*

With the demand for new equipment, various types of track-mounted shovels, capable of turning in all directions, were devised to remove the debris in mines and tunnels. *Westinghouse Air Brake Company*

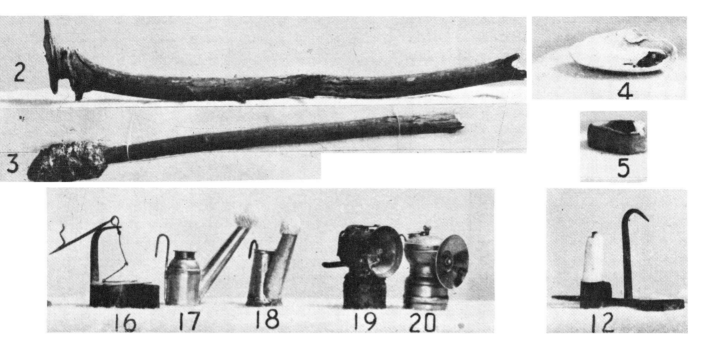

The first lights in mines were undoubtedly torches, such as the pine torch (2–3). Their use was followed by natural containers such as clamshells (4) and sometimes pottery containers (5). As candles were developed, various types were used for mining, some with hooks so the candleholder could be hung on rocks (12). In the 1600s, the "Betty" type of lamp (16) was used in the silver mines of Mexico, but this never became popular in the United States. Some coal-oil lamps (17–18) were used in the United States, but the popular lamp remained the carbide lamp (19–20), occasionally used in mines today. *Smithsonian Institution, Grant Wheat, Proceedings, Illinois Mining Institute, 1945*

A six-ton locomotive used for gathering loaded cars in the 1940s. *Westinghouse Air Brake Company*

The operation of this type of continuous miner is vertical rather than horizontal. The counter-rotating arms rip an arched tunnel through seams of bituminous coal. The loosened coal is picked up by a conveyor belt running through the heart of the machine, and is dumped at the rear onto a shuttle car for movement to the main mine transportation system. Such machines can produce up to eight tons of coal per minute. *Joy Manufacturing Company*

Continuous coal miner, capable of gouging its way underground much like a mole, at the Allen Mine in Colorado. It is one of the marvels of coal mining, and possibly accounts for the fewer miners working in coal mines today. *C. F. & I. Steel Corporation*

79

The coal barge *Bruce* at the Blue Mountain Dam of the Schuylkill Canal at the turn of the century. Mules pulled canal barges until the first quarter of the 1900s. *Smithsonian Institution*

The bulldozer at the right of the giant crawler on the electric stripping shovel at the Captain Mine of Southwestern Illinois Coal Corporation (Percy, Illinois) gives an indication of the shovel's size. When it went into service in 1965, this shovel was the world's largest mobile land machine. It has a 180-cubic yard dipper swung from a boom towering as tall as a 21-story building. Once every minute, it can take 270 tons of earth and rock in a single bite, swing it 450 feet away, and dump it on a pile as high as a 15-story building. The shovel mines two coal seams simultaneously, standing on the lower one. *National Coal Association*

A towboat pushes six huge bargeloads of coal along the Ohio River. In the background is the mine where the coal was produced and loaded. Low-cost water transportation helps keep coal competitive, particularly for plants located along inland waterways. *Consolidation Coal Company*

UNDERGROUND FIRES

Many mine fires have been burning for years. A fire in the Summit Hill Mine, near Lansford, Pennsylvania, broke out in 1859, raging through the early 1900s. Attempts to extinguish it were unsuccessful until the late 1930s when strip mining opened up the coal seams. In fact, the entire Summit Hill has since been removed by strip mining.

Later fires occurred: the Jersey Mine, underneath Plymouth Mountain, in 1902, burned into the 1940s; there is a still-burning fire (since 1915) near Shenandoah; the Kidder Mine, now known as the Laurel Run Mine, in 1917 destroyed the village of Laurel Hill, including 160 homes, and still burns under containment by state and federal cooperation to keep it from spreading; Carbondale was blackened with smoke in 1946, and though strip mining has excavated the area the fire will continue to burn unless the entire vein is stripped; Coal Run in 1949 had a major fire, now also contained; and a blaze near Hazleton was discovered in 1966. The Pennsylvania Department of Mines and Mineral Industries accounts for ninety-five underground coal-mine fires still burning in Pennsylvania—sixty-eight in bituminous and twenty-seven in anthracite mines.

Toward the close of 1969, almost a year after Consolidated Coal's Mannington explosion, the House and Senate each passed a mine health and safety bill, the toughest safety measures in seventy-five years. Major points covered are lighting, ventilation, rockfall protection, mine-train safety, and health standards.

Strip mining can go right along the sides of mountains, as in this recent view at Monogahela National Forest, West Virginia. *United States Forest Service*

THE LIFE OF A COAL MINER

Life at the Pennsylvania mines was rough. Besides the accidents, fires, and the deplorable working conditions, there were layoffs. A great many miners had come from Europe to escape even worse conditions. The Welsh, Irish, and Germans comprised the largest groups, each with its own community activities and celebrating its own holidays. Often the women helped support their families by sewing and taking in boarders. And the mines would capture the children, too.

Hocking Coal Company No. 3 Mine in the fall of 1903, photographed by a student. The ladies are Albia High School teachers, as is the man in the derby, who is the science teacher. The large man leaning on the post is the pit boss. The other two men are miners who acted as guides. *Clarence Q. Nelson*

CHILD LABOR IN THE MINES

Education was sadly neglected. In the 1860s and 1870s children went to school at six and to work at twelve—in the mines. It is almost impossible to set the exact date when child labor was introduced into the mining industry in the United States. There are records of children employed in textile mills in the 1830s, but the probabilities are that the first general use of children for mining occurred after the Civil War when slaves were no longer available and machinery was being developed for mining use.

By the 1870s children began to be employed extensively in the Pennsylvania coal mines, working from 7 o'clock in the morning until darkness for $1 to $3 weekly. By 1904 about 16,000 Pennsylvania youngsters were employed as "breaker-boys." The job of a breaker-boy, or slate-picker, required little skill. The boys sat on narrow seats over chutes, into which coal was dumped and carried to the washers. Their job was simply to pick out the pieces of slate, rock, or other debris, leaving nothing in the chutes but pure coal. The work was not particularly difficult but it was exceedingly tire-some. The boys became saturated with coal dust; their hands were scratched and bruised; and their fingernails were worn off by the constant rubbing of the discarded slate. Cut and crushed fingers were not uncommon. Although the legal age for employment generally was twelve years, many of the boys, some as young as eight, exaggerated their age because the income was needed at home. As the youngsters gained experience, they were slowly promoted to door-boys, or door tenders, switch-boys, and oiler boys, and some even became mule drivers. These were mostly the fourteen- or fifteen-year olds. Later the boys were graduated to laborers and finally to full-fledged miners. As late as 1907 most breaker-boys were only earning about sixty cents a day for twelve or more hours' work.

Actually, the number of children employed in the mines was no greater than those working in other industries. The 1870 census reported 700,000 children under fifteen at work, and by 1910, this figure had risen to almost two million. Ten years earlier, of Pennsylvania's 120,000 working children, only 16,000 were employed in the mines. Parents not only readily acquiesced to their childrens' em-

In the late 1800s in Pennsylvania and West Virginia these breaker boys, or slate pickers, worked the mines for $1 to $3 a week. United Mine Workers Journal

ployment because their meager earnings were welcome additions to the family income but also because they believed the children were learning a trade. And once a miner, always a miner. They could never accumulate enough money to improve themselves or escape their lot.

In 1874 miners were paid ninety-three cents a carload. This enabled a miner to earn about $3.50 for himself and about another $2.35 to pay his laborer. The wage scales had fluctuated greatly; ten years earlier they had received $1.68 a carload, but the postwar years brought a coal decline and an

8½ percent wage reduction, dropping by July, 1865, to $1.09. A general strike had brought wages to $1.31 a carload, followed by an unsuccessful strike and still further cuts.

The miners usually were paid monthly, in the intervening periods buying their food, clothing, and other necessities on credit so that by the time they received their pay they were frozen into the credit system for the following month. Among the German miners, some were able to save enough money to purchase or rent a farm and escape mining.

Young slate pickers working on the chutes in the mine. Note the large perforated drum in the upper right that graded the coal into its proper size before it fell into the chutes. The breaker boss standing at the left has a switch in his hand, and although generally it was used sparingly, it had its effect on keeping the boys working.

Breaker boys sitting straddling their chutes at a Scranton coal mine in 1904. The youngster in the right foreground is holding a crutch, and apparently has been excused from work. *William Culp Darrah Stereo Collection*

A closeup of a slate-picking operation using children exclusively. United Mine Workers Journal

As new legislation was passed prohibiting the use of child labor in coal and other mines, progress was also made in the methods of sorting coal. This is a picking table run on an automatic belt. The picking and cleaning is done by adults who not only remove the slate but also the large pieces of coal. *Bituminous Coal Institute*

Not all the youngsters employed in the mines were breaker boys or slate pickers; many were put in charge of the animals. *Bureau of Mines, Department of the Interior*

Some children were also employed as oiler boys. This youngster worked in a coal mine in Scranton. *Pennsylvania Historical and Museum Commission*

Children were also employed for general work and to bring food to the miners. This "miner" from Byesville, Ohio, was nine years old when this picture was taken in October, 1882. United Mine Workers Journal

Some idea of the large number of slate pickers who worked in the mines can be obtained from this 1889 group photo from the Pine Brook Colliery. In 1918 and 1922 child-labor laws were declared unconstitutional by the Supreme Court, and in 1924 a constitutional amendment was passed by Congress, but it was not ratified by enough states. Nevertheless, by then employment of children under sixteen was declining, and the Fair Labor Standards Act of 1938 virtually eliminated employment of children under sixteen. United Mine Workers Journal

WYOMING GOLD

But it was not coal that stirred men's souls but gold—even when they were not consciously looking for it. Hardly known as a gold producer today, Wyoming was the site of an 1842 gold discovery in the Sweetwater district of the South Pass country. An unknown Georgian had come to the district with the American Fur Company to recover his health, and stumbled on the find. He returned to Georgia a year later to organize a company to work the mines but is believed to have been killed en route by Indians.

About a forty-man group prospected along the Sweetwater River in 1855 and found gold both in the river and its tributaries. As winter approached, they moved to Fort Laramie and here gathered a year's mining supplies. Setting out again in the spring, they traveled barely two days when they were overtaken by the United States Dragoons who ordered them back to the fort. Later the expedition's leader was sentenced to prison, for a nonrecorded offense, and the group's company, including the property, was confiscated. The leader returned three years later, apparently having served his prison sentence. But not until 1860 did he and eight other prospectors begin mining on Strawberry Creek, a project that was abandoned a year later when the Overland Stage Company hired men away from mining at higher wages for the completion of its stage route. By early spring of 1862, fifty-two men were ready to recommence mining, and had even selected their locations near South Pass City. But they were raided by the hostile Shoshone Indians, robbed of their supplies, and driven from their stakes.

Our unknown hero-leader was undaunted. In 1866 he was back again, this time with a group from Virginia City, Montana. During the summer they were harassed by Indians and so decided to winter on Willow Creek, a tributary of the Sweetwater, where they would be free from winter attacks. They organized through the winter and identified their properties as the Shoshone Mining District, agreeing upon mining laws and regulations. As spring approached they returned to their claims.

The next year, the Carissa (Cariso) Lode was discovered. The mining claim was staked by one of the group, H. S. Reedall, who recovered $15,000 in gold, a huge amount considering the crude mining methods that were the only means of gold recovery at the time.

Indian raids soon recurred. One man was killed and his companions driven off, returning to Fort Bridger. Their reports of a new goldfield, greatly exaggerated, electrified the community. Soon lines

The Carissa Mine works. The Carissa proved a highly successful mine. It was vigorously developed, yielding an average of over $200 per ton for several years. Many other placer deposits and several important lodes were discovered while South Pass City was being erected. Major early placer discoveries were at Carissa Gulch, Rock Creek, Strawberry Creek, Big Atlantic Gulch, Promise Gulch, Jones Gulch, Smith's Gulch, Irish Gulch, Miner's Delight Gulch, Yankee Gulch, and Meadow Gulch. Some of the most important lode discoveries were the Young American, the Robert Emmett, later known as the Franklin; the Carrie Shields, the Doc Barr, the Duncan, the Mary Ellen, the Oriental, later known as the Groundhog; the Buckeye, later known as the Garfield the Soles and Perkins, the Caribou, the Lone Star, the Diana, and the Miner's Delight. In 1885, while the French were trying to salvage the Atlantic City placer property, Bolivar Roberts of Salt Lake City was the principal owner of the Carissa Mine. He organized a new company to resume operations. The company instituted an expansion and modernizing program, constructing a building, installing hoisting machinery, and sinking a shaft 200 feet to connect with the old workings. The connection was never made. Instead the mine was leased, and for twelve years operations continued without benefit of deep mining. In late 1896 a new body of ore was found, and the mine was purchased by John C. Spry upon the recommendation of the mine's future general manager, B. N. Dibbals. Active operations continued until 1904, by which time new shafts had been sunk over 400 feet. The Carissa continued operations until Mr. Spry's death in 1925, when his estate leased the property to Midwest Mines Corporation of Seattle, Washington. Midwest Mines purchased a 20-stamp mill in Atlantic City and installed it in 1929 to replace a 10-stamp mill that had been built earlier. Before completion, money ran out, the company was in the hands of a receiver, and the properties were involved in litigation. *University of Wyoming, J. E. Stimson Collection*

Carissa's interior with view of hoist and separator. *University of Wyoming, J. E. Stimson Collection*

of covered wagons and bands of frontiersmen in sufficient numbers to discourage Indian attacks were converging from every direction on South Pass City. Throughout summer and fall of 1867, a constant stream of goldseekers poured into Sweetwater—and as many poured out when they found the reports to be exaggerated. About 500 remained and laid out the South Pass City town site. Until sawmills could be established in the forests to supply lumber for construction, buildings were constructed of crude logs, with dirt-covered roofs and dirt floors. Within a year South Pass City had a population of 4,000, four hotels, three meat markets, two bakeries, four law firms, thirteen saloons, a bank, a newspaper, many business buildings, stores, and churches. Although more time had been spent in building the city than in mining, three gold-stamping mills with twenty-six stamps were in operation, and several arrastras were busy grinding away the quartz rock.

As miners filled up the South Pass country, the Indians grew more resentful. But by then they were so outnumbered that direct attacks were impractical. Nevertheless, as late as 1880 lone miners and small parties were still attacked.

By 1872 South Pass City was the largest in the Territory and had become the seat of Sweetwater County. Unfortunately, in the placer claims the major portions of the paydirt had been worked out, leaving only lower-grade material; even in the lodes most of the rich ore had been extracted and milled, and what little remained was of such low grade that the mines could not operate at a profit. In six years South Pass City was a ghost town and the county seat was in Green River. Some of its relics remain intact: about a block of old buildings, some dating to the 1860s, the general store built in 1868, the schoolhouse, dance hall, Wells Fargo office, and Exchange Saloon.

"Main Street," Atlantic City, 1884—heart of the South Pass district—when a group of French capitalists came to Atlantic City and acquired title to placer property along Rock Creek, which they felt could be mined profitably by hydraulic methods. The ore material was just not suitable for hydraulic mining, and the project failed. The property was sold in 1904 to the Dexter Mining Company and the Dexter Milling Company, owned by D. J. Cahoon. A mill was built at a cost of over $200,000, and more than 1,000 feet of tunnel was run, none of which served to expand the production of the property; it fell into the hands of creditors, who continued to operate the mine as a dredging operation well into the 1930s. It was just after the Frenchmen failed that Miner's Delight was discovered, about four miles north of Atlantic City, where Hamilton City was started. The town changed its name to Miner's Delight, and later the mine was sold to the Hub Company of Boston. Miner's Delight was at its height when the Young American opened, and a 20-stamp mill was built. *Wyoming State Archives and Historical Department*

Atlantic City still clings to mining. It is the center of a huge taconite mining operation owned by the U.S. Steel Corporation, of which this aerial view encompasses the taconite mining and beneficiation complex in the Wind River Mountains. Ore from the open-pit mine (upper right) is routed to primary and secondary crushers (center right), to the concentrator (large building to left of circular thickener), the pelletizing plant (center left), the conical storage building (beyond rail line), and finally to the loading unit (spanning tracks) where railway cars are loaded with pellets destined for steel mills at Provo, Utah. *U.S. Steel Corporation*

THE LAKE COPPERS

In 1830 Douglass Houghton, Michigan's first state geologist, while with the Schoolcraft expedition in search of the source of the Mississippi had become interested in the mineral wealth of the Lake Superior region. He returned ten years later, collected samples of native copper ore, studied the mineral possibilities in detail, and published a report that described the country and the probable extent of the copper deposits. Adventurous prospectors began to trickle in during the ensuing year, but not until a treaty with the Chippewa Indians was signed did the area open to settlement—and a mining boom. A mineral agency was opened by the federal government at Copper Harbor and the town mushroomed, which, together with the smaller Eagle Harbor, became a focal point for infiltrating miners. Because federal mining permits were required, obtainable at Sault Sainte Marie 200 miles from Copper Harbor, trading in them became an active business notwithstanding that they

were no guarantee of the presence of any metal. An early purchaser of a permit was David Henshaw, Secretary of the Navy under President Tyler. Henshaw and his associates organized the Lake Superior Copper Company in 1844, which in its first annual report described an assay of silver and copper values of over $3,000 per ton of rock. Its publication created a second rush to the area.

As prospecting over the Mineral Belt increased, Douglass Houghton switched to the federal government to continue his geological surveys. Eager to finish his work before the onset of winter, Houghton, in 1845, attempted a dangerous crossing near Eagle River in an open boat, but the boat overturned and he drowned. He was only thirty-six, but he left an imprint on the Lake Superior region felt to this day.

The Lake Superior Copper Company continued its optimistic annual reports but, despite continued copper production, the company showed successive losses and in 1849 went under; it was succeeded by the Phoenix Copper Company, which had no greater

"Douglass Houghton Finds Copper." This painting by Robert Thom is one of a series commissioned by the Michigan Bell Telephone Company and distributed by the Michigan Historical Commission through the John

M. Munson Michigan History Fund. © *Michigan Bell Telephone Company, 1965. All rights reserved. Used by special permission.*

Early print of the North American Mine on Lake Superior. *University of Michigan, Michigan Historical Collections*

success than its predecessor—its balance sheet showed a $2½ million expenditure against $20,000 income.

The Pittsburgh and Boston Company was more fortunate. It discovered a vein in 1845 near the little town of Eagle River in the Keweenaw district. Driving an adit into the vein, the miners discovered a copper lode about 70 feet from the entrance. The success of the Cliff Mine, by which it came to be known, sustained interest in the district when the district's reputation was in jeopardy because of the poor showing by Lake Superior Copper. Cliff Mine produced more than 38 million pounds of copper by 1880.

With the opening of the Cliff the federal permit system was discontinued and the land put on sale for $5 an acre, later reduced to $1.25 an acre. The abandonment of permits spurred the exploration of copper, which peaked in 1848. Soon thereafter, news

of the California gold rush reached the Michigan copper fields and many of the old timers headed west.

The copper beds in the peninsula lie in strata

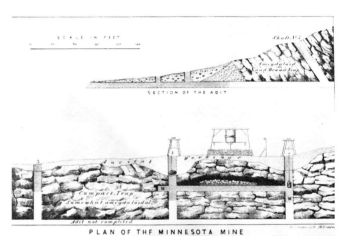

A plan of the Minnesota Mine. *University of Michigan, Michigan Historical Collections*

Cliff Mine on the "Copper Peninsula" (Keweenaw Peninsula in upper Michigan). From a print from *Report on the Geology of the Lake Superior Land District*, 1850. *New York Public Library Picture Collection*

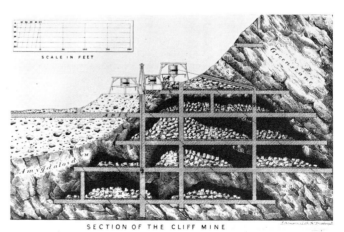

An old plan of a section of the Cliff Mine. *University of Michigan, Michigan Historical Collections*

89

of lava flows, sandstone, and conglomerate beds, stacked one upon the other and turned on edge by upheavals of the earth. From these diverge cross-fissures, wherein the early miners found most of the copper.

North of the Cliff Mine, almost in the center of the Peninsula, the Pewabic Lode was discovered, at Portage Lake, not in a fissure but in a lava flow just north of the lake. The Quincy Mining Company, which controlled most of the land containing the lode, became a great copper producer. Its developments opened the door to the possibility that great copper beds might lie directly in the extensive lavas and conglomerates. The Quincy expanded rapidly; during the Civil War it furnished the federal forces with virtually all the copper needed for war. In 1862 the company started paying dividends, which continued almost uninterruptedly into the 1920s. Today the Quincy underground mines are closed, but the remains of the surface operations can be seen along the highway between Hancock and Calumet.

This is not a ski lodge but the famous Quincy Mine shaft near Hancock, Michigan. The mine was abandoned in 1945, but in its time it was one of the world's deepest. The mine hoist within the building is now being renovated because of its historical interest; it is the largest steam-driven hoist in the world, built to lift 20 tons of ore from a depth of 10,000 feet along the incline. These mine structures required huge compounds that often were architectural marvels, sometimes looking more like elaborate resorts or hotels than mining buildings. They were usually well kept, neatly painted with window trim, and extremely complicated-looking buildings, with many roof lines. This occurred for several reasons. First, the structures were usually on a hillside or mountainside. Except for such prosaic buildings as an office or an assay building, the first true mining building usually housed the hoist and shaft. This protected the opening from snow, ice, and weather. As various refining processes were developed, it was most advantageous, wherever possible, to utilize the force of gravity. For this reason the hoist house was often the top structure so the crushed ore and water could travel with the aid of gravity through the various steps *down* the building, ending up at the base. Another reason for the unique architecture was that as the mines developed their new processes, additional buildings were required and added to the original structures. Light was a necessity, so large windows were used, and buildings that were on hillsides and subject to heavy snows had steeply angled A-frame roofs. *University of Michigan, Michigan Historical Collections*

Ascending the depths of a copper mine on the Upper Michigan Peninsula, circa 1910. *Michigan Historical Commission*

A mass of copper hanging from a Michigan copper mine, circa 1910. *Michigan Historical Commission*

CALUMET AND HECLA EMERGES

The development of copper lode mining changed the nature of copper mining in the Peninsula; the lodes were considerably larger in area, contained more tonnage, and were deeper and more uniform than the fissure deposits.

In 1858, just prior to Quincy's greatest expansion, another great discovery occurred when Edwin J. Hulbert, surveying for a military road in the Keweenaw, found what he thought to be a prehistoric copper pit and a huge block of conglomerate cemented together by copper. Recognizing the importance of his find, he quietly bought as much land as possible along what he presumed to be the

The Calumet and Hecla Mine around the turn of the twentieth century. *University of Michigan, Michigan Historical Collections*

copper lode. After accumulating nearly 2,000 acres, in 1861 together with J. W. Clarke, Horatio Bigelow, and some other investors from Boston, he formed the Hulbert Mining Company. That same year he bought an additional 200 acres and, with the same investors, formed the Calumet Mining Company.

Despite owning two mines, the Hulbert and the Calumet, Hulbert believed there were still great deposits to be found on the Keweenaw, and, to scure additional financing, in 1865 he went to Boston to borrow $16,800 from Quincy A. Shaw for additional land purchases for Calumet. For his services as manager, Hulbert was given controlling interest of Calumet stock. The company then leased the mine operation to Hulbert and Shaw, and mining began promptly. Dazzled by the rich veins, Hulbert became reckless in developing the property, attempting to mine by opening surface pits. These became filled with water in summer and snow and ice in winter. (His open pit idea was premature; machine technology had not reached the stage to make this practical.) Calumet ore was hauled by wagon thirteen miles to a mill, and supplies, at excessive prices, had to be purchased in Hancock and Houghton.

Hulbert also managed Shaw's Huron Mine, about fifteen miles from the Calumet. Hulbert, believing that the Huron, which was in financial difficulty, would eventually outproduce the Calumet,

Hardinge conical pebble mills, 8 feet by 18 feet, being installed in 1940 at the Calumet and Hecla plant, Lake Linden, Michigan, to grind copper ore. Banks of mills like this one are not uncommon in preparation plants today. *Koppers Company, Inc.*

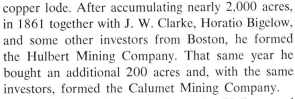

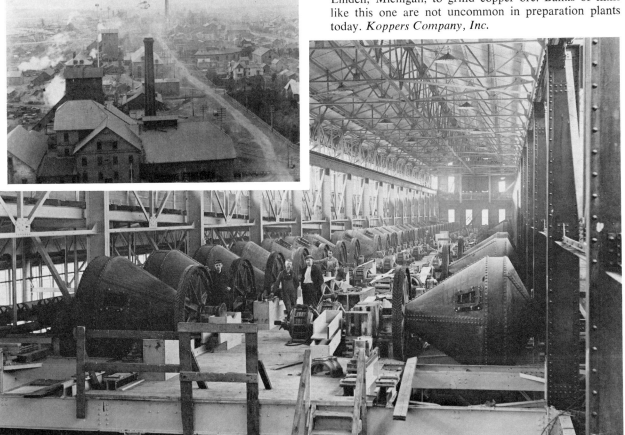

The old main Calumet and Hecla hoisting engine known as "The Celebrated Superior Engine—4700 horsepower." *University of Michigan, Michigan Historical Collections*

sacrificed his Calumet stock to salvage his stock holdings in the Huron. The Boston directors terminated the Hulbert-Shaw lease on Calumet, but Shaw had purchased land south of the Calumet and organized the Hecla Mining Company. Control of this company, too, evaded Hulbert; Shaw's brother-in-law, Alexander Agassiz, agreed to take over management of the Hecla, Hulbert, and Calumet mines.

When Agassiz arrived at Calumet he found that all the mines were in sad neglect—supplies were low, cash was virtually nonexistent, and authority for operations was lacking. Agassiz, assisted by Shaw, slowly but surely managed to reestablish the mines on an efficient basis. To provide additional working capital, assessments were levied on both the Hecla and Calumet stockholders, and within a

Surface installation, including headframe and rock house, at one of the mines at the Calumet Division. *Calumet & Hecla, Inc.*

year the Hecla became the largest producer in the district.

By 1868 the Calumet also was operating satisfactorily, despite aborted attempts by Hulbert to sabotage the Calumet dam and shut off the water supply to the mill. He did inflict minimal damage, but the dam was quickly repaired.

In 1869 Hecla paid its first dividend, and a year later Calumet did the same. In 1871 the two companies were consolidated with two others into the Calumet and Hecla Mining Company. Shaw remained on the board until his death in 1908; Agassiz was president from 1871 until he died in 1910.

In the meantime, Hulbert was continuing his unsuccessful ventures with the closing of the Huron Mine. At the time, to recompense Hulbert for his discovery of the Calumet, Shaw established a trust for him consisting of 2,000 shares of Calumet and Hecla stock, then worth $200,000, and considerably more later. Hulbert moved to ·Italy. He died in Rome in 1910, but not before Calumet and Hecla had produced 100 million pounds of copper, by 1906, and the stock was selling in 1907 for more than $1,000 a share. Since its inception, the company has paid out nearly $300 million in dividends.

COPPER RANGE

In 1899, while Calumet and Hecla were undergoing enormous growth, another important copper producer was organized. This was the Copper Range Company. Copper Range believed that new finds of copper might be uncovered south of Portage Lake, an area that had received relatively little attention. Five months after the company was organized, the Champion Mine was established, and in 1903 Copper Range obtained control of the adjacent Tri-Mountain and Baltic mines and additional adjoining property. With these acquisitions Copper Range became the second largest copper producer in Michigan. In 1926 Copper Range added Porcupine Mountains' White Pine Mine, six years dormant, to its holdings. During World War II copper was once again produced here, but since 1953 White Pine has become a chalcocite copper ore operation that now employs about 2,500 people.

Around 1935 the Copper Range Company embarked upon extensive drilling and exploration in the southwest end of the district occupied by the Porcupines. While studies disclosed tremendous deposits of copper, they were mostly low-grade and would require a huge investment to become profitable producers. In 1950 the federal government granted Copper Range a $64 million loan to develop the property, provided the company would add $13

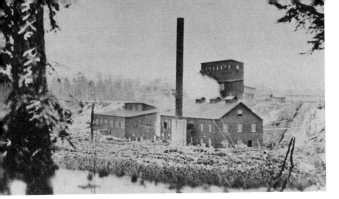

The White Pine Copper Company: mill and power plant, 1914. *White Pine Copper Company*

Centennial Copper Mine showing old- and new-type rock houses circa 1900. *University of Michigan, Michigan Historical Collections*

Loading a tramcar with a mechanical scraper in 1919. *Michigan Historical Commission and* Detroit News

Pouring copper into ingots (foreground) at Lake Linden, Michigan, before 1911. Copied from a postcard view. *Michigan Historical Commission*

Copper ingots on the wharf at Houghton, Michigan, await loading on the steamer *Tionesta,* circa 1912. *Michigan Historical Commission*

million for working capital. The government agreed to purchase the copper from the mine, which went into production in 1956 when nearly four million tons of ore, providing almost thirty-eight tons of copper, were mined.

The Lake Coppers, meaning the Michigan coppers, have become important factors in stabilizing prices and production of American copper. They allow the United States to be less dependent upon the political unrest of the principal foreign sources for copper—Africa and Chile. And they are major producers in their own right.

ISLE ROYALE

The same treaty between the Chippewa Indians and the United States in 1835 that opened the area to the "lake coppers" enabled the white man to explore Isle Royale for minerals. Though a few mineral locations were filed during the year with the War Department, not until 1846 did a rush to the island begin.

However, even as early as 1843 copper was known to be on the Isle and mining operations began with various stock companies, many pure and simple stock-sale operations, some underfinanced, and others guided by professional mining engineers and geologists. It was relatively simple to prospect on Isle Royale because fissures and veins, often exposed along the shore, could be tracked to where the prospects were most promising and a shaft could be sunk.

As for the miners, most worked on a contract basis. At some locations one-man log cabins were erected by prospectors; at other, settlements developed. By 1847 about 120 people were working the mines. Most of the work was done in summer; during winter, which was severe, the mines were manned by maintenance crews only. The work was unusually rugged, drownings were common, and accidents and injuries rarely received medical at-

93

An 1892 photograph of a section of an ancient copper mine on Isle Royale. The tunnel was being mined at the time the photograph was taken. Published in J. B. Griffin, *Lake Superior Copper and the Indians: Miscellaneous Studies of Great Lakes Prehistory. Smithsonian Office of Anthropology, Bureau of American Ethnology Collection*

The remains of a railroad connecting the Minong Mine to McCargoe Cove on Isle Royale. After their third year here, North American sold roughly 2,500 acres to the Minong Company, formed just for the purpose. The property contained hundreds of pits left by ancient Indians, and work began in 1875. A mining settlement developed, but after four years Minong discontinued active work, and instead leased portions of the property for a share of the profits. The mine closed for good in 1885. Some years earlier, a year after the Minong started, in 1874, the Island Mining Company was organized, and a number of shafts were sunk near Siskowit Bay. There was considerable construction, included a dam, dock, and warehouse, all of which burned almost immediately. Within a year of the company's founding, mining was discontinued except for a few leased operations. And two years later the Saginaw Mining Company, near Rock Harbor, began its operation, which was discontinued in 1879. *National Park Service. Photo by William W. Dunmire*

tention. And the island was infested with mosquitoes and flies, adding to the miners' discomfort. Underground workings were usually small vertical shafts sunk to a depth of about sixty feet, where stoping would begin. Generally, the ore was removed by hand windlass, although a few mines had horse-powered hoists. Only two stamp mills were employed in the 1840s. Most of the copper was shipped from Isle Royale to Sault Sainte Marie and then across the lower lakes to smelting plants. Throughout these years, including the 1850s as well, many small mines were started only to be abandoned.

Isle Royale today is a national park, with many visible mining remains. Visitors to this Michigan historic site can find piles of "poor rock" tailings (debris from shafts and excavations), eroded foundations of old houses, stamp mills, storehouses, and shaft holes from the old Smithwick and Siskowit mines. Vestiges of most of the remaining areas are accessible and are part of the island's trail tours.

THREE IRON RANGES

What is now Michigan's Upper Peninsula was once part of the Territory of Wisconsin. After Congress had awarded the Peninsula to Michigan, the federal government commissioned territorial land surveys. One surveyor, William A. Burt, working near Teal Lake, noticed that his magnetic compass was erratic—the needle was swinging in all directions. He quickly traced the cause of this unusual compass activity to chunks of iron-laden rock. That was in 1844. About eight months later, an exploring party from Jackson led by Philo M. Everett was at work in the area; the group had formed a company to mine copper and silver.

When Everett first arrived, in June, he had heard reports of the iron ore found at the lake and,

A magnificent log office building in the mining town of Ghyllbank, Windigo, about 1892. A final attempt to produce copper profitably fell to the Wendigo Copper Mine (Windigo) in 1889, but after two years they converted to a real-estate operation and sold the property for the development of homes and a resort area. *Fisher Collection photograph from glass negative owned by Michigan Tech, Isle Royale National Park*

The abandoned Jackson Mine with the ever-present water collected in the pit. It was the first iron mine in Michigan. *Free Library of Philadelphia*

Additional ore deposits were soon discovered, particularly in the Gogebic and Menominee ranges, but no attempts were made to mine these districts for years, not until the opening of the first ship canal at Sault Sainte Marie. With the opening of the canals it would be possible to ship iron ore through the Great Lakes without portaging. Nearly thirty years after the opening of the Jackson Mine, ore was first mined at the Menominee Range, and only because the Chicago Northwestern Railway extended its road into the area.

Most of the ore from the new districts was of a lower grade than that of the Jackson area, but as technology advanced it was possible to open the mines and to work the lower-grade ores more profitably. Many additional locations were found since the first discovery, but in 1882 the Menominee Range was way out in front—it had shipped over a million tons. In 1884 the railroads arrived and the Gogebic Range assumed greater importance—the Colby Mine at Bessemer became its principal ore producer. The Nipigon Pit at the Colby Mine was the first, and within a year seven additional mines were shipping in excess of a million tons of iron ore from the range's Michigan portion. Gogebic quickly grew to become Michigan's leading ore-producing range.

enlisting the aid of a Chippewa Indian chief, Marji-Gesick, found the spot. Everett now returned to Jackson with a glowing report of his discovery, and the resultant Jackson Mining Company staked claims. A year later the company obtained permits to mine the "Jackson Pit."

Jackson Mine No. 1, about 1860. Philo M. Everett laid claim to the rich ore-bearing land near Negaunee, and in 1847 the Jackson Mining Company, of which he was a stockholder, began taking out ore. It was an open-pit

operation at first, like most of the early Michigan iron mines. The pick, shovel, sledgehammer, drill, and horse-drawn carts were the tools of the miners. *University of Michigan, Michigan Historical Commission*

The Jackson Mine, 1890. After the surface supply of iron ore was depleted, inclined shafts were sunk to get to other rich veins of underground ore. *Marquette County Historical Society and Michigan Historical Commission*

Here is a tube mill, 6 feet by 6 feet, which was converted, by means of conical liners, into the first Hardinge conical mill. Early power mills hand-picked the ore before sending it through crushing operations. Tube mills were among the first type of crusher used, but late in the 1880s the cone crusher became the most popular. Some cone crushers are still used, although ball mills are far more popular. *Koppers Company, Inc.*

Crude equipment and laborious manual effort marked Michigan's early mining history in the sinking of this shaft at the Ashland Mine on the Gogebic Range about 1885. *Marquette County Historical Society and Michigan Historical Commission*

Hal Williams Hardinge, inventor of the conical mill, inspects the converted mill at Black Queen Mine, circa 1907. *Koppers Company, Inc.*

Six mills, 24 feet by 8 feet, in a Michigan iron ore beneficiation plant. The mills are the largest in use for the autogenous grinding of iron ore. *Koppers Company, Inc.*

This 250-ton hard-rock boring machine was built for use at White Pine Copper Company, White Pine, Michigan. The machine's head revolves while 63 bits, each 11 inches in diameter, bore an 18-foot tubular tunnel through solid rock. It is supposed to drill approximately 1,000 feet a month. *Copper Range Company*

TRANSPORTATION PROBLEMS

Poor transportation had hindered iron mining for years. Waterways were open only about half the year, and it became necessary to ship in advance an entire year's supplies to the mines. At the Marquette Range, the mines could be reached only by travel through dense forests and ridges of hills. Indians were employed to carry 200-pound bags of ore on their backs. By 1855, when these ranges were still under exploration, a road was laid to Marquette, and two years later, a railroad.

Even shipping facilities at Marquette were inadequate. Water was shallow, and ore had to reach the boats on barges. Livestock usually was shoved overboard and forced to swim to shore. A dock was built at this time, but it was soon smashed by violent storms. In 1859 a modern dock—solid rock pilings—extended into the lake 400 feet and contained a trestle with tracks for ore cars. Immediately after, docks were constructed at Marquette and elsewhere. The rapids on the Saint Marys River connecting Lake Superior and Lake Huron was a further transportation obstacle. Schooners were rolled on "greaseways" around the rapids, but barges still had to be loaded and unloaded. In 1851 a tramway had been constructed to bypass the rapids, but its capacity was now insufficient for the increased ore tonnage. The problem of iron-ore transportation was solved when a canal was built in 1855. Locks at Sault Sainte Marie permitted the ore to be shipped to the lower lakes ports. And from that day on locks were built continually to meet increasing demands.

Most transportation was by water, and great attention was given ship designs to ensure maximum results; early ore-bearing ships were wooden schooners, easily damaged by heavy chunks of ore. The first steam-propelled ore ship was the *R. J. Hackett*; it began to sail the lakes in 1869, and soon fleets of ore ships were roaming the lakes. Today, huge cargo ships over 700 feet long carry fantastic quantities year round.

Improvements in shipping also inspired new methods of increasing production. Until about 1875, about when the Menominee Range first started production, most operations were open pit, usually dug by hand, and animals carried the ore from the hole. Underground mining was in full operation by 1880, but it took fifteen years for the mule-drawn cars to be replaced by electric ones. Steam began to provide the power for hoisting ore and pumping water, but not until electricity came into common use in the early 1900s did it supplant steam. Until hoists were used to lower them in cages, miners often climbed down 500-foot ladders to get to the pits.

Electric lights were available in the early 1880s,

Iron ore docks at Marquette in the late nineteenth century. *Marquette County Historical Society and Michigan Historical Commission*

The days of Marquette are a far cry from the steamer *L. E. Block,* seen at Indiana Harbor. The ship is loaded with iron ore. *Inland Steel Company*

An 1886 view of the Aurora Mine open pit, looking west. *University of Michigan, Michigan Historical Collections*

Arrayed in the garb of the 1890s, these two miners are ready for their shift underground. Notice the candles on their caps. The scarf covering the head of the miner on the left is to keep the iron ore dust out of his hair. Most of the early miners were Irish or Cornish. *Marquette County Historical Society and Michigan Historical Commission*

but they were used mostly in the shafts and drifts. First candles and then oil lamps were used by miners, but not until about 1912 did carbide lamps come into use in Michigan. The carbide lamp was commonly used until the mid-1920s, when they were replaced by electric headlamps.

Today Michigan is an important source and reserve of low-grade iron ore. Even though competition from the Minnesota mines and from foreign sources have threatened the iron-ore economy of Michigan, its estimated 2 billion tons of low-grade iron ore reserves are not likely to allow Michigan to be forgotten as an important iron-ore source for the American economy. As new techniques are continually perfected, most Michigan low-grade ore ultimately will be processed economically.

Peck's Camp, built in 1883, for exploring parties at the Pabst Mine near Ironwood. Such crude log huts were built for the miners who went into the wilderness to mine ore. *Marquette County Historical Society and Michigan Historical Commission*

Aurora Street, Ironwood, Michigan, May, 1886. Notice the crude wooden buildings, many of which were still under construction, and the muddy, stump-filled roads and the dense forest. Aurora Street is now the main street of Ironwood. *Marquette County Historical Society and Michigan Historical Commission*

Lake Angeline Mine in Ishpeming about 1895. There were electric lights in the main tunnels, but the miners still relied on candles. A pegboard on the upper left tallied the number of carloads of ore mined by each shift. *University of Michigan, Michigan Historical Collections*

Tunnel at Ishpeming: gaping tunnels, like the one shown here, were cut into solid rock to get to the rich iron ore underground. Pillars were left to guard against cave-ins. *Marquette County Historical Society and Michigan Historical Commission*

OTHER SIGNIFICANT HISTORICAL EVENTS

The Pre-Boom Years

New Mexico

1800s: Early Pinos Altos gold mines: Langston, Pacific, Atlantic, Deep Down, Mountain Key, Night Bird, Family Lead, Golden Era, Golden Crown, Kept Woman, Wild Bill, Silver Belle, Silver Cell, Mammoth, Golfer. At White Oaks, North and South Homestake mines and the Old Abe Mine were worked.

1877: Hillsborough: A mining camp formed out of the Opportunity and the Ready Pay mines when gold was discovered by two prospectors on the east side of the Black Range. The name was later changed to Hillsboro, and the area produced about $6 million in gold and silver during the 1880s and 1890s. Hillsboro still exists along with old mining-day ruins.

North Carolina

1803: The Silvers Mine in Mitchell County was one of the state's first mica mines, later known as the Sinkhole Mine.

Illinois

1819: About this time one of the earliest known lodes, known as Gratiot's Grove, was discovered around Galena, near Shullsburg.

New York

1906: The Titanium Alloy Manufacturing Company was incorporated at Niagara Falls.

1908: Dr. A. J. Rossi demonstrated the use of titanium as a pigment.

1930s: Raw material for titanium pigments was imported from India, Norway, Senegal, Brazil.

1941: National Lead Company formed a Titanium Division and acquired MacIntyre Iron Company.

New York became the leading producer of titanium minerals; magnetite-ore mining was extensive; largest iron mine is the open-pit Benson Mine of Jones and Laughlin Steel Company. The state ranks second as a zinc producer; nation's largest zinc producing mine is the Balmat, nearby the Benson Mine. The Edwards Zinc Mine and Balmat are operated by St. Joseph Lead. Extensive talc mines surround Talcville.

Pennsylvania (early coal operators)

1838: Washington Coal Company (becoming Pennsylvania Coal).

1840: Scranton, Grant and Company.

1846: Scranton Platt Company.

1853: Lackawanna Iron and Coal Company.

North Carolina (post–Civil War)

Gold Hill, Reimer, Rudisil, Capps gold mines reopened. New ones were Coggins, Iola.

1933: Howie, Whitney-Isenhour, Portis gold mines reopened.

Virginia

1830s: Many gold mines here ran in a narrow band southwest between Charlottesville and Richmond.

1834: Tellerium Mine (quartz vein) formed eight miles from Columbia and operated twenty-five years.

1835: Ford's Mine (gold) discovered. After shafts were sunk, copper was discovered. Other mines in the area were Duncan (or Apperson), Bumpus, Ford, Hobson, Ayres.

Iowa

1840s: Coal mines at Douds opened.

1850s: Others involved in coal lands were the Delaware and Lackawanna Western railroads; both taken over by the Hudson Coal Company.

Wyoming

1882: New lode discoveries: Bullion Mine Lode, Hidden Hand, Iron Duke, Barr.

1843: Smithwick Mine discovered.

1844: Isle Royale Union Company founded; became Siskowit Mining Company in 1849; operated twelve years.

Michigan (Isle Royale copper)

1846: Copper and silver discovered at Siskowit Silver Mine at McCargoe Cove.

Settlements developed at Ransom, Siskowit, Snug Harbor, Todd Harbor.

1847: Ohio and Isle Royale Company mine discovered and Ransom advanced. Project abandoned in 1849 in favor of Portage Lake area discoveries on mainland.

1847: Pittsburgh and Isle Royale Mine began operations near Todd Harbor; continued for five years.

1848: Cleveland Mining Company started.

1849: Iron—Marquette Company started.

1871: North American Mineral Land Company began new explorations.

1877: First ore shipped from Menominee Range (Breen and Vulcan mines).

The California Years

Contrary to general belief, James Marshall's 1848 gold discovery was not the first in California, but it was Marshall's discovery that actually triggered the gold rush.

Small quantities of placer gold had been found earlier at many California sites, but the first commercially valued find occurred on March 9, 1842, when Francisco Lopez y Arballo accidentally uncovered it in Placerita Canyon while searching for stray cattle. Other Mexicans, including Francisco García, came from Sonora, Mexico, to work this mine. García later found gold in San Feliciana Canyon, and in about one and a half years he and his workers recovered over $40,000 worth from the two canyons. Operations were discontinued about 1847 when the deposits were exhausted, just in time for Marshall's discovery.

THE RUSH BEGINS

"Gone to the Diggings!" "Gone to the Diggings!"

San Francisco stores were plastered with such signs. Even the schools closed as teachers and students joined the gold stampede.

In May and June of 1849, without warning, San Francisco was a ghost town; lawyers were without clients (and clients without lawyers), newspapers were bereft of editors, printers, and readers; ships were abandoned in the harbor while crews rushed to the goldfields; stores closed, families were deserted, and soldiers left their posts, leaving nearby cities unguarded. Why this exodus?

MARSHALL'S DISCOVERY

The story begins in the summer of 1847 in the small Indian valley of Culluma (Coloma). Here Captain John A. Sutter, a feudal baron, and James W. Marshall signed a contract that would change not only the destiny of the western territory but ultimately the world. By the terms of the contract, Marshall was to erect and operate a sawmill; Sutter

Telegraph Hill in 1849. "The barren side of the Hill before us was covered with tents . . . in front a large 2-story building displayed the sign: Fremont Family Hotel," wrote Bayard Taylor, author of *El Dorado*, describing San Francisco in late 1849. The flag signals on the tower announce the arrival of ships in the Golden Gate. The original painting by an unknown artist of that day is a permanent exhibit in the Wells Fargo Bank History Room. *Wells Fargo Bank History Room*

was to furnish the necessary equipment, tools, supplies, and labor. Work began at once along an old river channel on the American River. It was to be widened and deepened to make the stream flow more freely, and thus provide adequate waterpower for the sawmill. The plan was to excavate during the day. At night the channel would be opened to allow the water to run through the entire ditch, washing away the loose dirt, clay, and gravel.

On one of his daily inspections of this tailrace, Marshall noticed something glittering in the clear water. Picking it up and examining it, he beat the stonelike piece between two rocks, and found that it was malleable. He retrieved additional pieces and, placing them around the crown of his hat, returned to the sawmill shouting to his workers, "Boys, I believe I've found a gold mine." The men gathered round and examined the material minutely, biting into the pieces, even pounding one into the shape and size of a $5 gold piece for comparison. Returning to the stream, more pieces were collected. Marshall agreed with his men to keep the discovery a secret, and with the samples left Sutter's Fort to show them to Captain Sutter. Marshall and Sutter located an encyclopedia and, using it as a standard, applied crude tests, even boiling the gold in soap! They decided that Marshall had indeed discovered gold. But Sutter's concern was that if the news leaked out he would never get his spring crops harvested, nor would his sawmill ever be completed.

THE NEWS LEAKS OUT

Despite attempted secrecy, news did leak out. Back at the fort, a teamster had paid for brandy with gold he claimed to be from Coloma. The storekeeper wrote to Sam Brannan, a Mormon elder, who as a result somehow obtained a bottle of glistening Coloma gold dust. Sam displayed it on the San Francisco streets.

The first newspaper account appeared in the *Californian* on March 15, 1848. Mormon mill workers wrote their friends and Sutter himself wrote to General Vallejo, at Sonoma, about the discovery. The news was also spread when Sutter sent one of his mill hands, Charles Bennett, to Monterey to

James W. Marshall who in 1848 started the greatest gold rush in the world. *Wells Fargo Bank History Room*

Cabin and monument (in background) of James Wilson Marshall, near Coloma, California, 1895. Marshall discovered gold near this spot on January 24, 1848. Sutter's Fort in Sacramento, like the Marshall Gold Discovery at Coloma, is a state historic park. The Marshall cabin stands opposite St. John's Catholic Church, and on a hilltop overlooking the cabin is the Marshall Monument, a shaft of granite surmounted by a statute of Marshall pointing to where the gold was first discovered. Beneath the statue lie the remains of the man who helped open the West. In addition, a Gold Rush Museum contains many relics from the hectic rush to find precious metal. *United States Forest Service. Photo by Charles Fitzgerald*

secure the property rights. Bennett displayed the gold nuggets along the way in Benicia, San Francisco, and Monterey. And when Colonel R. B. Mason, the military governor of California, visited Coloma that July, he confirmed the discovery and its richness, and the gold rush was on.

The news traveled east slowly. In September, 1848, the *Baltimore Sun* ran one of the first stories of the discovery, which precipitated an incredible exodus. Gold seekers raced to California from east and west, from Hawaii, Mexico, British Columbia, and South America. The few pre-*Sun* article gold stories that had reached the East had been discounted as rumors, but the *Sun* story and a statement by President Polk, in his message to Congress, dispelled all doubts. The President reported that "the accounts of the abundance of gold in that territory are of such an extraordinary character as would scarcely command belief were they not corroborated by the authentic reports of officers in the public service."

A few days later a government messenger arrived in Washington with a tea caddy filled with 230 ounces of gold. As with Sam Brannan's bottle of gold dust in the West, the tea caddy whipped the Eastern rush to a frenzy.

ON TO CALIFORNIA

Within a month over sixty ships were chartered and bound for California. According to *The New York Herald,* "In every Atlantic seaport, vessels are being fitted up, societies are being formed, husbands are preparing to leave their wives, sons are parting with their mothers, and bachelors are abandoning their comforts; all are rushing head over heels toward the El Dorado on the Pacific."

Packet ships carried no less than 15,000 gold seekers to the California gold region via Cape Horn, a 6- to 8-month trip covering 18,000 miles. *Free Library of Philadelphia*

Sutter's Mill, looking down the tailrace toward Marshall's Monument at Marshall Gold Discovery State Historical Park. *California Department of Parks and Recreation*

In the 1840s, even before the California gold rush, steamers such as this plied between San Francisco and Panama, transferring passengers, freight, and mail across the isthmus of steamers on the East Coast. These boats left San Francisco on the 1st and 16th of each month, known as "Steamer Days," days on which all businessmen closed their books and settled accounts. This practice continued until nearly 1900. The boats became an important link during the gold rush. (From an 1842 sketch.) *Wells Fargo Bank History Room*

Early in 1849, the artist Elton produced this cartoon. The balloon reads, "What's a paltry income of $2 or $3,000 a year, that's all I now make! I shall pick that up in a week in California, overland route through in fifty days and damn the expense!!" *New York Public Library Picture Collection*

The *Sonora*, one of the Pacific Mail Steamship Company's important ships in California's early oceangoing trade, made a record run between Panama and San Francisco in 1854 in 11 days and 21 hours. *Wells Fargo Bank History Room*

Within a year of Marshall's find, 80,000 people from all over the world reached the West Coast. About 15,000 of these gold seekers traveled a 14,000-mile sea route from New York to California via Cape Horn, averaging six to eight months. The difficulties and hazards of the caravans and wagon trains that rushed across the continent frequently are vividly enacted on television and in the movies, but the equally monstrous trip by water has long been neglected. Easterners preferred to go by sea, either around the Horn or across the Isthmus of Panama, and every conceivable type of vessel was put to use—passenger and fishing boats, cargo carriers, whaling ships, and others so unseaworthy as to have been better confined to dry dock. Space was

A San Francisco newspaper ad in 1855 of Wells Fargo and Company offering to carry treasure for shipment on the S.S. *Sonora. Wells Fargo Bank History Room*

WELLS, FARGO & CO.'S
EXPRESS NOTICE.

FOR THE STEAMER OF MAY 16th.

VIA PANAMA.

Our next Regular Express for the Atlantic States and Europe will be dispatched

 By the P. M. S. S. Co.'s Steamship
SONORA,
R. L. WHITING, Commander,

On WEDNESDAY, MAY 16th, 1855,
At 9 o'clock A. M.

In charge of a Special Messenger.

TREASURE received for shipment (and insured) until 12 o'clock on TUESDAY NIGHT, May 15th, and small packages and parcels received until one hour of the time of sailing.

m12   WELLS, FARGO & CO.,
corner Montgomery and California streets,

at a premium, and cargo holds were converted to living quarters. The demand was so great that some companies sold the same space several times over for the same trip. Forty-five ships from the East Coast arrived at San Francisco in one day alone. In a single month over sixty ships left Baltimore and Norfolk, and in February, 1849, sixty sailed from New York City, and seventy each from Philadelphia and Boston, among hundreds from many other, including European, ports. Life aboard ship was pleasant, if one didn't get seasick, and passengers enjoyed themselves pretty much as they do today; they fished, gambled, drank, sang, read, and a few even attended religious services. Holidays were celebrated and food was plentiful, especially vegetables to combat the usual scurvy that had been experienced on previous long journeys.

Supplies and rest required occasional stops, but passengers reaching the tropics discovered the heat often was unbearable. Although the over-thirty-day trip around the Horn could also be rugged—freezing and wet—passage through the Straits of Magellan was even worse. No one knew what weather might be encountered, and many of the ships were wrecked or foundered.

TO THE WEST VIA PANAMA

Steamship lines soon found a quicker, more profitable route to California via Panama. But cooperating steamship lines were only able to pick up travelers on the western side of the Isthmus, leaving passengers to their own means of crossing Panama, with token advice from the lines. For most, this proved to be harrowing and hazardous; the jungles were dangerous, the native guides who supplied pack animals and canoes charged exhorbitant prices, and the climate was conducive to dysentery, cholera, and yellow fever. Despite the three- or four-month wait for passage, those who crossed the Isthmus often found the trip quicker than the Cape route.

Spurred by government contracts for mail, the United States Mail Steamship Company serviced New York to Chagres in eastern Panama, and the Pacific Mail Steamship Company serviced western Panama to San Francisco and the northwest. Its original charter for mail service notwithstanding, hundreds of people waiting on the Isthmus swarmed onto Pacific Mail's boats. Tickets were sold for the entire journey, and the fares, by today's standards, were reasonable: New York City to San Francisco

"The way they go to California." This remarkable lithograph by N. Currier, 1849, anticipates air travel by more than a hundred years. The dirigible reads, "Air Line through by daylight passage $50. Each passenger must provide a boy to hold his hair on." Below the dirigible it reads, "Augustus, don't you wish we were down and not up. Yes, for I begin to feel air sick. Oh, dear! Oh, dear!" On the parachute it reads, "Passengers landed by parachute." Even more remarkable is the rocket reading, "Rocket Line through in advance of the Telegraph Passengers not found (if lost)." *Library of Congress*

The effects of the California gold discovery were quickly felt in England. This cartoon, which appeared in *Punch* in 1849, was titled "The Country for Convicts," and shows the imaginary consequences of *Punch*'s scheme for sending convicts to California. *New York Public Library Picture Collection*

The Flying Cloud, launched in 1851. It made record trips around the Horn in 89 days—once in 1852 and again in 1854. *The Flying Cloud* often carried Wells Fargo treasure shipments. *Wells Fargo Bank History Room*

cost $330 for a first-class cabin, $290 for a lower-class, and around $100 for steerage. Stowaways were common, and tickets were examined very carefully. Upon arrival in California, ships often were tied up in San Francisco Bay, unable to make the return trip because their crews deserted to look for gold. The usually crowded docks precipitated a

lucrative business—rowing passengers ashore for $3 a head.

Within several years, in 1851, Cornelius Vanderbilt inaugurated a service from New York to San Francisco via Nicaragua. He built a cross-country road for this purpose, but four years later the Panama Railroad was completed and by 1857 Vanderbilt ceased operations.

THE OVERLAND ROUTES

Nearly 60,000 gold seekers on wagons, oxen, horses, mules, whatever was available, had crossed the continent by northern and southern trails. Wagon trains rolled out from embarkation points in Missouri with loners and entire families. Caravans were formed and leaders appointed. Storms, tornadoes, heat, cold, rivers, mountains, sick animals, cholera, food shortages, stampedes, and Indians impeded the wagon trains. Crossing deep canyons, it was often necessary to lower the oxen, horses, and wagons by rope. Asiatic cholera killed more than 500 would-be prospectors on the 1849 overland routes.

Thus the gold rush of the Forty-Niners brought death and disaster for the many and gold for the

106

Crews deserted their ships in San Francisco harbor and
rushed to the goldfields in the 1850s, creating an unprecedented traffic jam. *Smithsonian Institution*

A gold hunter on his way to California, via St. Louis.
Lithograph by H. R. Robinson. *Library of Congress*

very, very few. The peak production years were
from 1850 to 1853, at an average of nearly $70
million in gold each year. By the late 1850s, however, the placers were depleted and Coloma, where
it all began, relaxed into a town of homes and
gardens, orchards and vineyards.

Neither Marshall nor Sutter profited from the
gold. Marshall, who lived in the cabin he built near
Coloma until 1868, died in nearby Kelsey in 1885.
Sutter, a German-born of Swiss parentage who had
earlier built a feudal empire, saw the gold rush
decimate his resources; merchants, storekeepers,

saloonkeepers, and others rented space at Sutter's
Fort and many unscrupulous borrowers took his
money, most of whom never repaid their debts.
Sutter's land was besieged by squatters, his debts
mounted, and he moved to a farm near Marysville.
The house burned in 1865 and he went to Lititz,
Pennsylvania, to live. He died in Washington, D.C.,
June 18, 1880.

PROSPECTING HAZARDS

It might be well to view the unremitting conditions that existed and the difficult problems that arose
as a result of Marshall's discovery. These will account
in part for the nature of the sometimes rugged and
violent mining camps and towns that would soon
appear in California and the West.

Thousands had rushed to the Sierra Nevada
in 1848 hoping to amass a fortune. Many did not
survive the rugged winter. Though most of the prospectors who concluded the trip were robust and
hardy, many were ill-equipped. Few realized the
severity of the mountain winters; the majority probably expected to return home rich and safe before
winter set in. Of what there was, some equipment
was inadequate or useless, and some prospectors
gambled on their ability to improvise. But almost
without exception they were wrong. As winter approached, they faced serious problems: should they
return to the coastal cities, where it was warmer,
or remain in the diggings and be among the first
in the hills with the thaw? Though broke, should
they gamble with their remaining provisions and
blankets against the luxury of returning? For many,

107

THE WAY THEY COME FROM CALIFORNIA.

Lithograph by N. Currier, 1849. *Library of Congress*

Placer gold workings at Sutter's Creek, Coloma, 1850. *Wells Fargo Bank History Room*

Although a miner's camp in the 1850s was not a stanchion of religion, it became common practice to devote Sunday mornings, if not the balance of the day, to rest and to cleaning up the camp, after a fashion.

This early sketch, labeled "Sunday Morning," shows the rest period. Perhaps the cleanup comes later. *New York Public Library Picture Collection*

Not all cabins were a horror—a miner's cabin around the 1860s in Colorado. Playing cards was a frequent way of passing time. Note the Franklin stove, shaving mugs along the shelf, the gun over the bed, and a

broom. The tablecloth seems to be the one concession to social amenities. *Denver Public Library, Western Collection. Photo by L. C. McClure*

The cabins looked no better in the 1940s. This is a typical prospector's cabin in Peek-a-Boo Gulch, San Isabel National Forest, Colorado. Notice the large bellows to the left of the cabin. *United States Forest Service*

Miners' housekeeping. Wood engraving in *Harper's,* October 3, 1857. *Library of Congress*

A prospector dreams of better days ahead. *Library of Congress*

a decision was less a matter of gold than one of life or death. Some miners, living in the open or in flimsy tents during the November rainy season, saw all they had wash out; the more fortunate lived in flimsy log cabins, hurriedly knocked together; few, especially the Easterners, realized how rapidly clothing and shoes would wear out.

Once begun, the snow never seemed to stop, building layer by layer, often blown by gale winds into drifts exceeding twenty feet. Working the mines was impossible—it was a gigantic effort just digging out of whatever meager shelters they had, even to

hunt food. Death from exposure and freezing afflicted almost every camp; in spring many of those rescued were so severely frozen that the loss of fingers and toes was common.

Many prospectors were lucky not to reach the goldfields between 1848 and 1849. Arriving between spring and autumn of 1850, they were forewarned, consequently better equipped when winter arrived to withstand the Sierra Nevada weather.

Cabins usually were without flooring, with sawdust or gunny sack, when available, thrown over the dirt. For beds, there were ordinary boards or canvas sacks of hay, and usually the miners slept in their clothes; clothing was worn until it rotted or shredded.

Few brought wives. Those who did inevitably found themselves operating a boardinghouse; among other chores, the women cooked while the miners worked. Women were in great demand also to nurse; many illnesses had besieged the miners: chills, fevers, malaria, dysentery, diarrhea, and probably ulcers were rampant.

Sanitation was restricted to piling refuse outdoors and burning it, where possible; crude outhouses were available, moved from time to time as the stench became unbearable.

With the exception of the few who became rich, mining remained a disillusioning experience; all suffered hardship and privation. Strikes were made in wilderness areas, without towns, saloons, or entertainment beyond the miners gambling among themselves or with neighboring miners. Not until enterprising newcomers developed commercial establishments did they get the relaxation they desperately wanted.

Mining laborers were scarce—occasional Indians, Chinese, or Mexicans were employed. Time hardly existed for mining, no less building. Food often was scarce and rations scanty. Miners lived on supplies they had lugged in, augmented by whatever they could hunt or trap in the wilderness. Coffee, pork, and beans hardly sufficed for men who worked long and hard, often panning for gold in ice-cold waters. The bitter winter weather took its toll.

The little towns begun by these hardy pioneers grew rapidly, but in their haste, safety was forgotten. All such towns, often semipermanent in construction —at first, shacks, lean-tos, tents, and shelters formed by blankets—were fire hazards. Business enterprises, too, were crude and inadequate. Who knew whether the bonanza would be over before construction was finished? Eateries were unfurnished; miners often ate sitting on planks. Inns or hotels were nonexistent; a few places had rooms where men by the dozens

"Lady's Chain" (miners' dance). Wood engraving in *Harper's*, October 3, 1857. *Library of Congress*

Faro gambling in Miner's Camp. Wood engraving in *Harper's*, October 3, 1857. *Library of Congress*

slept on open floors. Housekeeping was unheard of and no one thought to shave. They craved only entertainment and diversion after a hard day's labor, and accordingly saloons were the first public structures of any town. It was easy to spot the well-dressed swindlers and gamblers among the ragged, unkempt, often mud-covered miners who flocked there. Little, if any, legal restraint assured abundant profanity, fights, arguments, and gunfire. Food, whiskey, gambling, and women on a take-it-as-it-comes basis were the miner's greatest demands—quickly satisfied by enterprising entrepreneurs.

These remained meager diversions, and new schemes for entertainment were constantly being devised. Bull baiting, cockfights, and boxing matches offered relief from the tobacco- and alcohol-stenched saloons, and theatricals, whether tasteless and unprofessional or classic and expert, were received with great enthusiasm. As the towns progressed, performances of Shakespeare and operas became popular.

Three scenes of the Colorado gold rush from *Frank Leslie's Illustrated Weekly*, German edition, April, 1859. *Colorado State Historical Society Library*

Nearly all prospected land was public domain, and claim jumping and arguments of every kind were common. There being no jurisdiction over the staking of claims or federal enforcement, until about 1865, every mining camp passed its own rules and laws. Violators, claim jumpers, and others were tried immediately, in open court, because usually there were no jails. Proceedings generally took only an hour or two, including executing the sentences; either a man was hanged, flogged, or thrown out of camp.

As the mining frontier spread from California to Colorado and Arizona, and other western states, prospectors carried along these conditions, from strike to strike. In fact, chance meetings of miner friends hundreds of miles away from "home" ground were frequent. The Colorado gold find was interesting in that it created an eastern instead of western gold rush of new pioneers; many of these bonanza seekers were old hands, either disappointed miners from the California goldfields or from the North or South.

It continued thus through the gold strikes of Pikes Peak, the Colorado "fifty-niners," and the booms of Colorado's 1870s, Nevada's 1880s, and Cripple Creek's 1890s—retracing the unremitting life of the miner from the days of the Forty-Niners.

Unidentified miners in the Colorado gold rush. Note the violin hanging on the wall in the right-hand corner, the briefcases, and the "art." The sophistication of some of the appurtenances are in stark contrast with the general condition of the cabin. *Colorado State Historical Society Library*

THE OUTLAWS ARRIVE

Marshall and Sutter were by no means the most successful gold seekers in 1848 and 1849, but they inspired renewed and continued searches throughout California.

Only twenty miles from the site of John Marshall's gold discovery was Auburn, California, originally North Fork Dry Diggings. Auburn became headquarters for two of California's most famous bandits. One, Tom Bell, though himself never lucky enough to successfully complete a robbery, originated the idea of holding up stagecoaches for gold, a trend that continued for years. In 1856, Bell, with five companions, stopped a stage carrying $100,000 in gold. At that moment a horseman approached and when Bell and his associates turned to apprehend him, the stage driver whipped his horses and took off with the stagecoach. Bell and his gang started shooting at the fleeing stage, wounding several passengers and killing a woman. Bell eventually was caught by a posse, and permitted to write a letter to his mother—in which he blamed his demise on evil companions, gambling, saloons, and women—before they hanged him from a nearby tree.

Rattlesnake Dick, the other bandit, was an ex-prospector who never struck it rich. According to reports, unjustly accused of two unproved thefts, Rattlesnake acquired the reputation of a thief. If he were going to be known as a thief, he decided he might as well be one; thereafter he was called "Rattlesnake Dick (for stealing horses near Rattle-

Panorama of old Auburn, California, in the 1870s. Placer mining was successful here as early as 1848, and in two years about 2,000 people lived in the town. Auburn became an important shipping center for mining supplies and freight until the Central Pacific Railroad was built in 1865. *Mrs. May W. Perry, Placer County Museum*

Jim Sheridan was the owner and driver of this freight team that ran from Auburn to Forest Hills in Placer County in the 1880s. For several years after its discovery no roads led to the area. This did not deter prospectors, who had to walk miles, carrying their possessions or packing them on mules, burros, or horses. Shortly afterward, wagons driven by ox or horse teams were able to get through, and as mining increased along the nearby American River and up into the mountains, trails and rough roads were constructed. Long lines of pack mules, sometimes as many as eighty, carried the supplies. By 1850 standard roads were open to miners who would pay the tolls for their use. Freight rates were expensive, especially for a ten-hour ride from Sacramento. Ox-drawn teams cost from $10 to $40 a hundred pounds for haulage. When the stage started running, its fare was $10 one way and $16 for a round trip. By 1855 the fare was reduced considerably: $2 each way to and from Sacramento, with the round trip an easy one-day ride. *Mrs. May W. Perry, Placer County Museum*

snake Bar), the Pirate of the Placers," for six years robbing the gold miners.

But Rattlesnake Dick was a piker compared to the rough characters that infested Hangtown. Robberies and murders were so common here that citizens were forced into making their own law, flogging and hanging offenders without trial. And thus the settlement soon acquired the dubious name of Hangtown.

Hangtown had other, nonmining, claims to glory. It spawned some of the early giants in American business and industry. The Studebaker brothers began their careers here, building and repairing wagon wheels; Mark Hopkins, who sold groceries door to door, became a railroad builder and one of the incorporators of the Central Pacific Railroad; Philip Armour ran a butcher shop, the beginning of

"Old Dry Diggin's," first called Hangtown. It was one of many mining camps that grew out of the Mother Lode in 1848 following the Sutter's Mill gold discovery. Before a year, mining characters from all over the world overran the town. At the extreme right in this rare 1850 photo is the small building in which the Studebaker brothers built their first spring wagon. The old Empire Theater, clearly seen in the center background, is where famous stage celebrities of the day appeared, including the first of the Foys and Lily Langtry. The famous old hang-tree (center) gave the camp its name. On Jackass Hill (beyond center) Mark Twain built a cabin, where he lived with his mining partner, Jim Gillis. After six years of growth, a population of about 2,000, and with respectability exceeding rowdyism, Hangtown was incorporated as Placerville, with the principal mine, the Pacific, in plumb center of town. Placerville's decline was hastened by two disastrous fires. The latter, in 1856, seemed to signal its end; gold production had fallen off, and the outlook was bleak. Notwithstanding, the local citizenry rebuilt it, which proved to be a fortunate decision because the Comstock Lode in Nevada was discovered three years later and Placerville became the gateway to the historic Nevada mines. *University of Oklahoma Library, Division of Manuscripts (N. H. Rose Collection)*

one of the largest meat-packing houses in the country. And there were legendary characters. The tales of Snowshoe Thompson's deeds are equal to Paul Bunyan's. Thompson was a giant woodsman who crossed the Placerville–Genoa (near Carson City) trail, in winter, impassable to all but Thompson who managed to carry mail, supplies, and, once, a cast-iron stove. Hank Monk, a reckless, fearless stage-driver careened Horace Greeley, bellowing with rage, over the hair-raising Carson City–Placerville trail. Had Monk overturned Greeley's stage, which was imminent, Greeley might well have altered his famous utterance to "Stay East, young man, stay East!"

While Snowshoe Thompson was "beating the bush" out of Hangtown, Major Pierson B. Reading, from New Jersey, was scouring the Shasta section of California on a grant of land he had received from the Mexican governor. He discovered gold near the mouth of Clear Creek Canyon, in 1848. To the town's misfortune, the California and Oregon Railroad bypassed it in favor of the new town of Redding, and Shasta's decline followed rapidly.

Shasta is now a state historical monument consisting of several brick buildings, a store, and a courthouse that serves as a museum but with an excellent collection of relics of the period. The monument's outstanding features are the remains of the longest row of brick buildings, the widest main street, and the oldest lodge in California. An unusual site is the old jail, containing wrist and leg shackles, ball and chains, and an iron collar with a chain fastened to the floor where escapees were chained as an example for the rest of the prisoners. There is also a reconstructed gallows.

Portions of "brick row." Ruins of what was the longest brick row of buildings in California during the gold-rush days. *California Department of Parks and Recreation*

The Portuguese Mine in the Klamath National Forest near Shasta, a fine example of modern hydraulic mining. Between five and six million dollars in gold was shipped out of Shasta each year, mostly produced by hydraulicking. *United States Forest Service. Photo by A. K. Crabbin*

Clear Creek—Reading's Bar—Reading's Springs—Shasta City—Shasta, in the order of their name changes. Shasta never became an important gold-mining district despite the prospectors drawn from San Francisco and Oregon. It served as a supply camp for the more remote mining camps in the area; and throughout a devastating fire in 1852 and another six months later, the town still prospered. From 1852 to 1857, Shasta remained the center for mining supplies, keeping more than 2,000 mules busy hauling materials to the mines. By 1857 the population reached 3,000, not including many transients, who stopped at the numerous hotels and rooming houses, nor a Chinese quarter with about 1,000 workers. The photo shows the old Norton and Tucker Building in Shasta, a remnant of those old mining days. *California Department of Parks and Recreation*

Murphy's placer mining works, 1868. Murphy's Diggins, near Angel's Creek, was named for Daniel and John Murphy who discovered placer gold beds in July, 1848. In 1859, fire destroyed Murphys, its new name. However, a few of the original buildings remain—a hotel, bakery, stores, a Wells Fargo express office, and a schoolhouse. Murphys Hotel, then known as Mitchlers Hotel, had housed such guests as U. S. Grant, Henry Ward Beecher, Mark Twain, Horatio Alger, and Black Bart. Joaquin Murietta, another famous bandit, supposedly began his infamous career in Murphys. He was captured by a couple of railroad detectives, one of whom was said to be a woman. James Carson staked a claim in Carson Hill, eventually one of the richest of the mining camps. It produced the largest nugget of the California bonanza, a single piece of gold weighing 195 pounds, then valued at nearly $75,000. *William Culp Darrah Stereo Collection*

Mark Twain's famous short story "The Celebrated Jumping Frog of Calaveras County" had its genesis in a visit to Angel's Camp, in Calaveras County, California, in 1865. Angel's Camp was a trading post established in 1848 when James H. Carson and George Angel discovered placer deposits of gold here. Nine years later, eleven mills were operating, but they were soon exhausted. Quartz veins were discovered accidentally by a miner known simply as Raspberry. One day while out hunting with his muzzle-loader, the ramrod stuck in his gun barrel. Unable to remove it, he fired the rifle anyway, the ramrod hitting a rock on the ground. When Raspberry picked up the disintegrated rock, he found pieces of gold in it. He immediately staked a claim, and in three days removed over $10,000 in gold.

MEXICAN MINERS

Roaming over the Southwest looking for metals even before the Americans were the Mexicans, who never got as far north as Shasta. Some never returned to their homeland and were drawn like bees to honey to those camps reporting gold strikes. Such a town was Sonora, "Queen of the Southern Mines," which grew up around placer gold deposits discov-

ered by Mexican miners in August, 1848. It was a rowdy, rough-and-tumble California town, filled with Mexicans. But in 1850, at the instigation of Sonorans, the state legislature decided Sonora had too many Mexicans and Chinese. It imposed a $20 tax on every foreign-born miner, which forced many to leave. Though the Foreign Miners Tax was repealed in 1851, it was reinstated the year after at $3 a month, increased to $4 a month in the second year. It is interesting to note that many fires devastated the town during this period.

"OLD ABE" TO THE RESCUE

An interesting nearby town, Soldier's Gulch (changed to Volcano), also worked for gold, had, with the Civil War approaching, divided the miners into two factions: those who believed in states' rights and those who wished to abolish slavery. Should Volcano go to the North or South? As verbal arguments grew into fistfights, the abolitionists resurrected an ancient cannon, dubbed "Old Abe." Lacking cannonballs for ammunition, they selected round stones from the placer workings. Whether the cannon could have been fired was never determined. The Southern sympathizers, deciding not to test their mettle, retired. Volcano's gold by default went to the Union forces, probably contributing importantly to the outcome of the war. Along with other mining relics and the old jail at Volcano, "Old Abe" is still on public display.

But "Old Abe" was not around earlier at Mokelumne Hill to settle disputes between two other foreign elements—French and Chilean. It was a rough town—a murder a week was average. One riot nearly wrecked it when some French miners had raised the French flag over their workings. Another battle was fought against Chilean miners working the nearby gold areas in 1848 and 1849.

A local bandit, Joaquin Murietta, had so outraged the Mokelumne miners that, in the saloon one day, one miner reputedly threw a bag of gold on the bar, betting $500 that he would kill Murietta on sight. A Mexican, rising suddenly, accepted the bet, grabbed the bag and was out of the bar before anyone realized what was happening. He then jumped on a horse, and disappeared with the entire $500. Some of the miners believed he was Murietta, known for his cunning. A Frenchman once offered to sell him a bulletproof vest, and to be sure he wasn't buying a "pig in a poke," he ordered the Frenchman to put on the vest. Murietta shot him in the chest and the Frenchman fell to the floor, not hurt by the bullet but in a dead faint from fright.

DEATH VALLEY DAYS

More than bulletproof vests were needed to combat the natural forces working against the prospectors. As a result, while gold searches went on, other metals or minerals that would some day prove even more mine-worthy than gold were completely by-passed or ignored.

This was exactly what happened at Death Valley, which acquired its name and reputation when a group of avid gold seekers in 1849 attempted to cross the desert as a shortcut to the California goldfields. All but one perished in the barren wastes.

Virtually no gold was found in Death Valley, although borax, which became an important commodity, was discovered later. Death Valley owed its gold reputation to Walter Scott, known as Death Valley Scotty, an ex-rider in Buffalo Bill's Wild West Show. He established himself about 1903 at the northern boundary of the valley, posing as a prospector and building a "castle" reputedly costing more than $2 million. He claimed that his funds derived from a secret gold mine that he had discovered, but this was a complete fabrication. His money came from two Chicago backers.

South of Death Valley is the Mojave Desert, containing the world's largest borax deposit. Unlike Death Valley, the Mojave also contained gold, near the mountain town of Randsburg. Here the Yellow Astor Mine produced gold worth millions of dollars. But except for borax, perhaps the desert's greatest mineral contribution was a tungsten mine, the Scheelite Mine of the Atolia Mining Company, possibly the largest tungsten mine in the United States. However, in its borax and talc mines lies the true story and real value of mining in this desert region.

While no one may have wanted to own desolate land in Death Valley, ownership of other western lands was often complicated by land grants that had been issued by Mexican and even Spanish governments before the territory became part of the United States.

John C. Frémont's ranch had disclosed one of the first gold-bearing quartz veins discovered in California. However, Fremont became involved in litigation over the title to his ranch. His legal battles and shady partners, as well as high mine-operating costs, precluded any profits from mining, although by 1862 over $3 million in gold had been removed. Fremont lost control of the Mariposa a year later, which in the ensuing decade produced over $20 million in gold.

Death Valley Scotty relaxing in his $2,000,000 castle, reputedly built with funds from his "secret" gold mine in Death Valley. *Felix A. Peckham*

A twenty-mule team in Death Valley. *U.S. Borax and Chemical Corporation*

This relic from borax mining days is on display at Death Valley. *Felix A. Peckham*

CALIFORNIA BLACK GOLD

About 150 miles west, and slightly north of Mariposa, lying about midway between San Francisco and Sacramento, is a former roaring coal-mining region. A few coal dumps, some skeletal buildings, and many dangerous mine shafts are sole remnants

of past activity. The famous Black Diamond coal vein was discovered here in the early 1850s. Thousands of tons of coal were produced and shipped to the port of Pittsburg, California.

Because of the coal's low-grade quality, followed by an explosion in the Black Diamond Mine in 1876, the entire area witnessed a rapid decline. The old shafts still remain, some hundreds of feet deep, and are extremely dangerous for hikers or curiosity seekers.

These mule trains at the Nellie Mine were similar to the mule trains that ran from Downieville to Marysville in 1849 and 1850. Freight service was by pack trains, mules usually driven by Mexican drivers for their American employers; and the traffic between Downieville and the surrounding towns was almost unbelievable. More than 2,500 mules operated between Marysville and Downieville alone, requiring nearly 400 men, and as the trails wore smooth, wagon trains, each sometimes pulled by six or eight mules, became the accepted method of transport. *Colorado State Historical Society Library*

The Frémont Mill and vein, Mariposa, California. Gold extraction from the quartz mill utilized steam power (1850). Frémont was a famous soldier-explorer who lived at the southern end of the Mother Lode on his Mexican land grant of nearly 45,000 acres. Soon after the 1849 gold discovery, Frémont put twenty-five Mexican miners to work building a quartz mill, around which grew the town of Mariposa.

JUANITA'S TOWN

About 160 miles northwest, Downieville was having its own growing pains. When gold was found here in 1849 the usual stampede of prospectors followed. By spring, 1850, over 5,000 had established a mining camp, all within a twenty-mile radius.

And a discovery of rich nuggets at the Sailor Diggings about three miles above Downieville, resulted in an influx of Englishmen to the California goldfields. Owned by a group of English sailors, the Diggings in 1851 yielded a nugget of pure gold weighing 31 pounds, as well as a great number of others weighing from five to 15 pounds. The group returned to England with the nuggets in two canvas sacks. Rather than sell the gold, they found it more profitable to exhibit their collection in large towns and cities. The display spurred the wave of British gold-digging fever that brought many Englishmen to California.

Downieville is perhaps better known for being the only camp in the gold country to hang a woman, a Mexican dance-hall girl, Juanita, who had lived in town with her Mexican boyfriend. One night an uninvited drunk, a miner named Campbell, called on her. Rebuffed, he returned the next day and was met by Juanita's boyfriend; the two argued, then fought. During the fight Juanita fatally stabbed Campbell in the chest, in view of many witnesses. She was hanged by vigilantes despite her doctor's claim that she was pregnant. An autopsy disproved the doctor's testimony. Oddly enough, Juanita was said to have killed other men who had accosted her.

Another Downieville claim to fame is William "Bull" Meek, reputedly the only stage driver never held up and robbed. Local history records that "Bull" brought supplies to the neighborhood bawdy house, and that the madam exercised her important influence with the tougher element in town to assure Bull's safe passage.

Westward-bound gold seekers and travelers found the California Overland Trail spotted with watering places. Mud Spring was one, an inglorious name for a town boasting of placer gold in 1849. As it achieved the status of a booming mine camp, its name optimistically changed to El Dorado. The gold ran out two years later, and the town was abandoned, reverting to no more than a mud spring.

TONG WARS BEGIN

It is amazing how quickly the Chinese arrived at the mining camps—sometimes as quickly as the prostitutes! Enterprising groups found it profitable to import the Chinese as laborers. One such company was formed by Englishmen who founded Chinese Camp in 1849. The town became headquarters for four of six Chinese companies and within six years its population exceeded 5,000. Actually, these companies were tongs, and rivalry between these family clans was keen. The first tong war broke out in Weaverville (about 150 miles northwest of Downieville), the second in Chinese Camp (about fifty miles northwest of Mariposa).

Typical of the factions' sensitivities, when a boulder accidentally rolled from the diggings of one Chinese group to another, first words were exchanged, then blows, and finally they were at it hammer and tong. In an engagement between the 900-membership Yan Wo Tong and the 200 Sam Yap Tong at Crimea Flat, three miles from Chinese Camp, spears, axes, daggers, and rifles were employed. The battle was joined and ended October 25, 1856. Despite its ferocity, only four were killed and four wounded, but 250 were jailed—by Americans.

Some 2,500 Chinese worked in the vicinity of Weaverville, all hard workers, often restricted to working for hire or to reworking the tailings left by previous miners. Encouraged by whites, the Weaverville tong war erupted in the 1850s. Spears and squirt guns containing some disabling liquid served as weapons. Tin shields and helmets comprised armor. Despite their primitive means, eight Chinese and a Dutchman were killed before the skirmish ended.

The Weaverville Joss House is one of the town's most interesting present-day features, believed to be the oldest Chinese temple in continuous use in the United States, and the still partially denuded surrounding countryside remains witness to the extensive hydraulic mining that once went on.

Chinese workers in costume on the right. Thousands of Chinese joined the gold rush as traders, laborers, and independent miners. The photo was taken in the early 1850s at the head of the Auburn Ravine in California where gold was first discovered in 1848. *Wells Fargo Bank History Room*

Air view of "earthworms" formed as a result of gold
dredging in the 1940s in Eldorado County, California.
United States Forest Service. Photo by W. I. Hutchinson

Although most Chinese laborers working in mines were
under contract and paid by the day, there were some
who did mining on their own. This early sketch shows
a group of independent Chinese miners in California.
New York Public Library Picture Collection

In the 1940s dragline dredging had taken the place of hydraulic mining in the Trinity National Forest near Weaverville. *United States Forest Service. Photo by J. N. Gibson*

"SCUBA" DIVING IN THE 1870s

A short time earlier, in 1849, a strange story had come to light after an unknown miner came to the conclusion that gold, being heavy, would sink and ultimately come to rest at the bottom of the riverbed. He had engaged a Coloma, California, friend, an expert in "mechanical pursuits," to design and construct a suit of submarine armor to wear while exploring river bottoms.

Twenty-five years later he told of the results of his friend's engineering brilliance in an article in the September, 1874, issue of *Overland Monthly,* in which he described the diving suit:

> I had seen many hideous and repulsive things in my day, but they were things of beauty and joy to soothe the nerves forever, compared with this. Laid on its back, it looked a huge, misshapen burial casket; turned on its side, a pauper's coffin. Long India-rubber tubes, black and flexible; two glaring eyes; dust and rubbish adhering to every pitch-besmeared seam—it were hard to say whether the thing most resembled a sleeping crocodile or a curled-up devilfish lying in wait for prey.

A group, including Larry McShane, a bibulous companion sworn to secrecy, set off to find gold, but McShane, convinced that this was a plot to drown him, refused—despite the proffered reward of a bottle of whiskey. The miner-author would dive alone, later to write about it:

> As nothing could be done without a diver, I determined that I would take it upon myself to perform that grave service. Accordingly, securing the aid of a few trusty friends, we repaired with our accoutrements to a deep, still stretch in the river, a little above the mill, previously fixed on for the purpose. Here, divesting myself of my outer

As for more modern methods, dredges are expensive but expendable; derelicts are commonly found in old dredging areas. Unfortunately, the dredges could not be reversed after serving their purpose, and were abandoned after the machinery was removed. In the 1960s a few venturesome prospectors who could not afford hundreds of thousands of dollars for a dredge searched for gold in the pockets of rivers by using scuba or skin-diving equipment. The North Yuba River in the Tahoe National Forest in California is known for this, and here divers are using a pump on an elaborate raft to recover gold from the river bottom. *United States Forest Service. Photo by John W. Wicker*

garments, I was duly ensconced in my water-proof dress, feeling all the while very much like a wretch being prepared for public execution. If the mere sight of the machine had caused me to shudder, my frame of mind can hardly be conceived now that I was to be screwed up in it and anchored in five or six fathoms of snow-water. Though badly scared, I managed to conceal my fear, so that those assisting me really thought I was in excellent spirits and even relished the operation. Gladly would I have backed out as the cold and clammy folds of the rubber invested my limbs. After I had been fairly launched, and while my companions were poking away with a couple of poles, seeking to shove me out into deep water, I was on the eve of crying out and demanding to be pulled ashore, so horrible did my situation seem to me. But all was at stake—fortune, consistency, reputation for courage—to give up at this stage of proceeding was to be branded as a poltroon, and to dissipate the gorgeous dream of wealth in which myself and partner had so fondly indulged. Better drown than this; so I restrained myself from making an outcry, and, suffering the poling process to go on, soon found myself at the bottom of the pool, where I lost no time in filling the two large buckets, provided for the purpose, with such materials as I could most readily lay hands on. As I could no longer see after beginning to stir up the mud, I had no idea what this material might consist of, but flattered myself that a fair proportion of it, at least, was gold. Having filled the vessels to repletion, I gave the signal and was speedily hauled to the surface. It would be difficult to describe the solicitude with which we watched the washing of what I had brought up, or the dismay that seized us on finding that it contained not a particle of the precious metal we were in search of. Another effort was made here with a like result, and then we decided to go below and make trial in the mill-dam, from which we felt certain no gold could have escaped that had once been carried into it.

Moving down to this more promising location, another descent was made; but nothing having been obtained—the contents of the buckets consisting in every case of only barren gravel mixed with twigs, leaves, mud, and sand—still a fourth had to be undertaken. While being submerged this last time, the signal-rope became entangled with the air-supplying tube in such a manner as to prevent either of them acting freely. Beginning to experience a difficulty in breathing soon after I was let down, I signaled for more air and at the same time to be hauled up. No attention, however, was paid to my signal. Perceiving that something was wrong, I began to tug at the signal-rope with all my might; but it was of no use, it would not work. Soon I felt myself beginning to suffocate, and in this condition I was left till my companions above, alarmed at the length of time I had been under water, pulled me up and hauled me on shore, after which they were not long in discovering what was the matter. Stripping off the armor as quickly as possible, they found me in an unconscious state, respiration suspended, my features convulsed, and my veins black and swollen. Restorative measures were adopted, and I was at length resuscitated. For a time I laid in a condition of partial stupor, but as soon as I became fully conscious of what had happened, and had strength enough to stand on my feet, I got up, and, taking one look at the accursed contrivance, without saying a word to anyone, staggered away; disgusted beyond measure with my experience at diving, yet thankful, withal, that it had ended so well: nor did I ever after inquire what had become of the machine, or seek further to explore the deep places for gold.

Our underwater explorer was merely ahead of his time. Though no record exists as to whether he actually found any gold, in the winter of 1905-1906, Captain Henry Finch prospected near Nome under six feet of ice, at forty degrees below zero. Finch had outfitted his expedition with standard submarine armor and a diving tender.

GOLD OR SPIDERS!

Diving for gold was not destined to uncover an important part of gold's production but almost at the time our enterprising 1849 diver was struggling for his life on the river bottom, a major discovery was being made at Grass Valley, between

Captain Henry Finch prospecting for gold in Nome, Alaska, in 1905. Finch is seen descending below the six-foot-thick ice in a temperature that is 40 degrees below zero! *University of Alaska Museum, Mackay Collection*

Mariposa and Downieville. But whether little Grass Valley in the western foothills of the Sierra Nevada became better known for its fabulous Empire Mine or for its famous entertainer, Lola Montez, is a matter of opinion.

A year after Marshall's discovery, a small miners' camp grew up in Boston Ravine where the first gold-quartz find in California occurred. This marked a major turning point in California's mining history and opened the door for the development of deep mining in Colorado because, before its discovery, most gold mining had been done by placer and hydraulic methods, and of course quartz-rock mining required a completely different technique. At first the old placer miners tried to break the quartz rock with hand mortars. Soon crude, hand-worked stamp mills, made from large tree trunks attached to a base of iron, were found to be more practical. Later these mills were modified and powered by steam and electricity until more modern methods of rock crushing were developed. G. W. Wright built the first American mill to process gold-quartz ore in Grass Valley in 1850.

The quartz-rock find created little excitement

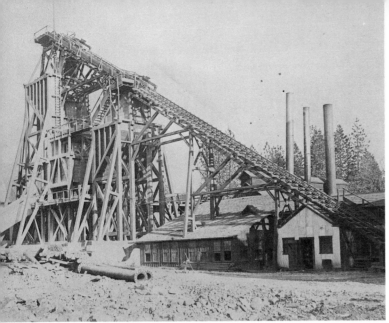

The headgear at the Empire Mine. This shaft goes down to a depth of 4,600 feet on an incline and then on the main horizontal drift for approximately one mile. It then enters another underground shaft, or winze, which drops to a depth of 8,000 feet. The stations or levels in this shaft are 450 feet apart. From this main shaft run hundreds of miles of drifts. The home of the Empire was famous Ophir Hill, and Grass Valley quartz ledges also were discovered at Rich Hill and Massachusetts Hill. Just a mile from Grass Valley George D. Roberts had staked a claim on Ophir Hill, never dreaming that it would develop into the state's most famous gold-quartz mine, one of the richest and deepest in California. During its first four years the Empire claim changed owners several times, and although by then it had produced over $1 million, its stock sold for comparatively very little money. In that period, Empire Mine's stamping mill was destroyed by fire, which also ruined the pumping and hoisting equipment, and the mine again changed hands a year afterward, followed by a new mill. By 1873, after 23 years in operation, 91 miners were employed, 11 in the mill. Shafts were dug 1,250 feet, while nearly 8,000 feet of drifts were chiseled through Ophir Hill. As the vein ran out, the company developed its adjacent Rich Hill vein. Within five years the mine proved unprofitable at such depths, and again new owners took over. In 1885 an addition was constructed to the stamping mill, and mine power was converted from steam to water. Utilizing a Cornish pump, the water-filled Ophir shafts were pumped out so that the Ophir, as well as the Rich Hill ledge, could be reworked. Within a couple of years still other shafts had been pumped dry and reopened. *Grass Valley, California, Mining Exhibit*

until the Gold Hill Ledge was discovered four months later on what was then called Gold Mountain, later known as Gold Hill. Prospecting hopefuls poured in from all over the state, causing the construction of more than 130 buildings in Grass Valley in under a year.

No history of Grass Valley can ignore Lola Montez, the internationally famous beauty and entertainer. As for any Spanish blood, it was all in her name. To her Irish parents she was Eliza Gilbert.

An 1885 photograph of the miners ascending from the Empire Mine. Note that they are carrying candles. The mine continued in operation until 1900, with some changes in ownership. By then the main shaft had reached a depth of 3,080 feet. The nearby Pennsylvania Mine had also been acquired. New equipment was continually being installed by the new owners, and the main shaft was extended to 3,600 feet. By 1924 it was the deepest in California, 6,200 feet, while at the 2,600-foot level, the shaft had been connected to the 2,400-foot level of the Pennsylvania Mine. *California, Division of Mines and Geology*

At 2,100 feet down at the Empire Mine, about 1890. *California, Division of Mines and Geology*

She had danced for royalty and had been a hostess to such notables as George Sand, Franz Liszt, and Alexander Dumas. As a mistress, for two years, she had charmed Ludwig of Bavaria, among unnamed others. She had gone to England, remarried without

The Sullivan stoping drills in the North Star Mine around 1895. In 1929 the Newmont Mining Corporation acquired the North Star and the Empire, and consolidated them into the Empire-Star Mines Company Limited. Despite the Depression, within a year the underground workings were extended to 18,200 feet, making the new Empire the largest gold producer in California. By 1942 Empire-Star Mines operated the Empire, North Star, and Pennsylvania mines at Grass Valley, in addition to the Pennsylvania and Dannebrog mines at Brown Valley in Yuba County. With the end of World War II, operations were suspended for a year. They reopened on a lease-operated basis, continuing until 1959 when the entire holdings were sold at public auction. At that juncture over 190 miles of tunnels crisscrossed the mine, the incline depth of its deepest shaft reaching over 11,000 feet. Should the price of gold ever reach a satisfactory level, the mine may one day reopen. *Grass Valley, California, Mining Exhibit*

An ore "skip" dumping at the North Star Mine. These skips, or ore cars, are loaded from the shaft chutes or bins by a man called a "skiptender." When it was loaded, he would signal to the hoist to surface, where it would dump the ore into a bin. This skip went to a depth of 3,600 feet (circa 1900). *Grass Valley, California, Mining Exhibit*

Lola Montez. *Wells Fargo Bank History Room*

benefit of divorce (she had deserted her army-officer husband) and had subsequently been tried for bigamy. She had then gone to New York City, as a dancer, finally ending in California.

Though her celebrated Spider Dance in which she fought off attacks by spiders left impressions in San Francisco, it did not create the sensation she expected at the mining camps. The crowds came to see her more for her notoriety than for her dancing. At Grass Valley Lola took a fancy to a neighbor's girl, Lotta Crabtree, and tutored her. Lotta became the miners' favorite at the age of

123

eight—when she toured the mining camps. She grew up being showered with nuggets and bags of gold dust, and had phenomenal successes as an actress in New York and San Francisco. While Lotta retired from show business with $4 million, the beautiful Lola Montez died in New York in 1860, penniless.

COLUMBIA—THE GEM OF THE MOTHER LODE

Like many other gold-rush towns, Columbia lay in the heart of the "Mother Lode," a mile-wide, 120-mile-long network of gold-bearing quartz that extended along the western edge of the Sierra Nevada Range, from Mariposa northward to Georgetown.

The Chinese influence here was quite strong. Many stayed on to work their own "diggins," while some became businessmen; a small Chinatown was established after the 1857 fire. Their original contract terms generally provided wages of $3 to $4 a month; $1.50 to $2 was withheld to cover subsistence for the coolies' families in China.

In roughness, Columbia was not equal to Bodie, but it had its usual Mexican fandango halls, gambling parlors, saloons, and "houses" of diversion; bullfights and bear baiting were common attractions. Serious attempts were made to raise the level of culture: small circuses and theatrical groups were well received, bands and choral societies were organized, and the miners paid well for quality entertainers, attracting such stars as Edwin Booth, Lotta Crabtree, and Lola Montez.

But by 1860 the town was in decline; in 1870 some buildings were razed and their sites mined. Columbia resisted a ghost-town status through its some 500 souls who remained in the surrounding area until the town became a state park.

THE RUSH MOVES EAST

The search for quartz gold continued with the trend now moving eastward—a trend that would later become a panic in Colorado. Near the crest of the

A relic of the gold-rush days is this old "ore car" at Columbia State Historic Park. Among other reconstructions are the Mills Bank, Fallon House Hotel, stage drivers' retreat, and the old firehouse. Set among the rocks is a replica of a mining cabin, and a real stagecoach features a ride and robbery. *Felix A. Peckham*

Columbia about 1860. Columbia is now a popular state historic park, and one of California's best preserved gold-rush towns, once called "The Gem of the Southern Mines." In only about eleven years of active quartz mining, it had produced over $87 million in gold. At today's prices that amount would more than double. When Dr. Thaddeus Hildreth and brother George discovered gold here on March 27, 1850, the stampede began. Miners converged, and in a month 5,000 prospectors were living in tents and shanties, some camping on the very site of future Columbia. The town began as Hildreth's Diggings, then changed to American Camp, finally incorporating as Columbia in 1854. Water was needed to wash the gold out of the dirt. Columbia had no natural streams or springs, so in 1851 a company was formed to bring it in. But the rates were excessive, and the miners formed their own company. They built a 60-mile aqueduct to supply the mines, but by the time the new system was completed, seven years later, most of the gold was gone, as were the miners. However, in the interim Columbia had grown. By the end of its second year, it was quite a town—150 places of business, including 30 saloons and a brewery, a church, Sunday school, Masonic lodge, and various other buildings. Columbia's first fire, in 1854, destroyed the entire center of the business district but for one brick building. In the next year and a half 30 new buildings were built, many from locally produced red brick. Three years after the first fire, a second ravaged the business district, wiping out the remaining frame structures and even many of the new brick buildings. However, rebuilding began immediately, and some of those structures still stand. *California Department of Parks and Recreation*

The gold scales in Wells Fargo's Columbia office were shipped around the Horn in 1853 and were an important part of the banking equipment of Wells Fargo's office in Columbia. These scales weighed out over $55 million in gold. *Wells Fargo Bank History Room*

One of the first buildings the state restored was the Wells Fargo and Company express office, Columbia's onetime hub of activity; it had been the center for shipping, freight, passengers, and supplies, and millions of dollars of gold dust and nuggets. The reconstructed Concord coach is an exact replica. *California Department of Parks and Recreation*

The old mining town of Johnsville, now part of Plumas-Eureka State Park. After about twenty years of operation, in 1872 British interests took over mining claims on Eureka Peak, emphasizing quartz mining. Placer operations subsequently were soon discontinued. The Quartz Mountain District property known as the Little Jamison, on Little Jamison Creek, about two miles south of Johnsville, represented an encouraging new mining development in the 1890s. The Jamison Mining Company had been incorporated. The terrain was suitable for both placer and tunnel mining, and expensive shaftwork and drifts were developed to remove the quartz gold. *California Department of Parks and Recreation*

Since it was often necessary to carry water for miles, a lone miner found it impossible to construct such a flume to his claim; some flumes extended ten miles or more. The scene is a flume at Parks' Bar on the Yuba River, California. *New York Public Library*

Old lithograph (circa 1855) showing how watercourses were turned to wash gold-bearing sands in California. *Free Library of Philadelphia*

A mill was constructed, and operations continued successfully until 1943, when mining became unprofitable. This building was the old powder cache, or magazine, used for the Johnsville stamp mill. *California Department of Parks and Recreation*

The State of California acquired much of the mining area now incorporated into Plumas-Eureka State Park. The state has repaired and restored the old Plumas-Eureka Stamp Mill, a 72-foot-high building that still has 10 of the original 48 stamps used to crush ore before the gold was extracted. The photo shows the ruins of the mill before restoration. Old mine tunnels and other buildings remain. When activity on the almost 8,000-foot Eureka Peak slowed down in winter, the Johnsville Track, a ski course of 1,676 feet, provided "snowshoe" races. Instead of snowshoes competitors used huge Norwegian cross-country skis. The races proved so popular that competitions were held with neighboring mining towns, establishing Johnsville as the birthplace of sport skiing in the United States. *California Department of Parks and Recreation*

eastern slopes of the Sierra Nevadas lies the historic California mining community of Johnsville. Although some mining was known here during 1849, the Eureka Ledge discovery—on Eureka Peak—two years later kicked off an intense lode-mining activity; placer mining sites and old flumes are still scattered over the Peak. Panning for gold along Jamison and Little Jamison creeks disclosed exceptionally large gold particles taken from the stream bottom.

FROM PAN TO HOSE

Despite the searches for quartz-gold and mother-lode veins, work on known deposits did not stop, and hydraulic mining was proving to be a more productive recovery method than panning.

Malakoff Diggins, the State Historic Park with modern swimming facilities, sitting at the edge of North Bloomfield about nineteen miles north of Nevada City, Nevada County, California, was quite different back in the good old days when it was a water storehouse for hydraulic mining. The extensive erosion induced by mining operations is permanently fixed in part of the reservoir shoreline, which resembles a miniature Bryce Canyon, Utah.

The good old days began in 1851 when a drunken prospector stumbled into a Nevada City saloon, dumped a handful of nuggets and dust on the bar and ordered drinks for the house. Bartenders were always alert to displays that might indicate windfalls, but this was a tight-lipped miner who would not disclose the source of his nuggets. Later he purchased supplies, mounted his burro, and rode a trail northwest of town, finally arriving at the bank of a small creek where two of his friends were washing gold from the creek gravels. But over twenty Nevada City prospectors were right behind their drinking but close-mouthed companion, at a safe distance. In time, they revealed themselves, staked their claims, unpacked their gold pans, and went to work—and panned nothing of value. Suspecting trickery, they dubbed the project "humbug." Thus the creek became Humbug Creek.

Later arrivals, of course, struck it rich, and little Humbug City in five years counted over 400 residents—saloon keepers, gamblers, dance-hall girls, merchants, and miners among them. Humbug was no longer a proper name for a dignified mining camp, and the townspeople changed it to Bloomfield. But there already was a Bloomfield in California, so they changed it to North Bloomfield.

Hydraulic washings in the Malakoff Pit, not unlike settings, in miniature, at Bryce Canyon. In 1856 millions of gallons of water, under high pressure, washed the towering gold-flaked and nugget-laden gravel banks here, and the former Humbug Creek became California's largest hydraulic mining center when two large reservoirs had been constructed high in the Sierra Nevada, 6,000 feet above sea level and about 3,000 feet above town; the intricate system of canals and flumes transporting water to the miners extended for over 100 miles. But hydraulic operations silted every stream and stream-fed lake and river, so polluting the water that antidebris laws were passed prohibiting dumping in any stream entering the Sacramento Valley. It was the beginning of the end of Malakoff Diggins, as they were soon put out of the hydraulicking business. The town peaked in 1880 with a population of about 1,800; now only a handful remain between the town and park area. *California Department of Parks and Recreation*

"GOOD-BYE, GOD, I'M GOING TO BODIE"

With few exceptions, the placer camps soon died out as the workings were depleted, unless more permanent lode deposits were found. Nevertheless some camps developed into towns that lived for twenty-five or thirty years or more. In its heyday, Bodie was probably the roughest, toughest, wickedest city in the United States. In 1852 gold had been discovered by a United States Army Infantry detachment in search of Yosemite Valley Indians. A trek of prospectors came hard after them, traveling over

The Standard Mill, the principal gold mine at Bodie, opened within months. First called the Bunker Hill, it was registered in August, and its name later changed to the Standard Mine and Mill Company, and again, in 1877, to the Standard Company. A block of ground was leased to twenty-five-year-old James Cain, who, with Joe Maguire, in ninety days removed $90,000 in gold. Standard reneged on a renewal, but Cain, through court action, later acquired the entire mine, and became the town's principal property owner. *California Department of Parks and Recreation*

Remnants of old mining machinery lie about the old buildings of Bodie. By 1883 only two mines remained, and these consolidated four years later, and in 1893 tried a unique experiment—transmitting electricity 13 miles, starting at Green Creek. (The mineowners had insisted that the line be put in absolutely straight so that the power could not jump off at the curves.) By 1890, about 2,000 people remained, with only the hardiest staying through the turn of the century. A disastrous fire in 1932 wiped out many of the abandoned buildings, and until the state took over, visitors stole many antique furnishings and artifacts, seriously degrading the remaining buildings. Today, visitors are given a detailed pamphlet outlining a self-guided tour to the "arrested disintegration." *California Department of Parks and Recreation*

the Mono Trail from Big Oak Flat through what is today Yosemite National Park. Among them was Waterman S. Body (Bodey) who rediscovered the precious metal in 1859 on the site of the town that would bear his name. (Though the "Bodie" spelling is attributed to an illiterate sign painter, the local citizens felt it aided proper pronunciation.) Body, in the winter of his discovery, died of exposure in a snow storm. He was found by friends the following spring and buried where he had died.

In the interim, about 1878, prospectors discovered a "new Comstock," a gold zone two-and-one-half miles long and one mile wide. It created an immediate gold rush, and in one year the population rose from under 100 to over 10,000, including miners, gamblers, and entrepreneurs. And a year later, Bodie, "The Shooter's Town," was a synonym for violence. The popular phrase "badman from Bodie" described any ruffian who savored the raw whiskey and climate of Bodie. But as many died from disease. At an elevation of 8,400 feet, long, cold winters provided heavy, hazardous snows, while poorly constructed buildings offered slight protection.

127

Stories of gold strikes were sometimes spread to conceal thefts of high-grade ores taken from the workings of others. Miners who suddenly seemed to acquire an undue amount of money were always suspect. In one such theft, reportedly from an unnamed California placer camp in 1852, a kangaroo court sentenced the perpetrator to hanging. Before dying he begged that his aged mother "back East" be notified, but without the details of his death. A committee was formed to compose a letter of condolence to his mother; to conceal the manner of his demise they simply wrote her that her son had fallen to his death "when the platform on which he was standing suddenly collapsed under him, while he was participating in a public function."

"Goodbye, God, I'm going to Bodie" was a common California comment. Killings occurred at the rate of about one a day; robberies, stage holdups, and street fights were frequent and the town's sixty-five saloons added fuel and fire to the miners "relaxing" after a hard day at the mines. According to Rev. F. M. Warrington, in 1881, Bodie was a "sea of sin, lashed by the tempests of lust and passion." Thirty mines supported saloons, pothouses, restaurants, gin mills, bawdy houses, and breweries. The Chinese, who ran the laundries, peddled vegetables (shipped in by express), and brought in much of the wood, provided Bodie with a joss house, tongs, opium dens, and faro and fantan games.

The shipment of gold became increasingly hazardous; robberies were common and nothing exceeding $500 in value could be transported safely without armed messengers. One gold shipment amounting to half a million dollars was guarded by six Wells Fargo messengers: two riding up front, two behind, and two inside the stage. As for the jails, "guests" could be bailed out for $5!

As with most bonanzas, activity gradually decreased and the town slowly atrophied.

Like Bodie, Kernville quickly developed into a vintage mining camp, lasting for forty years. A wandering mule had precipitated the discovery of the Big Blue Mine. After unsuccessfully chasing his

The story is told of Second Garrote, California, named for a tree from which sixty men were reputedly hanged. When Bret Harte wrote his gold-rush stories, he included one entitled "Tennessee's Partner." The story is about James Chaffee and Jason Chamberlain who came to Second Garrote in 1852. Harte was supposed to have stayed there as a guest in their typical miner's cabin, which still remains and can be visited for a small admission fee.

wandering mule along the bank of the Kern River, "Lovely" Rogers, a miner, had heaved a rock at it in anger. The rock hit a piece of quartz, uncovering its gold-studded interior, and Quartzburg and another boom were created in 1853.

In the meantime, prospector Adam Hamilton decided that there was more money in whiskey than in gold, and set up two whiskey barrels with a plank spanning the tops, declaring his bar open for business. Because it was situated at the mining flats below Quartzburg, he christened it Whiskey Flat, which soon developed into a bonanza camp. For some reason the name of the town was changed to Kernville, which though it was a leading mining town by 1867, endured as such only briefly. By 1870 fewer than twenty people lived there. Some felt there still was gold to be salvaged. Senator John P. Jones, the bonanza king from Virginia City, bought the Big Blue Mine and brought in Cornish miners. It continued to be active until the late 1880s, but Cornish miners sabotaged it in 1890, closing it and terminating Kernville's mining life. A favorite Kernville story involved the Lost Mine of the Padres. Sometime during the mid-1850s, a prospector staggered out of the hills and fell down in a field. When rescued by soldiers from Old Fort Tejon, his heavy sack was found to contain quartz held together with wiregold, a form of gold that runs through the rocklike wires. He claimed that he had been prospecting in the northeast mountains when his burros were stolen. While hunting for his animals he had encountered an outcropping of rock held together with wiregold like the samples in his sack. Following his recovery at the fort, he agreed to guide a party to his find, but before it could be organized, he was thrown from a horse and killed. Thanks to a Samuel Bishop, a sketch was found among the dead man's clothing, apparently a map locating the discovery. It led to the site and the old man's saddle and equipment, but not the gold.

THE EXPRESS COMPANIES

Law enforcement was strictly a local matter. Some form of protection was needed to guarantee that the precious metals would reach their destination and that people and supplies could be transported safely. The express company was·the answer.

Along with others, in 1850, Henry Wells, William G. Fargo, and John Butterfield combined their express interests to form the American Express Company; in 1852 Wells and Fargo organized Wells Fargo and Company to handle the New York–San Francisco express service created by the California

Gold dust was often measured in three-fingered pinches, and it was customary for the seller to measure the gold dust from the buyer's bag. For this reason it was advantageous to have large-size fingers. *Wells Fargo Bank History Room*

These bits of metal are gold slugs, issued and stamped by private firms to furnish badly needed business currency during the 1850s in San Francisco. The center coin is dated 1852. Smaller transactions were usually settled in gold dust. *Wells Fargo Bank History Room*

It was at No. 114, between Sacramento and California streets, that Wells Fargo and Company, Express and Banking, opened for business in July, 1852, to take advantage of existing services, which required three to six months for the coast-to-coast trip around the Horn; the new companies were able to haul staples and perishables in just over a month via the Isthmus of Panama. *Wells Fargo Bank History Room*

gold rush. Today the company is a leader in American banking (the Wells Fargo Bank) and transportation.

Express companies had been in existence in California as early as 1849 since there was no postal service or any other reliable method of carrying packages and gold bullion. With the expansion of gold mining, two companies, Adams and Wells Fargo, came to dominate the express business.

Both Adams and Wells Fargo speculated in gold dust, which is how they entered the banking

The treasure boxes with their heavy locks were carefully guarded until they were brought to the Wells Fargo banks where the gold dust was weighed and receipts given for the correct amount. *Wells Fargo Bank History Room*

The sketch by contemporary engraver Durbin Van Vleck shows Wells Fargo's interior offices and banking department. From 1856 to 1876, the Parrott Building served as Wells Fargo's San Francisco Express and Banking headquarters. It was built by Chinese laborers who were brought here to assemble the building stones, which had been cut to fit in China. The Parrott Building stood on the northwest corner of California and Montgomery streets until 1926, when it was torn down for a modern replacement. *Wells Fargo Bank History Room*

Wells Fargo's only known direct venture into mining was made in the Comstock. This scene shows the Wells Fargo Mining Company property, which, because its development required heavy machinery, was never developed as a mine. *Wells Fargo Bank History Room*

business. They paid as little as $10 an ounce when gold was first found, and a few years later, slightly less than the $18 price paid at the federal mint. Adams' failure during the Panic of 1855 left the field to its rival.

Competition among stagecoach lines kept pace with increased mining activity; many independent companies ran short hauls between all the important mining points. Around 1854 most of these combined into the California Stage Company, which did not survive the year. But this did not discourage competition; other independents still covered about half the routes.

In 1858 John Butterfield started a Missouri-Texas-Arizona-Los Angeles-San Francisco route as the Overland Mail Company. In 1860 it was the Pony Express, but its reputation outlived the company, which collapsed after about eighteen months.

Robberies, bandits, and holdups kept pace with the increased frequency and wealth of the shipments, reaching millions in a single day. Wells Fargo, the largest carrier, suffered the largest losses. Actually, holdups started up right along with the express companies. Wells Fargo not only assumed the responsibility for transporting the valuable cargoes but also for depositing the gold and currency in its own

bank branches, giving receipts that were always honored. No company for which they worked ever lost money, and they offered large rewards for captured robbers and recovered treasure. Their first holdup occurred in 1855 when a mule train carrying $80,000 in gold dust was stopped by "Rattlesnake Dick" the bandit from Auburn. Rattlesnake Dick and four of his gang were captured by Wells Fargo police near Folsom; they killed a fifth member. Dick was jailed at Auburn but escaped to San Francisco where he was again arrested and again escaped. This cycle continued for a while until 1859 when he was shot while avoiding arrest.

There was no respite in burglary attempts so Wells Fargo expanded its police and detective force, which, in its later years, was headed by James B. Hume. Hume became an expert criminal detective, and under his leadership the force became a potent

The celebrated Concord coach, pulled by six horses, was the most popular method of travel. In the rough mountain passages "mud wagons" were sometimes used. These were built low to the ground and were not easily tipped, but the Concord's assets were its supporting heavy leather straps, or braces, providing a passenger with the comfort that comes from riding a "cradle" that absorbed the shocks and bumps of the road. *Wells Fargo Bank History Room*

Famous wash drawing by Charles Russell, "Coach Overturned." Stagecoach drivers in general were experts, but traveled at a fast pace, and sometimes the coaches were overturned in their hectic races against time. A network of stagecoaches carried mail, gold, and passengers, covering Nevada and California, and later Oregon, Washington, and other points. *Wells Fargo Bank History Room*

Sometimes rewards were as much as 40 percent of the recovered treasure. This poster offers more than one-third. *Wells Fargo Bank History Room*

$2500
REWARD

On Sunday night, 27th inst., the Stage from Colfax to Grass Valley was stopped by four highwaymen and our treasure box robbed of following amounts:

$7,000 IN COIN.

In a leather pouch, and three packages of coin containing respectively $50, $18 and $10. We will pay the above

REWARD OF $2500

in Gold Coin for the capture of the robbers and the recovery of the Coin; or

$1250 FOR THE CAPTURE
of the Robbers, and

$1250 FOR THE RECOVERY
Of the Coin.

L. F. ROWELL,
Ass't. Supt. of Wells, Fargo & Co.

deterrent to stagecoach robbers. Neill C. Wilson's *Treasure Express* lists a Wells Fargo 1884 tabulation of robberies:

Number of Stage Robberies	313
Attempted Stage Robberies	34
Burglaries	23
Train Robberies	4
Attempted Train Robberies	4
Number of Wells Fargo Guards Killed	2
Number of Wells Fargo Guards Wounded	6
Number of Stage Drivers Killed	4
Number of Stage Drivers Wounded	4
Number of Stage Robbers Killed	16
Number of Stage Robbers Hanged by Citizens	7
Number of Horses Killed	7
Number of Horses Stolen from Teams	14
Convictions	240

Treasure Stolen	
(promptly made good to customers)	$415,312.55
Rewards Paid	73,451.00
Prosecutions and Incidental Expenses	90,079.00
Salaries of Guards and	
Special Officers	326,417.00

Total cost to Wells Fargo due to highwaymen operating against 8 trains and 347 stages during 14 years	$905,259.55

So closely was Wells Fargo related to the gold-mining rushes of the 1850s that the Wells Fargo Bank now features a historical collection in its History Room at 420 Montgomery Street, San Francisco, California, including symbols and relics of gold-mining days.

The *Antelope,* once the fastest boat on the Sacramento River. It was known as the "Gold Boat." Chosen by Wells Fargo to carry express and gold shipments from Sacramento to San Francisco, it carried millions in its famous "Gold Room." This room's floor was especially braced to take the weight of the golden treasure. From Sacramento, it was a fast eight-hour run to San Francisco. She carried the first westward Pony Express mail on its final lap. *Wells Fargo Bank History Room*

Perhaps the end of the line for the California gold rush, Coulterville is the subject of an amusing story of a town whose streets were rumored to be paved with gold. In 1899 the town was ravaged by a great fire, and some of the rubble from the old buildings was used to fill up the holes in the streets. Immediately afterward, a heavy rain revealed gold deposits in the streets, and soon the entire town, armed with picks, shovels, and any implements at hand, was digging up the pavement. However, any gold the town derived was that paid out for repaving the streets! It seems that someone, gambler, miner, or bandit, had hidden gold in the wall of one of the demolished buildings, and in the fire, the gold had melted into the rubble used to pave the streets.

OTHER SIGNIFICANT HISTORICAL EVENTS

The California Years

1850s: Nevada City: Originated as mining camp on Deer Creek, near North Bloomfield, whose population it exceeded in the 1880s.

1852: Somersville, Nortonville, Jetsonville, Empire, Stewartsville were all early coal-mining towns.
    Downieville: nearby were the gold-mining camps of Forest, Alleghany (Sixteen to One Mine), still mined, Goodyear's Bar (the Bush Creek Mine still operates).
    Columbia: Some of the gold mines along the mother lode are the Mariposa, Sonora, Jackson, Placerville (Hangtown), Auburn, Bear Valley, Tuttletown, Chinese Camp.

1860s: Auburn: Principal operating gold mines were Todd's Valley, Michigan Bluff, Dutch Flat, Gold Run, Yankee Jim's, Iowa Hill; adjacent areas also developed hydraulic and river mining: Rattlesnake Bar on American River, Horseshoe Bar, Bean Poker Flat.
    Death Valley: The California Rand Silver Mine produced millions in silver, as did the King Solomon Mines in gold.

The Forty-Niners Move On

When it became obvious that there was not enough gold to go around, the search changed direction—from California to the east, toward Colorado, and then back to the north. The Mojave Desert and Death Valley border on Nevada, the first state east of California; and crossing the desert was considered a shortcut to the east. It was not long before Nevada became the new stamping ground.

Possibly with the exception of transient Mexicans, the first whites in Nevada were the Franciscan Fathers, in 1766. Aided by Mexican converts, they worked gold-placer and silver-lode mines and turquoise deposits. Some of the mines have provided interesting relics of their operations.

THE MORMONS

In 1849, when Nevada was part of the Mormon "State of Deseret," a Mormon company was formed to visit the newly discovered California placer gold mines. On the return trip, in July, Abner Blackburn, a member of the party, found placer gold at Gold Canyon, near Dayton.

Before leaving for his next trip to California, Blackburn told H. S. Beatie, the secretary of the company, about his discoveries, with the result that some Mormons, along with immigrants headed for California, worked Gold Canyon gravels and founded the little placer-mining camp of Johnstown—Nevada's first mining town.

During these years the old Spanish Trail was used extensively as a route through Las Vegas to southern California. When in 1855 a Mormon group, returning on the trail from San Bernardino, discovered the Potosi Mine in Clark County, futile attempts were made to smelt lead ore on the site. Thereafter the ore was shipped to Las Vegas, a way station on the trail, where five tons of lead were produced and the title "the first lead-smelting works in Nevada."

But the most important Nevada mining strike was the discovery of the Comstock Lode, in 1859, a discovery that rivaled Marshall's ten years earlier. The Comstock Lode is described in a following chapter.

NEVADA'S MINING TOWNS

At Austin, an unforgettable sight was the camel team used to pack salt from Columbus Marsh

A new tent at a new mine location. Note the barrel at the extreme right. It could be "red eye" but probably contained water, which sometimes was nearly as expensive as whiskey. None of the people are identified. (Caption by Malapai Mike, last of the breed of old-time prospectors, who was associated with Central Nevada Newspapers, for whom he wrote a booklet, "Reel History and Hysterical Events of Nevada." Several of the captions for the Nevada photographs in this book were written for that booklet.) While the Comstock sky-rocketed, this Humboldt Range yielded ore, and a year later Star City became the largest mining town in Northwestern Nevada with the opening of the Sheba Silver Mine. Star City featured a stamp mill, two hotels, and, among other buildings, a Wells Fargo express office. But after a brief eight years, in 1868, the mines petered out and the town disappeared. *Central Nevada Newspapers*

An 1881 lithograph of the Manhattan Silver Mining Company, Austin. Notice the "Toonerville trolley" locomotive pulling the load in the foreground. This area began with William L. Talcott's ore sample find in a stream in the Reese River region, the basis of a claim he and several friends staked out. The silver ore proved to have a high assay, and within a year prospectors rushed to the area, settling the little towns of Clifton and Austin, a mile apart. By 1864, in Austin alone between 6,000 and 10,000 people were working. Austin ore was largely silver with some gold, and assay reports of from $700 to as high as $5,000 a ton created a boom in Austin mining stock in San Francisco. From Austin, which was one hundred miles directly north of Esmerelda, other important silver strikes were made due east, at Eureka and Hamilton, among other towns. At its peak, Austin had nearly 400 brick, adobe, and frame buildings, and it had become the county seat. Its best year was 1868, when over $2½ million in metal was produced, after which the action rapidly moved downhill as the mines neared exhaustion. By the mid-1890s Austin's population had dwindled to about 600, but still the Reese River district managed to produce over $50 million in ore. *New York Public Library Picture Collection*

Malapai Mike (Magnus F. Peterson), who was always looking for the next big strike. He died in 1968 at seventy-nine. *Central Nevada Newspapers*

to the Austin mills. Camels had been used as pack animals by the United States Army during the Indian wars, especially in California and Arizona, but in Austin the teamsters complained that the camels frightened their horses, as well as their mules and burros. Eventually an ordinance was passed restricting the camel train in town to nights only. The operation proved so unprofitable that the camels were turned loose on the desert, where they lived for years in Smoky Valley.

During its first four years, Aurora managed to sustain a violence record of about one murder every six weeks, until a vigilante committee took over, hanging some of the gangsters and murderers and driving the rest from town. Mark Twain had tried mining near Aurora but without success; by 1864 Aurora mines were almost depleted, while disastrous fires in 1866 and 1873 nearly made it a ghost town. By 1880 most of the population had moved to Bodie, twelve miles across the California border, where gold had been found, along with murder and mayhem.

Because Hamilton was originally built on an exposed mountainside, the biting winds and high altitude made it necessary to build with rock for warmth and insulation. Of course, it was not unusual that some of this rock contained valuable ore, and when it was discovered, such houses were torn down and shipped as ore. Only a few stone walls remain—those without ore.

As Nevada gold- and silver-bullion production increased with the addition of the Comstock Lode material, it was obvious that so much metal could not be handled by the San Francisco mint. From the beginning of the Civil War to 1880, over $365 million in metal had been mined in Nevada, making it second only to California. Construction of a new United States mint began in 1866, in Carson City (about thirty miles south of Reno, hanging over California's border); it was operating by 1869. However, operations were slowed by the silver panic of 1893, reducing the mint to the Federal Assay Office. Today it belongs to the State of Nevada and contains an interesting mining exhibit.

First ore shipment from Manhattan, Nevada, October 19, 1905. It assayed $1,000 per ton. This team was driven by jerk line, and the horses were trained to respond to the commands "gee" and "haw." A long-line skinner was the top in his profession. *Central Nevada Newspapers (caption by Malapai Mike)*

The Belmont Mine, Tonopah, Nevada. While the Civil War was being concluded, an Indian and a man named C. L. Straight were discovering silver quartz veins in Belmont, which during the next twenty years produced over $15 million in silver. Stampeding to Straight's discovery, miners organized the Philadelphia Mining District and founded Belmont. Within a year three stamp mills were operating and the camp swelled to 1,500 miners. The Combination Mill Company's town smelter still remains, though as a ruin in the town that died in the early 1900s. *Nevada Historical Society*

Aurora. Ore was hoisted to the surface by horsepower in Nevada's early days. Note the horsewhim at right in the picture. Not many houses at this period. Miners lived mostly in tents, in some cases, caves (*caption by Malapai Mike*). Following the Comstock discovery, Aurora was founded on August 25, 1860, when three California prospectors in the Esmeralda Mining District, just over the California border, uncovered silver ore. At about this time, many of the '49ers and others who had come to California had begun prospecting to the east, thus moving the mining frontier first into western Nevada, then throughout the state, and ultimately into most western states. In 1863–1864 estimates of Aurora's population ranged from 6,000 to 10,000. It was an active town, with 17 quartz mills, 20 stores, 12 hotels, and many boardinghouses and saloons. Aurora's productive mines reopened during World War I for a brief period, but by 1930 the town was completely deserted. *Central Nevada Newspapers*

Starting at a base in Austin, another important discovery of major quantities of lead and silver was made at Eureka in 1864. It did not occasion any stampede, however, because the combination of lead and silver was then difficult to smelt. But in 1869, Major W. W. McCoy built a small smelter to process ore, the first lead-silver smelter in the United States. The result was the expansion of Eureka. The next year the Eureka Consolidated Mining Company was incorporated in San Francisco, and a year later the Richmond Consolidated Mining Company was financed from London.

In 1874 a narrow-gauge railroad was constructed, and within two years no less than nineteen smelters were separating gold, silver, and lead. At first the smelters produced a partially refined ore that was sent to Salt Lake City for further refinement, but six years after the introduction of the first smelter the Richmond Consolidated Mine smelter featured an improved process that was entirely capable of recovering the Eureka silver. In the 1870s Eureka produced over $26 million in silver and 225,000 tons of lead. Although Eureka was devastated by fire and flood on several occasions, it remained an important mining center until 1891, when the ore bodies were exhausted and water flooded the mines, forcing them, as well as the smelters, to shut down.

The Monitor Silver Mine and Mill in White Pine County where, as the fever spread, speculators rushed to buy stock in the White Pine mines; more than $50 million in securities were sold, just about twice the value of all the metals taken from the Treasure Hill mines up to 1887, twenty years after it all started. Actually, by 1875 all but one of the mines had stopped working, and within five years the population dropped to about 500. As for Hamilton, two disastrous fires, one in 1873 and another in 1886, finally destroyed most of it. *Nevada Historical Society*

The horseless carriage comes to Tonopah. This congregation of late deluxe models has gathered for an excursion trek to Kawich. The date is June 10, 1905. Right after the picture was taken, they took off at breakneck speed some 13 to 15 miles per hour. How many made it back was not noted. *Central Nevada Newspapers (caption by Malapai Mike)*

Urban Renewal, Hamilton, 1905. The mansion on the right is making some progress in the war against poverty. The one on the left seems to have lost the battle *(caption by Malapai Mike).* Also at Hamilton, coincidental with Straight's discovery, two former Austin prospectors discovered silver, at which time the White Pine District (just east of Eureka) was organized. Originally, Hamilton was called Cave City until Albert Leathers, guided by an Indian, in 1867, located the Hid-

den Treasure Mine. The mine, on Treasure Hill, contained extremely rich silver ore, and as word spread, it seemed that the White Pine District would rival Comstock. The stampede to Hamilton enriched its population in the winter of 1868–1869 to 10,000 in town and 25,000 in the district, incredible, considering its handicap of an 8,000-foot altitude. But many of the prospectors had to live in tents or nearby caves. *Central Nevada Newspapers*

Kennecott's Liberty Pit, exceeding a mile in diameter and 1,000 feet deep, Ruth, Nevada. Ruth (almost in the center of the White Pine District), once a goldmining camp in 1868, was virtually forgotten until Edward F. Gray and David P. Bartley, in 1900, examined some outcroppings of copper that had intrigued them. Securing samples and, subsequently, financing, they formed the White Pine Copper Company, in 1904 becoming the Nevada Consolidated Copper Company. Development work progressed in Ruth for several years, including a 140-mile railroad and a smelter that began operating in their fifth year. However, copper had been taken out by about their third year, and from 1907 to

1917 Nevada Consolidated was able to pay out almost $76 million in dividends. While still in the grip of the depression, in 1933 the Kennecott Copper Corporation acquired control, and ten years later changed the name to Kennecott Copper Corporation, Nevada Mines Division. And in 1958 Kennecott acquired the contiguous Consolidated Copper Mines Corporation. Liberty and Consolidated's Morris-Brooks Pit are major producers of copper, and are among the largest in Nevada. The old smelter has been modernized and moved to McGill about twenty miles north. *University of Nevada, Mackay School of Mines*

Hauling rich ore from a Tonopah mine in 1906. With the impending demise of Belmont just prior to 1900, James L. Butler went looking for gold, and on May 17, 1900, discovered silver at Tonopah (hanging on Esmeralda's eastern border). Butler found it more advantageous to lease his various claims, and for a 25 percent interest in the gross output, he arranged for Casper L. Oddie and Wilse Brougher to work the properties that August. All that Oddie and Brougher were able to take out during the remainder of 1900 was about one ton of silver, worth $600. But as the news went round, and more prospectors descended, by the following year about $4 million in ore was extracted. The camp, which began to grow, was in need of a name, and the prospectors chose Butler, but Mrs. Butler decided it would be Tonopah, from "tono," a shrub used by Indians for food, and "pah," Indian for water. Notwithstanding that it was established in the twentieth century, when the West was less remote, Scott Hicker as Tonopah's first chief of police had to keep a strong hand on gangsterism. Tonopah consequently was one of the most orderly mining camps in the West. Any man with a reputation who did not meet Hicker's rigid standards was ordered out of town: one was no less than Wyatt Earp. *New York Public Library Picture Collection*

Overall view of the Florence Mine and Mill at Goldfield in the Pioche District. William Hamblin, a Mormon missionary, discovered the district (directly south of White Pine) when he was shown a silver site by a Paiute Indian in 1863. The district was organized as the Meadow Valley District, but little work was done until five years later when F. L. A. Pioche purchased claims, later turned over to the Meadow Valley Mining Company. In 1869 a failing mill from another district was brought to Bullionville, near Pioche; the owners bought a mine, set up a mill, and were an instant success as the Raymond and Ely Mining Company. As the district boomed, they rivaled even the Meadow Valley Mining Company. Pioche reached its peak in 1872, almost in a decade of its founding, but three years later activity gradually diminished. In 1905 the Pioche District revived somewhat and continued to produce metals until 1921. About then, lead and zinc shipments from Pioche increased, and in the 1940s, with a war going on, the Combined Metals Reduction Company increased its mill capacity from 500 to 1,000 tons a day for the production of lead-zinc concentrates. This company and the Bristol Silver Mines Company continued to produce lead, zinc, and copper well into the 1950s. *Nevada Historical Society*

Pouring bullion at a Tonopah smelter around 1906. After its first year, despite all the activity, most of the ore remained in Tonopah. Inadequate transportation and a lack of local smelting capacity were responsible. In 1902 the Tonopah Mining Company bought the property, and built a railroad two years later. By 1906 they were operating cyanide mills to reduce the silver from the ore. Almost from its inception, the Tonopah District was a major silver producer; in the first twenty years of its existence, over $115 million in ore was taken from the ground. *Nevada Historical Society*

Anaconda's Yerington Pit, Weed Heights. *Nevada Historical Society*

A celebration in Tonopah on July 4, 1906. This is pictorial evidence that Tonopah was never a one-horse town, not to mention the burros *(caption by Malapai Mike)*. The more than 100 miles of tunneling still remaining under the streets of Tonopah accounted for about $200 million in silver in all. Modern Tonopah abounds with relics of the old mining days. Superstructures of some of the mines can be seen from the main street, and it is common to find discarded mining machinery lying around the old sites. Rock hounds daily seek jasper, turquoise, agate, jade, and petrified wood, but more important to the economy of the city is the nearby test range operated by the Sandia Corporation for the Atomic Energy Commission. *Central Nevada Newspapers*

The 407-foot stope of the Mohawk Mine, Goldfield, circa 1904. One of the last Nevada gold discoveries of the early 1900s occurred here. On December 2, 1902, William Marsh and Harry Stimler staked the first claim in the district, and soon struck gold. Other prospectors moved in rapidly, but because no other ore bodies were found, most of the miners left just as rapidly. In the interim, the original claims lapsed. But only months later, on May 24, 1903, A. D. Meyers and R. C. Hart found the Combination Lode, and when shipments began by the end of the year, a big Goldfield rush followed. The town was built almost entirely of tents, but when the railroad reached Goldfield in 1905, the population, which had been around 8,000, doubled, and hundreds of brick and wooden structures were built. The Goldfield Consolidated Mines Company, one of the largest in the district, completed the first mill, containing 100 stamps, in 1908. By then the town had grown to a population of 20,000 and in 1910 added the $500,000 200-room Goldfield Hotel. Over $11 million in gold was mined that year. Although the district yielded about $85 million from 1903 to 1921, production declined rapidly in 1922, dropping to only $150,000. The following year a fire destroyed 53 blocks in the center of town, and whatever remained of the town was ruined by flood in 1932. After that, most mining consisted of reworking the old tailings. Just before that happened, though, a fight had erupted between the owners and workers. The owners had ruled that miners were to change their clothes when coming off shift. The men had been in the habit of coming out dirty, and a few dollars richer in gold each day. Troops were brought in and order was restored. Although for years Nevada's biggest gold producer, Goldfield's output today is very small, and only a few of the town's earlier buildings remain, including the hotel, the Esmeralda County Courthouse, and a firehouse built simultaneously with the first mill. Southwestern Nevada's third mining camp of the 1900s was Rhyolite, named for the rock that abounds in the area. Its 1907 population of 7,000 was considerable for this rough and otherwise deserted country, connected by railroad with Tonopah and Las Vegas. The town never amounted to much, producing only about $3 million in gold. By 1910 it was a ghost town. *Nevada Historical Society*

OIL BEGINS TO RIVAL GOLD

Even while California's active coal mining region boomed, simultaneously in Pennsylvania, the oil industry was taking root. Of course the Indians and later the early settlers knew that there was oil along Oil Creek and at other places in western Pennsylvania, West Virginia, Ohio, and Kentucky, but they knew nothing about whales: the oil they found along the streams was a nuisance, sometimes contaminating the water, and occasionally it was skimmed off to be used for medicinal purposes. A few used the oil as a lubricant, but its thick smoke and disagreeable smell discouraged its use for lighting. But whale oil and candles remained the best illuminants until about 1840. Whale oil was becoming scarcer and scarcer, even with more and more whales being killed, and candles were expensive. A suitable replacement had to be found. A Pittsburgh businessman, Samuel Kier, in the early 1850s succeeded in producing a fairly successful illuminant by distilling petroleum from oil he had found at Tarentum, twenty miles north of Pittsburgh. His success was confirmed by Dartmouth and Yale scientists when they corroborated the possibility of distilling a satisfactory illuminant from oil.

THE DRAKE WELL IS BEGUN

A company was organized to drill for oil. George Bissel, a New York lawyer, sold shares to investors in New York and New Haven, while James H. Townsend, a New Haven banker, gained control of the company and commissioned his friend Edwin L. Drake to go to Titusville, Pennsylvania, to bring up the oil in the spring of 1858. Drake was an unemployed train conductor whose total experience included a clerkship and a stint as an express agent.

In Titusville, since he could not hire a driller, Drake tried to drill an artesian well to excavate for the oil, but water filled up the holes as fast as he made them. He obtained help from William A. "Uncle Billy" Smith, a blacksmith experienced in shutting off water at salt wells. Smith drove a six-inch pipe into the drill holes to stop the flow, but the water collapsed the sides of the holes. All this had cost about $2,500, and Townsend sent word to Drake to abandon the operation. But before Townsend's decision reached him, Drake had borrowed $500 and drove sections of cast-iron pipe thirty-two feet to the bedrock. Now, in August, 1859, he started drilling at the thirty-two-foot level, and on Sunday afternoon, August 28, "Uncle Billy" peered down the pipe and saw oil floating just below the derrick floor.

According to the Wheeling *Intelligencer* (about 1913), reviewing West Virginia's oil industry, an oil well existed on the banks of Charleston's Kanawha River "fifty-one years before the Drake Well

The first oil field found in hilly country was along Pioneer Run, a branch of Oil Creek seen in this 1864 photo. All previous oil fields had been found on the flatlands in the vicinity of Oil Creek, Pennsylvania. *Shell Oil Company*

Drake Well, circa 1860. *Shell Oil Company*

"Oil Region Boys" from an early (circa 1864) West Virginia well. *William Culp Darrah Stereo Collection*

Derricks blotted out the landscape in the intensive drilling along the oceanfront at Huntington Beach, California. *Bureau of Mines, Department of the Interior*

at Titusville, Pennsylvania, ushered in the petroleum industry of the world."

There were other wells in other states. Kentucky had one at an early, unknown date, but no one knew what to do with the oil except for a limited portion that was bottled and sold as a liniment. But the Drake Well was the first *organized* oil well in the United States.

With the discovery of the Drake, the countryside soon was covered with hastily built derricks, shafts, and tanks. The fever spread so quickly that the hillsides were cluttered with these crude wooden derricks, the beginning of a colorful chapter in the history of industrial America.

At first, oil was transported to the refineries by wagon, eventually replaced by boat, barge, and pipelines. Dams were built to equalize water levels of the various water bodies, but oil losses continued as vessels frequently collided, often grounding in shallow water. Once an ice gorge broke loose, crashing into 350 oil boats; half were destroyed along with about 30,000 barrels of oil.

Since the early 1900s derricks no longer were constructed like so many wooden boxes. Here drillers add "stand" of pipe to a drill string. The drill string must be completely removed from the hole to change drill bits when they are worn out. While out of the hole, the pipe is stacked upright in the derrick in stands of three joints each.

One of the early refiners, the Great Western Refinery, Pennsylvania, 1860s. *William Culp Darrah Stereo Collection*

Teams of horses were used to haul heavy equipment to early-day drilling locations, which were often a morass of mud. The topheavy load has tilted the vehicle over. *Humble Oil and Refining Company*

Displacing the barrels were the bulk-oil barges, around 1861, but they only partially solved the problem—most leaked significant quantities of oil, and crashes usually meant the loss of the entire cargo. By war's end, the railroads had expanded into the oil districts and were hauling much of the oil. Wooden tank cars were developed almost immediately, and although they, too, leaked and were beset by frequent accidents, they were the best transportation method available.

Pioneering in oil pumps. Troutman well, Pennsylvania, 1868–1878. *William Culp Darrah Stereo Collection*

Distillery, 1875, Oil City, Pennsylvania. Stills with a capacity of 1,400 barrels are nearly filled with crude oil before the fires beneath them are started. Distillation commenced almost immediately. *William Culp Darrah Stereo Collection*

JOHN D. ROCKEFELLER

But within twenty years of the Drake discovery John D. Rockefeller would gain control of the Pennsylvania oil industry. It was oil refining, which kept pace or led the demand for more highly refined merchandise, that brought John D. into the oil business.

With his partner, Maurice B. Clark, their firm of Clark and Rockefeller had already been a financial success in the produce business in Cleveland. In addition, in 1863, Clark, Rockefeller, and a Samuel Andrews had financed and operated the Excelsior Works, an oil refinery. But Rockefeller decided to leave the produce business two years later, and he obtained the refinery for himself and Andrews for $72,500 under a plan that gave Clark sole right to the produce business. The new firm of Rockefeller and Andrews expanded rapidly, and Rockefeller's brother William and a brother of Andrews were hired. In their second year, Henry M. Flagler and Stephen Harkness joined them.

In January, 1870, the growing firm was consolidated into a new company, the Standard Oil Company of Ohio, capitalized at $1 million. John D. Rockefeller was president; William Rockefeller, vice president; Flagler, secretary; and Andrews, superintendent. Ten thousand shares of stock were divided: John D. Rockefeller, 2,667; Harkness, 1,334; Flagler, William Rockefeller, and Andrews, 1,333 each; 1,000 to the separate firm of Rockefeller, Andrews, and Flagler; and 1,000 to William Rockefeller's brother-in-law, O. B. Jennings.

At that point, competition had been keen, with production costs about equal for all refiners. Some sources credit Rockefeller with having obtained special concessions from railroads and other transportation companies, allowing oil shipments at slightly reduced prices in return for shipping all products exclusively over the concessioners' lines—in some instances contracting not to build pipelines, which would be direct competition. Standard Oil subsequently increased its refining capacity considerably, which in turn strengthened its bargaining power to obtain further transportation concessions.

The years 1871 and 1872 were marked by the consolidation of refining and freight companies in the industry, and by mid-1872 the Rockefeller interests controlled about a quarter of the oil industry's output. Rockefeller followed up by acquiring more refining companies and corporations, particularly those that were unable to withstand the competition from his rapidly growing Standard.

That year the industry's refining and producing interests united to form an organization (the National Refiners' Association) to act as sole purchasers of crude oil for all member refiners, as well as to assign refining quotas, set prices, and negotiate freight rates. Despite their objections, all the oil producers were forced to go along with the refiners' plan.

The opposition formed a counterassociation (the Petroleum Producers Association) whose members agreed to a six-month moratorium on drilling for new wells, boosting oil nearly $1 a barrel. However, the producers could not enforce a second six-month suspension and the increased output cut prices about 50 percent and forced out the producers' agency.

At the same time, the National Refiners' Association had its difficulties enforcing its quota and price requirements, and the Association was dissolved by the mutual consent of its members. This "oil war" eventually resulted in the buildup and final fragmentation of the Standard Oil Company, and others, including the disputes between the railroads, the pipelines, and the refineries.

PITHOLE CITY

Among the many burgeoning towns was Pithole City. On January 7, 1865, Ian Frazier and James Faulkner drilled the famous Frazier Well on Pithole Creek, which in time became the most productive oil well in the oil country. Soon the Homestead Oil Well began producing, and it looked as though this was an entirely new oil field several miles from Oil Creek. War-weary men were looking for something to do, and oil looked like the answer. (During and immediately after the Civil War, speculation in crude-oil stocks raged at fever pitch and an "oil-stock-company epidemic" spread throughout the country. In New York, the Petroleum Board—an oil-stock exchange—was organized and within months over 500 stock companies had been formed; James A. Garfield, not yet president, together with

The United States well, struck in Pithole, Pennsylvania, January, 1865. It flowed 800 barrels a day. Within six months several large flowing wells were struck. *William Culp Darrah Stereo Collection*

The beginning of Pithole—and its end. In nine months it grew from a few dozen people to a population of nearly 16,000. It practically disappeared in 1865 when the "oil bubble" burst. *William Culp Darrah Stereo Collection*

other congressional members formed an oil speculation company.) By May, 500 building lots and twenty-two streets were laid out above Pithole Creek, and the town began to fill up with varied structures, some built in four or five days. Almost overnight there were two banks, two telegraph offices, a newspaper, a waterworks, a fire company, two churches, various boardinghouses, grocery and hardware stores, machine shops, brothels, and saloons. Several hotels were built; the Chase House was the best, which accommodated 200 guests (100 in the dining room). The world's first pipeline, built by Samuel Van Syckel, ran from Pithole to the closest railroad, five and one-half miles away, at a rail charge of $1 a barrel. This was against $3 a barrel by wagon. Sections of Van Syckel's two-inch pipeline were joined by fitted screw sockets. Two pump stations provided the pipeline with a capacity of about eighty barrels a·day.

Burning of the Imperial Refinery, near Oil City, Pennsylvania, September 14, 1875. *William Culp Darrah Stereo Collection*

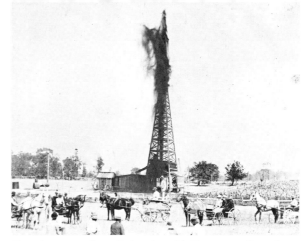

Shooting an oil well in the old Trenton oil and gas field, circa 1900.

Suddenly, in August, 1865, the Homestead Well stopped flowing. It had to be pumped to raise the oil. Then a long series of fires swept through the oil fields, and many of the town's buildings were gutted. And in November the Frazier Well played out. Speculation excesses, the post–Civil War falloff in domestic demand and a subsequent drop in crude-oil prices—from $10–$12 to $4.50–$6.50 a barrel—many disastrous fires, and a $1-per-barrel federal tax, contributed to a complete collapse, marked by a depression. By 1867 Pithole was destitute; only a handful of people remained.

Among the first firms to go was the Culver, Penn, and Company, operator of five oil-region banks and a railroad, setting off a chain reaction: nearly all the new companies failed—8,000 drilling projects were abandoned; crude-oil prices dropped to $1.35 (averaging only about $3.75 for the year even with the tax dropped); and the oil boom fell into the less glamorous routine of the general mining industry.

But dreams of wealth spurred renewed exploration. New discoveries spread throughout Pennsylvania's oil region. In seven years gushers obscured the landscape in defiance of all organized attempts to curb production. Increased production leaped forward with the new steam-drilling techniques and the recent development of "torpedoing"—clearing clogged drill holes. But not without cost. Nitroglycerin torpedoes were dangerous and caused many deaths. Pumping costs now had become a cost factor; some wells had been drilled 1,600 feet.

In 1872 a pipeline five and one-half miles long and capable of carrying four million cubic feet of gas a day was constructed to transport the waste gas from the oil wells to Titusville. Actually, the first production of natural gas in the United States occurred in 1821 in western New York, when gas leaked from the banks of Canadaway Creek and was accidentally ignited. It proved that natural gas was an excellent fuel. As a result, a well was drilled to a depth of twenty-seven feet and the gas was used for lighting. Thus gas superseded the use of petroleum.

OIL EXPANDS

The search for oil spread. West Virginia, Tennessee, Kentucky, Colorado, and California soon began to produce small amounts, and by 1876, Ohio had a substantial output, joined later by Indiana, Illinois, and Texas.

One of the most famous oil wells in the country is the Norman No. 1, the first commercially successful well of the Mid-Continent Field, the nation's largest oil field, spreading over Kansas, Oklahoma, and Texas.

W. M. Mills, a Pennsylvanian, drilled the well in 1892 to a depth of 832 feet, at which point the hole began to fill with oil. Mills, a shrewd operator, plugged the well, reported that it was a dud, and then began to drill another one. He went back to Pittsburgh bringing oil samples with him and organized a company that leased a million acres of land, during which time the Norman No. 1 remained secretly plugged for ten months. Within two years he had drilled 100 wells, and finally sold out to Standard Oil Company. The first oil well was actually drilled in Kansas, near Paola, in 1860 but it never amounted to anything.

With so many wells, drilling encroachments on

The famous Spindletop region, circa 1900. The cottages in the foreground are the homes of oil workers' families. *William Culp Darrah Stereo Collection*

the same oil body rapidly cut output and retaliatory flooding wasted considerable oil. In 1878 laws were enacted requiring the plugging or casing of wells before they could be abandoned. This proved a useful conservation plan considering all the abandoned wells, careless operations, and other widespread practices.

The automobile had not yet been invented, and oil was refined mainly for illumination (kerosene, gasoline), solvents (naphtha), lubrication, paraffin wax, and gas illumination. Fuel usage saw great expansion between 1862 and 1873; petroleum jelly went into use about 1870. Gasoline was then widely used to operate air-gas engines.

New oil fields continually were found in western Pennsylvania, and the discoveries that slowly spread

Spindletop, completed January 10, 1901, near Beaumont, Texas. This well, known as Lucas Number 1, was directly responsible for the birth of Gulf Oil Corporation. *Gulf Oil Corporation*

Scene on a lake straddling the Louisiana/Texas border where, in 1911, Gulf undertook the first water-drilling project. *Gulf Oil Corporation*

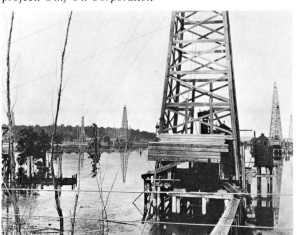

Traffic jam (circa 1918), at Northwest Field, Burkburnett, Texas.

Signal Hill, California. Before Shell discovered oil on Signal Hill, most of the front side of the hill had been subdivided into building lots and sold. Because of the lack of unitization practices in those days, the result of this widely dispersed ownership of small tracts of land was a tremendous number of wells, with the feet of one derrick often interlocking the feet of another. This excessive drilling would doubtless have been unprofitable except for one thing: Signal Hill proved to be the world's richest oil deposit in terms of barrels produced per acre. The bristling derricks shown here, once a Signal Hill trademark, are now rapidly disappearing. *Shell Oil Company*

Submersible barge rigs, perfected by the oil industry in the thirties, made possible the development of major reserves in shallow inland waters and coastal marshes along the entire Gulf Coast. In more recent years the drillers have taken to the sea with their equipment for drilling in deep water. *Humble Oil and Refining Company*

A computerized drilling system on Penrod Rig 44, a submersible drilling barge that is operating in the marshlands of St. Mary Parish, west of Morgan City, Louisiana. The system represents the first use of a high-speed digital computer to control oil-well drilling operations. *Humble Oil and Refining Company*

into Ohio, made it a major producer by the mid-1880s.

At first the Ohio strikes were considered insignificant since the oil had a high sulfur content, making refining a problem. Ohio oil was tagged with the name "skunk oil" because of its odor, which resisted removal methods then known. By this time oil demands increased not only for heat but for use in locomotives, ocean steamers, and such manufacturing industries as glass, steel, clay products, ceramics, and others. Meanwhile, Standard Oil became more active in producing and marketing natural gas. The development of better refining methods, particularly for use in converting "skunk oil," spread the oil business as far west as Whiting, Indiana, where Standard opened a refinery in 1890. The method of converting "skunk oil" was developed by Herman Frasch who also developed the methods used for sulfur refining.

NEVADA "COTTONBALL"

It was almost axiomatic that one discovery produced other minerals as by-products since the nature of minerals and chemicals is such that they are almost always found in combinations. Sometimes a use for these by-products was not developed until later, and meanwhile the material was discarded as a nuisance; sometimes the demand for a new mineral warranted prospecting for it exclusively; and sometimes material that was known to have limited use was found to be valuable for other purposes. Borax was in the latter class.

Borax was discovered January 8, 1856, at a mineral spring a few miles north of San Francisco. At the time, borax was an expensive import used in glassblowing and gold refining. But increases in gold production created a greater demand for the material. It took eight years to raise the capital to start operations, which began as the Borax Company of California, but the first year's production amounted to only twelve tons. United States imports that year dropped from $200,000 to $9,000, as did the price—from fifty cents to thirty cents a pound. As the result of driving an artesian well, the lake from which borax was recovered flooded, and in 1868 operations ceased. Another borax lake in the vicinity, Hachinhama, later renamed Little Borax Lake, was then developed to supply the domestic demand.

The borax industry zoomed in 1870 when "cottonball" was found in quantity on the Nevada desert. Cottonball is ulexite, one of the borate minerals. A dry lakebed at Columbus Marsh was

Crystals of dehydrated borax ore samples. Borax is used in making such items as sealed-beam headlights for automobiles, fiberglass, heat-resistant household glassware, and porcelain enamel. It is also used in the manufacture of ceramics, soaps, starches, adhesives, drugs, cosmetics, insulation material, antifreeze preparations, and fire retardants. Boron compounds are used in the electronic and metalworking fields. In agriculture, the borates have found an increasing market as weed-killers and plant foods, and they are used along railroad tracks as herbicides. The second largest borax producer is the American Potash and Chemical Company, which recovers borax from the brine at Searles Lake in California, as does the Stauffer Chemical Company, another leader. *United States Borax and Chemical Corporation*

covered with masses of it. Within a year, operations were started at Columbus, and also at Salt Wells. Borax soon was being produced for a great deal less than the foreign imports since the mineral could be harvested with a shovel and was easily processed. But a greater discovery was still to come.

F. M. Smith had left Michigan in search of gold. In 1872, learning of the operations at Columbus Marsh, he headed for the desert to sell firewood to the borax-producing plants. Their operations had

been simple: the borax was collected, shoveled into iron tanks, and boiled in order to separate and crystalize the produce. Huge quantities of fuel were consumed by the boilers. Smith's wood ranch ten miles from Columbus Marsh prospered, and he soon investigated another alkali flat, Teel's Marsh, which proved to have the richest specimen of cottonball ever discovered. Slowly, he began to buy out his competitors.

In the meantime, Smith had been shipping his borax to William T. Coleman and Company of San Francisco. Coleman was a prominent business-man who believed in the future of borax and sent scouts searching the desert for new material. While they explored, in 1881, Aaron Winters, an unsuc-cessful gold prospector who had been looking at fields of cottonball every day without realizing what it was, finally staked a claim. A scout had told Winters how to test for borax by pouring sulfuric acid and alcohol on the ore, then lighting it. If it were borax it would burn with a green flame. The claim covered hundreds of acres in Death Valley, one of the richest cottonball finds of all time. William Coleman bought the Winters claim for $20,000 and built the Harmony Borax Works.

Coleman's problem was getting the borax 165 miles across California desert to the Mojave railroad junction. The solution was two ten-mule teams hitched to form a 100-foot-long twenty-mule team. The wagons had to be designed to carry the borax and withstand the rugged trip across the desert.

Aerial view shows open-pit borate mine and adjacent processing plants owned and operated by United States Borax and Chemical Corporation at Boron, California. This is the only open-pit borate mine in the world. Ore is moved from the pit by a 1,300-foot mechanized con-veyor belt system visible in the center foreground. The development of the Boron Mine revolutionized the borax industry. In order to make borax from all borate ores other than sodium borates, the associated element must first be removed and replaced with sodium. The boron ore body already consisted of rich sodium borates, and automatically eliminated the expensive steps used in the manufacture of borax. *United States Borax and Chemical Corporation*

The wagons, built in Mojave, cost $900 and had seven-foot rear wheels and five-foot front wheels, each wagon weighing nearly 8,000 pounds empty and nearly 32,000 pounds loaded with borax. Each load included a 1,200-gallon water tank weighing 9,600 pounds. The total weight of a loaded wagon was thirty-six and one-half tons. From 1883 to 1889 the twenty-mule teams hauled borax between fifteen and eighteen miles a day, through Death Valley, across the Panamint Mountains, and through the desert to the railroad. Some twenty million pounds of borax later, the twenty-mule team was world famous and the trademark of the Pacific Coast Borax Company.

Meanwhile, Coleman's scouts had found new borate deposits in the mountains east of Death Valley and to the south in the Calico Mountains. But Coleman could do nothing about it. His widespread financial interests led to bankruptcy, and in 1890 F. M. Smith acquired all of Coleman's borax properties, which Smith incorporated into the Pacific Coast Borax Company. Thus, a new industry was born.

Within six years, Smith was looking for new outlets. He found them by amalgamating with a British chemical firm, combining their operations into Borax Consolidated Limited, a worldwide operation. Smith further expanded his activities, building new plants and railroads. Like Coleman, Smith overextended operations. He sold his borax stock in 1940 and resigned from the company.

In 1956, through a transfer of stock, the United

Both old-timers and modern television viewers are familiar with the famous twenty-mule-team trademark representing household laundry products. This is the world-famous twenty-mule team at the Boron Mine. *United States Borax and Chemical Corporation*

A New York artist's fantasy of Smith Brothers' borax refinery in 1876 (note mule teams pulling covered wagons) from *Album of American Manufacturers*. Smith's Pacific Coast Borax prospered as a division of Borax Consolidated Limited. From 1913 until 1925, borax deposits were found beneath the desert, thirty miles east of Mojave. Exploratory work indicated the ore body to be large, extending for hundreds of acres, and development of a mine and processing plants were begun simultaneously. Production began in 1927. The community that grew up around the mine was called Boron. *Pacific Coast Borax Company (United States Borax and Chemical Corporation)*

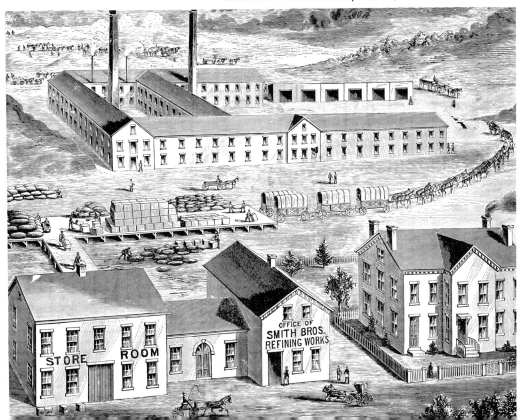

States assets of the British corporation reverted to the Pacific Coast Borax Company, a strictly American corporation, which, later that year, merged with the United States Potash Company. Together with this New Mexico mining and refining company, they formed the present United States Borax and Chemical Corporation, today the world's leading producer of borates and boron chemicals, and a major potash producer. In 1957, the boron deposits, which until then were mined by conventional underground methods, succumbed to the open-pit technique.

Since the early glassblowing and gold-refining uses, borax has become essential in more than 100 industrial processes, the glass and enamel industries being the most important.

A RETURN NORTH

As general movement away from California fanned out in an easterly direction, the farthest northern spot reached was Oregon. Late in 1851, rich placer deposits were discovered in Jacksonville along Jackson Creek, some twenty-five miles north of the California border. At about the same time, highly productive diggings were found on Sterling Creek, and a year later, in the headwaters of the Illinois River, the famous Sailors Diggings deposits were found. (Sailors Diggings was named for a group of sailors who deserted their ship at Crescent

The Sterling Hydraulic Mine near Jacksonville, Oregon, in operation around 1880. The Jacksonville District was the center of important hydraulic works for many years. The placers here had been quickly worked out, followed by large-scale hydraulic mining, many operations continuing into the twentieth century; hydraulic workings at Sterling Creek ceased only in 1914. Minor lode-mining operations, principally from small gold pockets, quickly faded. But by 1853 Jacksonville had become the county seat, population nearly 1,000. The citizens were plagued with Indian attacks; the Rogue River Indian War delayed mining considerably. Twenty years later, fire destroyed most of the Jacksonville business section, which was summarily rebuilt. But bypassed by the railroad, and its county seat lost to Medford, in 1927 Jacksonville lapsed into mining obscurity. About 60 buildings remain from those days, some still used for their original purposes. *Oregon State Department of Geology*

City, California, to prospect.) Jacksonville and Waldo were officially founded soon after, though today nothing remains of Waldo.

COMBING THE SALT BEACHES

Gold and Silver in Oregon, published by the Oregon Department of Geology and Mineral Industries, recounts a gold discovery in 1852 on southern Oregon's beaches. About twenty years later, similar gold-bearing black sand was found on some of Oregon's ancient elevated beaches. According to C. A. Spreen's 1939 Oregon University master's thesis, *A History of Placer Gold Mining in Oregon, 1850–1870,* quoted here from the above-mentioned book:

> The earliest beach mining in Oregon, of which there is any record, was in 1852, at the mouth of Whiskey Run, a few miles north of the Coquille River. A few half-breed Indians discovered gold-bearing sand on the beach and worked their placers quietly for a portion of two summers and undoubtedly saved a considerable amount of gold. In the summer of 1853 they sold out to the McNamara brothers for $20,000. Pans of black sand from this claim yielded from $8 to $10. It has been estimated that during the 50's and 60's more than one hundred thousand dollars was taken from this one claim. The town of Randolph sprang into existence overnight on Whiskey Run. In the fall of 1853 more than a thousand men were there. Its lodging houses could not accommodate all the miners so Randolph became a tent city. It was a typical mining camp. Poker tables were adorned with cocked pistols; and whisky, straight and mixed, went gurgling down the throats of those who sat around waiting for spring. Books were opened on "bedrock" credit, and all went merry as a marriage ball. But the sand, outside the one claim, did not pay.

INLAND SALT BRINE

We have discussed salt earlier, but these early salt-mining works of New York (1652, 1788, 1793), Massachusetts, and Missouri (1800s) were generally small local operations. In Virginia, around Saltville —in the 1850s one of the first major salt-brine producers—about 230 feet below the surface, a bed of fossil salt was recovered.

The demand for salt in the western states paralleled the development of the chlorination process of ore reduction in silver recovery. Pioneers at Salt Lake Valley met miners' needs for salt by boiling Great Salt Lake water in huge iron kettles.

The site of the first rock-salt mine in North America is marked by this plaque. The first American patent was for the manufacture of salt. Samuel Winslow (Massachusetts Bay Colony) acquired a ten-year exclusive right to make salt under a process he developed. But until the early nineteenth century most of the salt in the colonies came from England, and what was not imported was obtained by boiling brine taken from saline springs. *International Salt Company*

An 1857 *Harper's Monthly* sketch of blocks of kettles used to boil salt out of the brine at Saltville. At Saltville, wells were sunk into the bed. The wells were filled with water to within 45 feet of the surface and from there pumped into large tanks that held a saturated salt solution equal to 22 gallons of pure salt for every 100 gallons of pumped brine. The brine was then processed in 100- to 150-foot-long arched furnaces, with doors at one end and a chimney at the other. Rows of heavy iron kettles were built into the top of the furnace; in large plants there were often as many as 100 kettles. The brine was conveyed in wooden pipes from the tanks to the kettles, where the water was evaporated by boiling. Crystallized salt remained, dipped out manually with huge ladles, and dumped into woven mesh baskets that permitted the water to drain, thus leaving pure white salt as a residue. Barrelsful were shipped from Saltville along the Holston River to points along the Eastern Seaboard and westward.

Dipping out the salt into wicker baskets that allowed the water to drain, leaving pure white salt as a residue. Harper's New Monthly Magazine, *September, 1857*

Exterior view of Saltville works. Salt was not manufactured in the United States until about 1788, when the first plants went into production near Syracuse, New York. By 1793 saltworks were established at Salt Point (Salina, New York) on the shores of Lake Onondaga where William Val Vleck and Moses De Witt built potash kettles. This was the first saltwork of any size in the East. But Virginia soon had the largest salt plants at Saltville. *From* Harper's New Monthly Magazine, *September, 1857*

By 1885 Great Salt Lake became an important salt producer. Shipments were going to silver mines in Utah, Nevada, Colorado, Idaho, and Montana. Nearly 100,000 tons of salt were collected around the lake by 1886, and rock-salt mines were opened in several Utah locations. Of the thirty-five million tons of salt consumed in the United States annually, about half is produced from salt brine, a quarter from rock salt from underground mines, and the remainder from solar, vacuum pan, or open pan, evaporation. It occurs in tremendous bedded rock-salt deposits; as domes of rock salt under the earth's surface, and in lakes, springs, and underground brines, as well as in the oceans of the world. Yet table salt in American kitchens accounts for only 3 percent.

Salt mines on the Isle Petite Auce, Louisiana. Wood engraving in *Harper's,* August 22, 1868, after A. R. Waud. *Library of Congress*

Around 1900, crude salts were harvested from the solar vats at the edge of Great Salt Lake, Utah. Tractors and wagons were used to haul the salt to the Utah-Salduro Company. Their plant can be seen in the background between the last two vehicles. *Utah State Historical Society*

The 140-foot ceilings of a section of the Avery Island Mine, Avery Island, Louisiana, may hold the world's record for height. The ledge that appears about a third of the way up the salt pillar is approximately 40 feet from the mine floor. The old mine-floor level used to be at the ledge level in the photograph. *International Salt Company*

The first step in preparing a room for blasting is to undercut a channel ten feet deep and about six inches high at floor level. *International Salt Company*

Drill platform. Holes are drilled in the salt face for insertion of explosives. *International Salt Company*

Mountain of blasted rock salt. *International Salt Company*.

The primary crusher is self-propelled and operates right at the face. Portable conveyor belts pick up the crushed salt directly from the crusher. Semiportable belts then carry it to a permanent conveyor system. *International Salt Company*

Crushed and screened, rock salt heads for the shaft bottom. Conveyor belt carries the salt to a weighing station and on to measuring hoppers that automatically fill the skips at the shaft bottom. *International Salt Company*

Rock salt leaves the secondary crusher and climbs a steep slope on its way to underground storage. *International Salt Company*

Meanwhile, the mine cars continue to fill up with blasted rock salt. *International Salt Company*

Built from above and drawn off from below, thousands of tons of rock salt are stored in the Avery Island Mine. *International Salt Company*

Rock salt is drawn from the storage pile and conveyed to a surge bin. *International Salt Company*

Skip-loading station at the bottom of the production shaft. *International Salt Company*

Rock-salt mining is similar in many ways to mining other types of metals or minerals. Salt is recaptured from underground deposits by dissolving it with water—hydraulic mining vastly different from the hydraulic mining of gold. Holes are drilled into underground deposits, water is pumped in to dissolve the salt, and the brine is then brought to the surface for refining. Rock salt has been dissolved at a number of factories with steam and hot water for use as table salt. And as solar-evaporation plants developed, production increased, accounting in the 1960s for some 300,000 tons of salt a year. Artificial heat is still another method.

ZINC IN NEW JERSEY

Near the time of salt mining's expansion in Virginia, some 500 miles northeast, the earliest zinc mine in the United States was first being worked around 1850 at Franklin, New Jersey. The Franklin Mine produced zinc exclusively, which was exceptional since zinc ores are usually found in association with other metals, especially lead; zinc ores also frequently include copper, gold, and silver. Franklin's deposits were unusually pure, completely free of the usual accompanying sulfur. The mine operated 104 years until New Jersey Zinc shut it down in the mid-1950s when the zinc bodies were depleted.

Airplane view of the Tennessee Copper Company, Copper Hill, Tennessee. This represents Southeast's lone copper-producing area, near the North Carolina–Georgia border lying between Ducktown and Copper Hill. These large deposits were discovered in the late 1850s, the principal modern operations of which are Tennessee Copper's five copper mines at Copper Hill. Tennessee zinc is completely devoid of lead, though low in zinc content. However, deposits are large, and its quantity production makes for profitable mining. Four major zinc companies operate nine mines in the Jefferson-Mascot District. *Denver Equipment Company*

A salt stockpile. Salt, which is a chemical compound of sodium and chlorine, called sodium chloride, and its compounds probably have more uses than any other mineral: as a nutrient, or flavor, for heat tablets and other medicinals, for cattle blocks, as a preservative for commercial and domestic use, for metallurgical processing. Salt makes possible refrigerating brines and the manufacture of ice and ice cream; it de-ices highways and helps form antifreeze; it tans leather, dyes textiles, stabilizes soils, softens water, colors fireworks, kills weeds, and grinds prisms. From salt we get soda ash, sodium, sodium sulfate, hydrochloric acid, chlorine, and castic soda. Without salt the world as we know it would cease to exist. The largest consumer is the chemical industry, accounting for about two-thirds of the total United States production, about 65 percent of which is provided by six salt companies. Of six states that supply about 90 percent of the total United States output, Louisiana is the leading producer, followed closely by Texas and New York; Michigan, Ohio, and California rank fourth, fifth, and sixth respectively. *Salt Institute*

The Pittsburg-Tennessee Mine, April 12, 1892. Four months after this photograph was taken, insurrections arose throughout the state against employing convicts as miners. This was the second such insurrection in Tennessee. *Tennessee State Library and Archives*

An 1852 woodcut of the manufacture of zinc by means of "sublimation." The process of sublimation involves the use of sulfide ore that is roasted to the oxide and mixed with coal. It is then heated to 1,200 degrees centigrade, vaporizing the zinc that is condensed outside the reaction chamber, where it is formed into blocks or ingots called "spelter." *American Zinc Institute, Inc.*

MONTANA GOLD AND OUTLAWS

In the meantime, the great northern search for gold had reached Montana, with still no hint of the great Montana copper deposits that were still to be exploited.

Montana's first recorded gold discovery was François Finlay's 1852 find at Deer Lodge Valley, just west of Butte. Finlay was a half-breed Indian known as Benetsee. In 1856 a John Silverthorn, who traded gold for supplies at the American Fur Company at Fort Benton (about 175 miles northeast), may have obtained his gold from Benetsee, whom he knew. However, Benetsee's discovery remained unexploited for six years—until James Stuart, Granville Stuart, and Reece Anderson wintered in Montana en route from the California gold rush. The Stuarts prospected in Deer Lodge Valley at Gold Creek. They found insignificant amounts of gold, and were driven off by Blackfoot Indians. After retiring to Fort Bridger, they returned in 1860, exploring for three years before uncovering a promising find. In the meantime, constantly passing pros-

pectors heading through Montana for the Idaho mines caused the group to reconsider whether their find would be worth working. One would-be Idaho prospector, John White, from Colorado, stopped to winter in the Valley, some seventy-five miles east of Idaho, and made a major gold discovery at White's Bar, on Willard Creek—now Grasshopper Creek. When the Stuarts heard about it, they made their decision and rushed to the creek. About two and one-half miles above the site, Bannack was founded, and quickly populated by some 500 people during the winter of 1862–1863.

Bannack was better known for its Plummer gang than for its gold. Henry Plummer had come to Bannack from Idaho in 1862 and had organized

The once-famous Hotel Meade stands deserted at Bannack, first territorial capital of Montana. The first placer deposits here were usually found a short distance above the stream banks, where prospectors were often able to pull up the rooted plants and sagebrush, then shake the surrounding dirt and gravel into a pan, and perhaps work out $1 or $2 in gold. But well before the winter expired, a gold lode was discovered, the Decotah Lode, the first in the state, and a water-powered mill was built to process its ore. An Alder Gulch find, near Virginia City, in southwestern Montana, virtually emptied Bannack, and for two or three years both Grasshopper Creek and Bannack remained deserted. The area was somewhat revived from 1866 to 1870 when water ditches were brought in for hydraulic mining on Zoller's Bar. A smelter was built in Bannack to process the increasing finds of the white metal, but in a few years both towns declined as mining centers. Bannack has been made a state monument, and is being carefully preserved without commercialization. Visitors can poke around among the ruins and visit historic placer diggings where fortunes in gold were mined. *Montana Highway Commission*

Now overgrown with weeds, this was the first church in Bannack. *Montana Highway Commission*

a band of robbers, operating there and, later, in Virginia City. The gang is credited with at least 100 murders. One gang member was a former henchman, Jack Cleveland; another was an Indian chief. One of Plummer's band, married to an Indian, had mistreated his squaw so badly that she returned to her tribe. The Indian chief was killed in retaliation, and three of the gang were brought to trial, but the jurors, intimidated by Plummer and his men, voted eleven to one for acquittal. They finally reached a compromise—banishment for the three killers. Unfortunately, it was never enforced, and criminals consequently ran rampant in Bannack. Within five months of the trial, nine of the men who had contributed to the sentence were dead and about a dozen had fled in fear. And Plummer was elected sheriff! In 1864, in a vigilante action, Bannack residents hanged Plummer at nearby Hangman's Gulch.

WASHINGTON GOLD AND RUBY

The northern gold search reached the State of Washington in 1855, hardly causing a ripple on the "gold front" as Washington played only a very small part in the nation's early gold-mining history, principally at the port of Seattle (described in the Alaska chapter). One short-lived gold discovery occurred in 1855 near Fort Colville, a Hudson Bay Company fur-trading post close to the Canadian border. Once the gold was gone, many of the miners chose to remain and became farmers. Two 1886 discoveries created some excitement though. The first was a find along the edge of Salmon Creek by two prospectors just prior to 1886, but not worked until then. Their activity brought others into the general northeastern area, founding Salmon City and working the Homestake and Tough Nut mines near the town of Ruby in the extreme northeastern part of the state. Salmon City prospered, benefiting from an abundant water supply for placer mining, and in 1888 was renamed Conconully. But the new name brought with it a series of disasters, beginning almost immediately with its loss of the county seat to Ruby and, four years later, a disastrous fire, followed in another two years by an equally disastrous flood. In between, the depression of 1893 helped demoralize the town, which never recovered.

On the other hand, Ruby, the scene of the second of the 1866 exciting events, was more suc-

Deer Lodge. In 1865 freight for mines was often hauled from here by trains of oxen. *Montana Bureau of Mines and Geology, C. Owen Smith Collection*

Bannack, from Cemetery Hill. The track in the right foreground is part of the old wagon road to Virginia City. *Montana Highway Commission*

cessful. Also, prior to 1886, some prospecting had been done, though illegally, on the Moses Indian Reservation near Ruby Mountain. But in 1886 the government declared part of the reservation public domain, and a rush began, with some 1,000 prospectors seemingly appearing from nowhere. Although they found small quantities of gold, their biggest success was in silver, and a year later they organized the Ruby Mining District. Ruby's undoing was the silver-market crash of 1893; its population immediately declined and what remained of the town was mostly wiped out by fire in 1900.

A NEW "COPPER CULTURE"

Like the distant rumbling of thunder across the waters, the first warning of great new copper, silver, and gold storms began to be heard in 1854 with copper finds in Arizona, gold strikes in Colorado, and silver in Nevada. A new mining era was about to be born.

The first Spanish visitors to the Ajo, Arizona, area were so aware of the odor of wild onions, or garlic, which permeated the air, that they named it *ajo,* Spanish for a flowering type of garlic. When the first Americans arrived in 1854 they, too, en-

countered *ajo* but also found abandoned workings, rawhide ore buckets, and crude tools, relics of early attempts to mine the small veins of native copper occurring in three small hills. They were undoubtedly left by Mexican miners who had come from the silver mines in Sonora in 1750 to prospect for gold or silver. Apparently they had worked the veins for a short time and found them unprofitable.

In the 1890s, an era balanced between weird and shady operations began with A. J. Shotwell, a fake mine promoter and swindler, and John R. Boddie. They formed the St. Louis Copper Company, which soon failed. Shotwell then organized the Rescue Copper Company to rescue the St. Louis Company; then another company, the Cornelia Copper Company, named for Boddie's wife; and even a fourth, the Shotwell Tri-Mountain Copper Company. All but the St. Louis finally merged under the ownership of the Cornelia Copper Company. And between 1900 and 1907, there was the "Rendall Process" tried by the Rendall Ore Reduction Com-

Remains of an arrastra and hoist house near the old town of Liberty and an old stamp mill near Blewett Pass, not far from Granite, where in 1896 gold was discovered on Granite Creek. This resulted in portions of the Colville Indian Reservation opening to miners. A lively rush ensued, and the tent city of Eureka was formed, later changed to Republic for its leading mine. Some fifty log and canvas shacks, a number of stores, blacksmith shops, and other businesses, including several saloons, were established. By 1900, "several" saloons became twenty-eight as Republic grew into one of eastern Washington's largest towns, even boasting an opera house. Scheduled Republic-Spokane stages carried miners and supplies. Mining continued in the area until recent years, accounting for about half of Washington's silver production. Republic is a modern town today; fire destroyed its original buildings in 1938. *United States Forest Service*

pany, which had optioned some of the Ajo claims. The company claimed the process "would treat all classes of copper ore with equal facility," but it was a complete failure.

Immediately after, "Professor" Fred L. McGahn's mysterious "McGahn Vacuum Smelter" was built at a cost of $34,000. It was supposed to "melt the ore in pure gold, silver, copper, and so forth, which would then be drawn off in separate spigots. After the furnace was once started, the oxygen and hydrogen gases, which escape from the ore, would be used to fire the furnace, and the purchase of any other fuel would be unnecessary." The McGahn Smelter produced nothing but a vacuum in the pockets of its investors while Shotwell and McGahn disappeared. Other stockholders invested $20,000 in a hydrofluoric-acid leaching process almost as fantastic as the vacuum smelter. It extracted copper at the ridiculous cost of $1 a pound!

Ajo was deserted during the Panic of 1907. Meanwhile, during the next three years, the Utah Copper Company, of Bingham Canyon, Utah, was developing new methods for profitably processing low-grade copper, and was looking for new copper deposits. But big copper companies bid against each other for a chance to develop Arizona's Verde Valley ores, and an option on the reorganized Cornelia Copper Company went to the General Development Company.

Although the search for copper continued, no one drilled in the hills. Consequently the main ore body remained undiscovered until 1911, when Cap-

tain John C. Greenway of the Calumet and Arizona Mining Company directed his geologists to make a concentrated search under the Ajo hills. Convinced of the existence of large copper deposits, Greenway optioned 70 percent of the New Cornelia Copper Company's stock from John R. Boddie, and within two years and 25,000 feet of drilling, he was proven right. The hills were underlain with millions of tons of low-grade ore. This was the beginning of Arizona's great copper development, now the nation's largest producer.

Diesel-electric locomotives at work in the New Cornelia pit. New Cornelia consolidated with the Calumet and Arizona in 1929, and in 1931 all merged with the Phelps Dodge Corporation. After shutting down operations for a couple of years, production was resumed in 1934. The New Cornelia Branch of the Phelps Dodge Corporation became one of the great open-pit copper mines of the world. It is the fourth largest producer in the United States, and Ajo is a modern prosperous company mining town. *Phelps Dodge Corporation*

The New Cornelia Plant and the open-pit copper mine at Ajo, Arizona. In the foreground are the crushing plant and mill containing the concentrating flotation plant. The plant has a capacity for treating in excess of 31,000 tons of ore every 24 hours. The smelting plant treats all the concentrate produced by the concentrator, ultimately refining it into anode bars weighing about 700 pounds each. The first serious attempt to mine this region was in 1854, when the Arizona Mining and Trading Company worked small bodies of native copper, which had to be hauled by horse and mule teams to Yuma, Arizona, and San Diego, California, then transferred to sailing ships and brought all the way to Swansea, Wales, for smelting. It was an expensive operation. Understandably, the Arizona Mining and Trading Company failed, in 1859, and for forty years mining in Arizona was virtually dormant. *Phelps Dodge Corporation*

Old Gold Road, ghost town near Kingman. Nearly $8 million came out of this site. *Arizona Department of Library and Archives*

Converter for the recovery of copper at the Cornelia Plant of Phelps Dodge Corporation. *Phelps Dodge Corporation*

"PIKE'S PEAK OR BUST"—A REAL BUST

The thunder of the oncoming storm grew louder as "Pike's Peak or Bust" became a national slogan in 1859.

Denver, Colorado, contradicting the rumors of gold in and around Pikes Peak farther south, never experienced a real gold rush. Many who had lost out in California felt that if there was gold on one side of the Rockies it should be true for the other. Accordingly, gold-hungry hordes had rushed East to Pikes Peak.

Among the first were the three Russell brothers, William Green, Oliver, and Levi. They found gold about ninety miles north of Pikes Peak, at Cherry Creek, and there they settled, calling their little community Auraria after their home town in Georgia. A miniscule settlement of tents and Indians, which occupied the opposite side of the Creek, could be

Charcoal "beehive" burners, sometimes called "smelting furnaces," at the old Silver Belle Smelter, near Tucson. They were used for copper. *Arizona Department of Library and Archives*

Early Arizona silver mine. *New York Public Library Picture Collection*

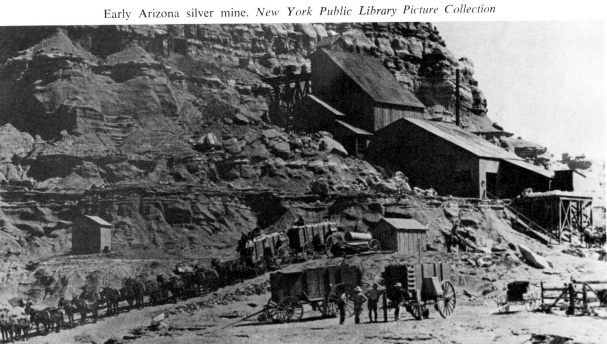

Interesting and unusual view of Auraria and Denver in 1858 and 1859, looking west. The stream running from the lower left-hand corner is Cherry Creek running into the South Platt River, lined by trees. At the left-hand end of the river is a ferry. The section with the tents to the left of the creek was Auraria, while Denver City was on the opposite side of the creek. In the background are the Table Mountains near Golden, Colorado. Auraria and Denver City combined in 1860 to form Denver. *Colorado State Historical Society Library*

This Colorado flume spanned a difficult rocky gorge. Note men at right end of flume. *Denver Public Library Western Collection. Photo by Thomas McKee*

A group of embryonic miners leaving Denver on a prospecting trip during the Colorado gold rush. Published in *Frank Leslie's Illustrated Newspaper* on May 21, 1859. *Colorado State Historical Society Library*

reached by ferry. In 1860 both communities joined to form the city of Denver.

The Cherry Creek finds would not qualify as a major strike, but they did add credence to exaggerated rumors of the abundance of gold. The influx from east and west continued, only to subside at Cherry Creek where the rumors were proved groundless, especially since the Russells had returned to Georgia. With winter approaching, many remained at Cherry Creek.

But the East learned a different story. Newspapers, songs, and articles extolled the Colorado finds. Endless teams and wagons transported farmers and workers, bearing the slogan, "Pike's Peak or Bust." Of 100,000 gold seekers who started west, half turned back after hearing the disappointing news, and the remainder eventually reached Denver.

Were it not for gold strikes at Idaho Springs, John Gregory's find at Black Hawk, and Central City's success, all "Pike's Peak or Bust" expeditions would have been an unadulterated bust. To this day, no significant gold finds have been uncovered in the immediate Denver vicinity.

The exaggerated newspaper accounts had been responsible for stampeding frontiersmen, the unemployed, businessmen, and disappointed miners, in fact, anyone who ever dreamed of gold, of striking

The rush to the gold areas around Denver and the routes to Pikes Peak inspired songs written and published about Pikes Peak, this one called "The Pike's Peak Gallop." The drawing on the cover is highly imaginative. Hordes of miners are seen climbing the peak, some falling off into the valley below. The little building in the center of the picture is labeled "grocery," but apparently all it sold was whiskey, and victims in all stages of drunkenness surround it. Off to the right, the covered wagon pulled by oxen is surrounded by fighting men. The wagon was named the Fizzle, and on its top was a plaque reading "Ax No Questions." In the foreground a man hangs high in the tree. The song was published in 1859 in southern Ohio. *Colorado State Historical Society Library*

it rich. They came in prairie schooners and light carriages, on horses, pack animals, and oxen, and on foot, some pushing two-wheel hand carts. Guidebooks were published, and the newspapers even located nonexistent finds. But almost all came to know that they had been "humbugged"; there was little available.

This did not prevent Denver from becoming the financial center for those commercial interests that developed important gold finds elsewhere in Colorado. And Denver was a natural geographical junction point for the railroads that were slowly being built to ultimately connect all the mining centers.

During the 1870s and the 1880s, silver exceeded gold as an important commodity in Denver, which now boomed from the wealth of its mining interests. It was the metropolis of the bonanza kings. Horace Tabor built his Tabor Grand Opera House, and the Silver Dollar Saloon became famous.

When the 1893 silver panic hit, Denver's opulent days ended suddenly. Banks closed, smelting plants shut down, and silver kings became paupers. New gold and silver discoveries, particularly at Cripple Creek, prevented Denver's complete disaster, but the city slowly turned to farming, cattle raising, and sheep ranching. Commerce and industry developed rapidly. Following World War II, the westward shift in American population sharply stimulated further growth. Denver is still important to the mining industry. It remains Colorado's mining capital, although its gold, silver, lead, and copper are secondary to uranium, molybdenum, zinc, and vanadium. Its Mining Exchange Building, erected in 1890 and 1891, topped by a statue of an old prospector holding a pick in one hand and a gold brick in the other, is attributed to many of Colorado's most prominent citizens among the original subscribers for construction funds. Among the buildings' tenants were a group of men who during the 1890s frequently lunched together at various Denver restaurants. These luncheon gatherings were the nucleus of the Denver Mining Club, a luncheon club for anyone connected or indirectly associated with the mining industry. The club has no dues or fees and visitors pay their own luncheon checks. Probably there is no other club in the world with as many "old timers" as members. The president of the club, Guy L. V. Emerson, also president of the Treasure Mountain Gold Mining Company, at ninety-three years young, is still active. H. W. C. Prommel, eighty-three, a member and prominent mining engineer and geologist, is still actively prospecting for gold in the high altitudes of the Colorado mountains. The world-famous annual Sowbelly Dinners in February are sponsored by the Colorado Mining Association, one of the nation's leading mining groups. In attendance are governors, senators, congressmen, and many others of equal rank and fame throughout the country.

Black Hawk, looking up Gregory's and Chase's gulches. Lithograph by J. Bien in Alfred E. Mathews' "Pencil Sketches of Colorado," 1866. *Library of Congress*

Results of a good day's work at the Boston and Colorado Smelting Company in Black Hawk, scene of a second strike below Central City's, about 1876. *Denver Public Library, Western Collection*

Gregory Gulch, site of the richest dirt of the 1859 gold strike. This 1909 photo shows the stamp mills of Black Hawk, "The Mill City" in the Gulch. A famous stamp mill was the one built by a Professor Hill, in 1867, in Black Hawk. Most of Central City's ore was processed by the Black Hill Smelter, passed through the stamp mill and reduction furnaces, and formed into "matt"—a mass of gold, silver, copper, and iron—and sent to Swansea, Wales, where the gold and silver were extracted. Just for the copper residue, the lengthy trip was warranted. *Gilpin County, Colorado, Chamber of Commerce*

160

Gregory gold diggings, May, 1859. Wood engraving in Albert D. Richardson's *Beyond the Mississippi,* 1867. *Library of Congress*

The cross in the lower left-hand corner marks the exact spot where John H. Gregory found gold on Gregory Hill, May 6, 1859. The picture was taken around 1866. *Gilpin County, Colorado, Chamber of Commerce*

Sketch of Gregory's Quartz Mill, Pikes Peak, made by Colonel D. H. Huyett on April 21, 1860. It was published in *Frank Leslie's Illustrated Newspaper* in December of that year. The name on the mill reads Gregory Quartz Mill, Konklin and Company. *Colorado State Historical Society Library*

THE MINER'S CODE

John H. Gregory's gold find on Vasquez Fork (Clear Creek) in April, 1859, is often credited as Colorado's first (the Russells had preceded him in 1858 at a point six miles above Denver). This discovery was a gold-quartz lode in the mountains. His find was made simultaneously with another near Boulder and Idaho Springs, at the Jackson Diggings. But the Gregory Mining District had been recorded first, and under agreement with other groups that had staked claims, it was decided that each prospector could claim 100 feet along a vein, while the discoverer could claim twice this by virtue of his

discovery. These and other rules later became the basis for United States mining law.

It had been the practice in most mining camps and towns for local committees of miners to establish themselves as mining districts, and to adopt a code for mining operations. By this democratic process did they evolve into local government agencies, and the rules and regulations were usually rigidly enforced.

In 1859 in Central City a major body of this type was formed. The adopted code named a president, a recorder, and a sheriff, and established regulations pertaining to mining claims. In general, regulations were based upon those commonly agreed upon in other mining areas operating under specific rules and regulations. Its principal feature was the award of a double-size claim to the discoverer of a mineral site, while all subsequent claimants were entitled to a single claim. Regulations permitted a group or partnership to make individual claims for each member, and if there were no previous claim-

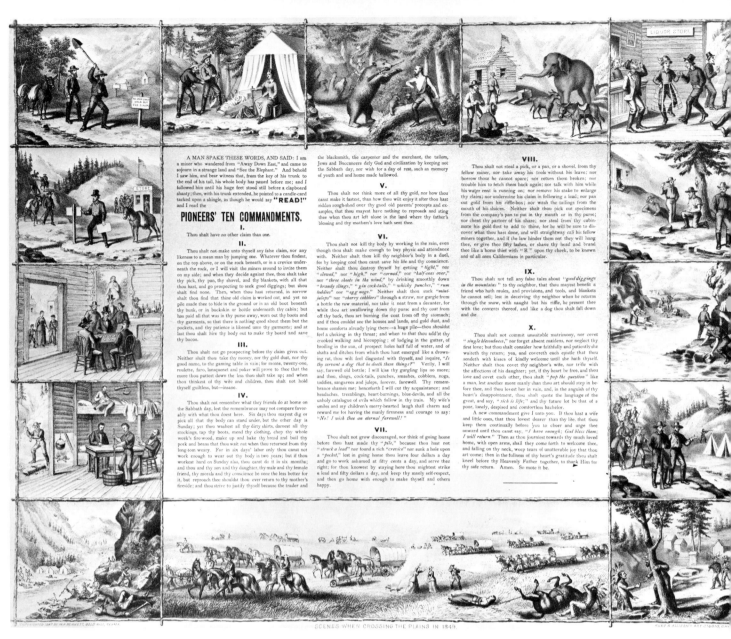

The miners' ten commandments of 1849. Lithograph by Kurz and Allison, 1887. *Library of Congress*

ants, such claims could be placed adjacent to each other. Special boards, very similar to modern arbitration courts, were set up to arbitrate disputes over mining claims or mining rights. Participants were legally bound to the decisions, but, under certain conditions, disputants could appeal before a jury or general assembly of miners from the district. These were miners' courts, which usually did not permit technicalities to defeat their purposes (often with the effect of prohibiting lawyers from appearing at the trial). Penalties (rather than sentences) ranged from forfeiture of property, to flogging, banishment from the district, and hanging. In 1860 Colorado itself became a territory, separate from Kansas, and the laws established under the local codes were declared valid by the courts. Other states, too, had regulations pertaining to placer mining, mill sites, timbering, building construction, etc., but Colorado was the first to establish regulations for tunnel or lode mining, where a gold lode might extend for quite a distance. The regulations stipulated that each partner or association could claim a mining extension limited to 200 feet for each person, along what he presumed was the lode, provided that the claim was first marked on the surface of the ground before tunnel digging began. This required foresight, clairvoyance, or plain guesswork to determine the direction in which the lode might conceivably run. An incorrect guess could be costly. Nevertheless, it became law, and, with some modification, the United States Congress adopted these basic tenets in the United States Mining Law of 1872.

Mountain City (later Central City), from a sketch in *Frank Leslie's Illustrated Newspaper* in 1860. The left-hand cabin bears a sign that reads "Rocky Mountain Gold Reporter." The next cabin is the express office. Note the use of oxen for hauling, and the timbering activity on the hills. *Denver Public Library, Western Collection*

Gilpin County miners as they came off shift (circa 1910). Note the children. *Gilpin County, Colorado, Chamber of Commerce*

CENTRAL CITY EXPANDS

Gregory Diggings was altered to Mountain City, and as mining activity surrounding the diggings increased, Gregory decided to rename the fast-growing town Central City, just in time for Horace Greeley, representing the *New York Tribune,* and A. D. Richardson, of the *Boston Journal,* to come riding into town on mules. A meeting called that evening to celebrate the event drew nearly 3,000 people to hear the visiting journalists. The next day they inspected

Central City remained lawful, a balanced community that by the mid-1860s offered churches, banks, a post office, schools, and legitimate theatres to offset its saloons, gambling joints, and brothels. Sixty mills, with

30 arrastras, and some 15,000 people helped sustain a thriving commerce. The photo shows Central City in 1864. *Denver Public Library, Western Collection*

the workings—sluice boxes, shafts, and other mining operations—and wrote a joint report, which was reprinted by newspapers across the country. By summer Central City's population went from 5,000 to 20,000.

As for Gregory, he prospered enormously, shipping in one month alone $5,000 in gold. In September when he returned to Georgia for the winter, he brought out $30,000, not including another $30,000 or more in claims he had sold.

Some fortunes derived from sources other than gold. W. L. Douglas repaired shoes here before establishing his nationally known shoe-manufacturing company; George M. Pullman had invented the sleeping car, but unable to finance its manufacture, came to Gilpin County where he acquired enough gold to start his business; and following his tenure as a Central City miner, W. A. Clark became famous as a copper king and a Montana senator. As the city's reputation grew, famous visitors began to arrive to look over the unusual town. Schuyler Colfax, who became Grant's vice-president, visited in 1865; A. D. Richardson made his fourth trip, gathering

Central City, from the side of Mammoth Hill looking up Gregory and Eureka gulches. Lithograph by J. Bien in Alfred E. Mathews' "Pencil Sketches of Colorado," 1866. After the destruction by fire in 1874 of most of its original buildings, only six were spared; the city was immediately rebuilt, more solidly than before. Some placer mining continued until around 1919, and in Gilpin County still does. Central City is probably the best preserved of the Colorado mining towns. *Library of Congress*

The area surrounding Central City was one of mountains and of canyons known as gulches, and mining here was known as gulch mining, as in this scene. In these gulches were the mills, furnaces, buildings, mine openings and mouths of tunnels, and even deserted claims. The flumes and sluices usually ran along the bottom of the canyon, and waterwheels often supplied the power. Almost weekly, new lodes were found. From the original discovery in April to the first of July, over 100 sluices were operating in Gregory Gulch, averaging about $30 a day per man. By the end of September, 900 men in the district were producing $50,000 worth of gold a week; during eight months a total of over $1 million had been removed.

Brokers thrived on the burgeoning mines. Some even sold shares in nonexistent mines at the height of the Central City-Black Hawk-Leadville rush. *Colorado State Historical Society Library*

The shaft of the Buel (Buell) Mine was entered by the long ladders shown in this 1870 sketch. The forerunners of modern tunnel and shaft mining can be traced to the mines around Central City. Cornish miners, experienced in extending drifts long distances, had been recruited from the British Isles to work with others from Michigan copper and Wisconsin lead mines; the pleasant Cornish personalities were heartily welcomed by the populace.

From its heading, the auriferous ore was loaded into mine cars and shuttled away along the tracks. Notice the men shoring up the side walls of the drift.

material for his book *Across the Mississippi;* Henry M. Stanley arrived in 1867 just before he went to look for Dr. Livingstone in Africa, and General Grant—accompanied by his son Ulysses Jr., and Generals Sherman, Dent, and Sheridan—arrived in 1868, shortly before he was elected president. In 1872 Henry Moore Teller, a Colorado leading citizen, opened the four-story Teller House at a cost of $80,000. On revisiting Central City in 1873, President Grant traversed the Teller House's $14,000 silver-bricked entranceway paved for the special occasion.

Central Cityites could recall a lynching in 1860 and the shooting of Charlie Switz by rival theatre owner George Harrison two years later. Harrison was tried for murder, but no one seemed to like Switz so the jury rendered a verdict of "not guilty."

A wild era of stock speculation flourished, caused by many claims falling into the hands of eastern speculators. Pat Casey, an Irish laborer, had sold a Nevadaville claim to a Wall Street syndicate for about $150,000. This started the Central City trading in mining stocks; by Civil War days many claims had "gone East" with speculators who had come looking for likely deals. They paid fantastic prices for stock as well as for Colorado mine interests; their profits on resale were even more fantastic. They bought anything and everything—mines completely exhausted, impractical to work, inundated beyond a Cornish pump's capacities, and some that were simply nonexistent. Lacking a knowledge of mining operations, they brought in useless machinery, including expensive and often fraudulent smelting processes, and burdened all Colorado mines with a terrible reputation among investors, who would no longer put money into even the most legitimate operations.

As for Pat Casey, he was now a famous Central City light, leaving his past far behind. Following his arrival, in steerage, in the United States, he had walked from the east coast to Colorado, where his friendly personality had soon made him one of Central City's favorites. As a mining claim of his prospered, he became a town leader. The road he built between his mine and mill on Bates Hill is still known as "The Casey." Casey could neither read nor write. Caroline Bancroft in her excellent book *Historic Central City* recalls that although Pat was unable to tell time, he carried an enormous gold watch (with chain and fob) "in ostentatious prosperity across his brawny middle." When greeted by a friend one day, and asked the time, he replied: "Sure and ye better be seein' for yerself. Ye wouldn't believe me if I told ye." The friend persuaded everyone

A Central City bar in the 1880s. *Denver Public Library, Western Collection*

he met to ask Pat the time, which always elicited, "Sure and ye . . ." When Pat was asked if he would make a donation to the Catholic church to help purchase a chandelier, he replied, "Sure, here is $50. But who's goin' to play it for ye?"

Despite the recurrence of silver booms in the 1870s and 1880s, a generally declining silver market followed. It turned many miners toward other Colorado areas in a hunt for gold, which grew increasingly more attractive as the United States further inclined toward establishing a gold standard. Nevertheless, Central City grew to become Colorado's second city.

With Denver as the hub, Colorado mining had literally fanned out westward. Barely twenty miles northwest of Denver is Boulder; directly west are the famous mining towns of Golden, Idaho Springs, Black Hawk, and Central City, all within a thirty-five-mile radius. Here the principal highways turn southwest toward nearby Leadville and Aspen. Georgetown is on the road to Leadville.

Long before the Leadville strikes of 1878, Georgetown was Colorado's leading mining town. Its hotels, newspapers, theatres, and recreation places went quickly into full swing. Georgetown even became known for its paperweights—silver bricks used

A late 1860 sketch of Georgetown, Colorado, showing the attractive layout of the town, the Clear Creek River running through it, and the rugged, mountainous background. Gold was first discovered here in 1859 by George and David Griffith, and the area around "George's Town" soon filled with gold miners. By 1864 the area's surface workings were relatively unimportant, but that was the year of the rich Belmont Silver Lode discovery. In no time 2,000 miners rushed in. By 1866, two mining camps combined to form Georgetown, whose rapid growth within the next couple of years captured the county seat from Idaho Springs.

166

Georgetown around 1873. By the early 1870s, the immediate Georgetown District was producing almost as much silver as the Central City-Black Hawk area, mostly from mines along the Belmont Lode, the Anglo-Saxon Lode, and from the Stephenson Baker Mines. The richest of these silver-bearing veins were near Silver Plume and Georgetown. *William Culp Darrah Stereo Collection*

When trails were too rough for wagons or rails, ore was pulled on these little burro carts. *Colorado State Historical Society Library*

at bank counters. (Their extreme weight contributed to their not being stolen.)

The narrow-gauge Colorado Central Railroad reached Georgetown in 1877, and the Georgetown Loop, constructed in 1884, extended the service to Silver Plume. Its passenger trains carried sightseers, picnickers, and vacationers to the scenic mountainous area as late as 1939.

In 1894 silver-lead mining reached its peak and began to decline. World Wars I and II created a new

An 1877 drawing of silver mining in Colorado. The upper left-hand drawing is titled, "Foreman Inspecting After a Shot"; the upper right-hand is "Cornish Boys Driving Tunnel"; the center drawing is called "View of a District"; the lower left-hand drawing is "Exploring Old Workings"; and the lower right-hand drawing, "Cleaning Out After a Tap." *New York Public Library*

interest in the lead and zinc in the old silver mines, and some were reopened and actively worked. The Georgetown–Silver Plume Mining District today is a national historic landmark. Under a Union Pacific Foundation grant, the State Historical Society and the Highway Department have preserved the site. Various methods of ore recovery, use of sluices, arrastras, and stamp mills are demonstrated at the original locations, and work is being done at the nearby Lebanon Tunnel, one of the oldest mining tunnels in Colorado.

GOLD IN LEADVILLE

Almost in the shadow of Mount Massive, Colorado's second highest peak (elevation 14,418 feet), lies Leadville, in California Gulch. Leadville is known today for lead and zinc, but the Leadville story began in April, 1860, when gold seekers, panning around the Mosquito Range base, stumbled into California Gulch and found rich mantles of gold in the surface dirt. Gold is an impossible secret; in less than a month, Horace Tabor (of Denver's Grand Opera House fame) and his wife Augusta were among the first to arrive, and would become Colorado's richest couple. They settled in the Gulch with 10,000 other miners who crowded into its seven-mile length. Here a string of habitations—log cabins, tents, and wagon homes—dotted a narrow stretch later known as Oro City.

Almost every California Gulch claim proved profitable; more than $2 million in gold was removed that first summer. Tabor's share was only about $5,000. But there was some compensation in Augusta Tabor's looming as a popular town figure. She ran a boardinghouse and laundry, and later was appointed postmistress.

Oro City was a rough mining town, but few

167

The newly discovered mines in the Rocky Mountains. Prospectors climb the perilous and difficult corduroy road 13,000 feet above sea level into Leadville. Wood engraving in *Leslie's,* May 24, 1879. *Library of Congress*

Colorado, a new El Dorado. Interior of a Leadville "dance house" on State Street. Wood engraving in *Leslie's,* May 17, 1879. *Library of Congress*

168

claim jumpers, robbers, or murderers would be comfortable there. Of course the inevitable gambling dens, sporting houses, saloons, and dance halls were common, at least for two years, until the gold ran out.

Not far from Oro City, other prospectors, from Central City, had been pushing westward into the South Park region, near Leadville, where they discovered gold along a small stream. The news spread, and the stream was named Tarryall Creek because everybody staked claims and tarried and panned

Prospectors crossing the peaks among the mountains, 10,000 feet above the sea, en route to Leadville. Wood engraving in *Leslie's,* May 24, 1879. *Library of Congress*

Just before the epidemic, on July 26, 1860, along Tarryall Creek, a little town had been established bearing the name "Hamilton Post Office." By 1861 its population had grown to 5,000, served by stores and saloons that catered to the rich placer working community on Tarryall Creek about a mile above the town. But Hamilton died in 1875 when Como was built alongside the new railroad running from Denver to Leadville. Hamilton, near Fairplay, is now extinct. In 1841 this ranch house was all that remained of the town that once had a population of 5,000, including miners, storekeepers, prostitutes, and a saloonkeeper. In 1941 the Cooley Gravel Company tested the area for coal, and the tent seen at the right background contained their equipment and an air furnace. Later, the company wrecked the ranch house, the bunkhouse, and the barns, recovering more than $1 per cubic yard in gold. *Cooley Gravel Company*

gold. The ground was soon completely staked, and unwelcome newcomers continued westward to the North Branch of the South Platt River. Here they found new placer gold where everybody could expect "fair play" in staking a claim, and the town of Fairplay was born.

By the early 1860s, Fairplay's mining camps experienced a smallpox epidemic. Nurses were unheard of, but one of the real Florence Nightingales, from the neighboring town of Alma, was a dancehall girl known only as Silver Heels. (It seemed her dancing slippers, or her heels, were made of silver.) She nursed the miners day and night. After the epidemic she simply vanished. The miners remembered her when they named a high mountain lying between Tarryall Creek and the North Branch of the South Platt River. They called it Silver Heels Mountain.

While Hamilton had been growing, in 1861 Oro City celebrated a new strike on the south side of the Gulch, the Printer Boy Mine, and a new group of boomers invaded an area three miles from town. And the Tabors, who had had their fling with mining, opened a store. One day August Rische and

James Joseph Brown, who made a small fortune in the Leadville district. "Leadville Johnny" had a roving eye, and was sued for alienation of affection in 1903 and again for $100,000 in 1919. From a photo by the Post Studio, Denver, Colorado. *Colorado State Historical Society Library*

Horace Austin Warner Tabor, who became one of Colorado's richest mining magnates but died penniless. *Colorado State Historical Society Library*

Augusta L. Tabor, the first Mrs. H. A. W. Tabor, from a photo by Curtis and Ross, Lewiston, Maine. *Colorado State Historical Society Library*

A "Rogers" sketch from *Harper's New Monthly Magazine* in 1879 describes this scene as depicting an Eastern "capitalist" who had dismounted from a stagecoach, and, "starting to walk to the hotel, found himself followed by a gradually lengthening single file of jocular residents, all keeping step with him."

Baby Doe Tabor (Elizabeth Bonduel McCourt Tabor), the second Mrs. H. A. W. Tabor and the central figure in the Tabor triangle. *Colorado State Historical Society Library*

George Hook persuaded Tabor to grubstake them for supplies, worth under $20, which they repeated twice more, for a total investment of about $50 against a one-third interest in any discoveries. On their first strike, May 1, 1878, they were able to bring out a wagonload of ore, but it was silver, not gold, so rich that the load assayed at $200.

TABOR STRIKES IT RICH

They named the mine Little Pittsburgh, which in two months was producing nearly $50,000 monthly. Five months after the discovery, Hook sold his third for $98,000; in seven months Rische got over a quarter of a million dollars for his; and short of a year, Tabor exchanged his share for a million dollars.

In the meantime, in July, 1877, Harvey Doe and his bride, the former Elizabeth McCourt, had arrived in Central City from Oshkosh, Wisconsin. Harvey's father owned a parcel of mines there and had promised to give him his half interest in the Fourth of July Mine. While perpetually pushing her inefficient husband to make a success of the mining business, Lizzie McCourt Doe made herself popular as a coquette, known as Baby Doe to the miners with whom she flirted. She eventually left her husband believing he would never get rich, and preferring her loose contacts with the miners. She moved to Leadville where, though she had little money, her coquettish demeanor caught Horace Tabor's eye. He staked her to $5,000 to pay her debts and furnished a place for her in Leadville. His wife, Augusta, re-

sided in Denver. Tabor by now had bought the Matchless Mine, on Fryer Hill, for about $120,000, and an interest in a Denver bank, an iron mine on Breece Hill, a gold interest in the San Juan Mountains, and an interest in Aspen silver mines, and had made other purchases that contributed to his great wealth.

He became Lieutenant Governor of Colorado, and divorced his ambitious New England wife. Meanwhile, Baby Doe, with the Tabor assets behind her, became a Leadville citizen of some affluence, but she remained unaccepted by polite local society. In 1883 she and Tabor were married in Washington, D.C. where he was serving as a United States senator, filling an unexpired term. The wedding was attended by President Arthur. By 1889 Baby Doe had given birth to five children (two were stillborn and one died within hours).

Four years later, the Tabors were broke, ruined by the silver panic when the United States went on the gold standard. The Eclipse Mine, a Tabor gold holding, proved worthless, and the Matchless Mine shut. However, because Tabor had always believed that silver would come back, he urged Baby Doe never to let the Matchless Mine go, as it would surely make her rich again. Because of his former prominence, Tabor was appointed postmaster of Denver. He died in 1899 from an appendicitis attack, which provided Denver with the largest funeral in its history. Baby Doe returned to a rooming house

Baby Doe Tabor's cabin at the Matchless Mine, where she died in 1935. *Arthur Lake's Library, Colorado School of Mines*

The Robert E. Lee Mine in Leadville, one of the state's greatest producers. The mine, on Fryer Hill, produced nearly $120,000 in a 17-hour stretch of mining in 1880. It was the Matchless Mine's biggest rival. Other mines, Little Chief, Chrysolite, Morning and Evening stars, were equally successful. Despite the poor start, even 1880s production reached $15 million. The Leadville district (Lake County) was topped only in 1892, by Aspen (Pitkin County). But Cripple Creek would surpass them all when the government went on the gold standard. *William Culp Darrah Stereo Collection*

in Leadville, living off the remnants of the jewelry she had secreted in a Denver safe-deposit vault. Her older daughter had gone to live in Chicago. Her younger daughter eventually moved to Chicago also, on the pretext of joining a convent, but she was later found murdered in a cheap rooming house there.

Meanwhile the Matchless Mine was being foreclosed by the mortgagee, but J. K. Mullen, a friend of Baby Doe, bailed her out with $14,000. The mine was temporarily saved, but it was a wasted effort as it slowly filled with water. Baby Doe despaired and moved from Leadville to a cabin at the mine, living in rags and on the charity of friends for many years, always hoping that some day the Matchless would recoup her fortune. She was found dead, frozen on her cabin floor, on March 7, 1935, and was buried

California Gulch showing the Moyer, Sellers, and other mines around 1875. *Colorado Division of State Archives and Public Records*

Tabor's Matchless Mine in 1929, six years before Baby Doe Tabor's death. *Colorado State Historical Society Library*

in Denver next to her husband, thirty-six years after his death.

The Matchless Mine today is in operational condition and, if silver prices warrant, may again go into production, realizing Tabor's prediction.

THE UNSINKABLE MOLLY BROWN

Those who saw the musical comedy or the movie version of *The Unsinkable Molly Brown* know the story of Maggie Brown who chose to be called Molly. She was born Margaret Tobin, the daughter of an Irish laborer, in Hannibal, Missouri. Maggie had visions of wealth and social prominence. While her boyfriend Daniel sold newspapers, Maggie was a waitress who learned about gold and silver waiting on Mark Twain. She persuaded Daniel to go to Leadville, and she soon followed him. She found work as a waitress in a boardinghouse, where she met James J. Brown, the manager of the Louisville Mine. She dropped Daniel to marry Brown. Brown became superintendent of the Little Jonny Mine, which he managed so successfully—finding and developing gold after the silver panic of 1893—that the owners gave him a one-eighth interest.

Molly was a social climber and although Jim never acquired anything like Horace Tabor's fortune, he had made successful investments. They moved to Denver where Molly decided to crash the social set. She hired tutors to teach her proper English, singing, and etiquette, and she traveled extensively. Despite affluence and self-improvement, no

Mrs. James Joseph Brown who became the famous "Unsinkable Molly Brown." *Colorado State Historical Society Library*

one in Leadville or Denver would accept her social invitations. It took the sinking of the *Titanic* and Molly's subsequent heroic feats and unselfish efforts to finally open the door to Denver society on her return as a heroine, thereafter known as "The Unsinkable Molly Brown." She proved to be generous and somewhat profligate, giving away large sums of money, and even offered to redeem the mortgage on the Matchless Mine for Baby Doe Tabor. But Mrs. Brown was almost broke. She and Jim had been divorced many years before, and her diminished fortune made it impossible to fulfill her extensive promises of charity. The Unsinkable Molly Brown

Lithograph of Leadville, Lake County, Colorado, 1879, by Ramsey, Millet and Hudson. About 6,000 prospectors scrambled to stake claims around Little Pittsburgh, which was nicknamed "Cloud City" because

of its 10,000-foot elevation. Later, Leadville became its new official name, and Tabor its mayor. *Library of Congress*

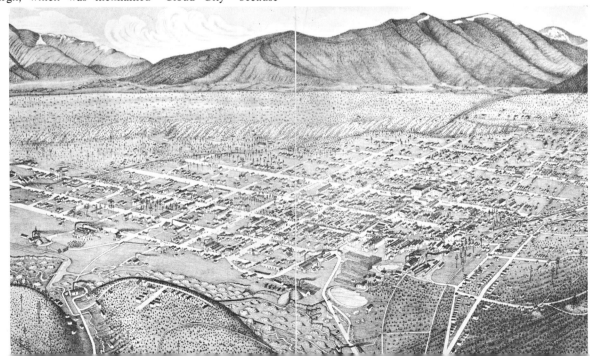

died in New York City on October 25, 1932, at the age of sixty-five. Caroline Bancroft called her "the woman with a heart as big as a ham, a vigorous relic of Leadville's bonanza days."

While the events of Baby Doe Tabor and Unsinkable Molly Brown were taking place, Leadville continued to boom. In 1878 and 1879, following the Little Pittsburgh strike, the city had grown so fast that it developed an "urban-renewal" complex; authorities ordered shanties to be torn down within ten days; streets were relaid; a new hotel was built; and other improvements were made, all creating a second boom—a land boom for lots.

It was a lawless town. In 1879, thefts, holdups, and burglaries were common. Anyone walking the streets at night carried a pistol in his hand for protection. A vigilante organization was formed and quickly hanged a bandit and a murderer, and drove out many undesirables. Though it stopped the robberies and murders, it did not close the gambling houses, saloons, and dance halls that remained open seven days a week; nor did it stop horse racing at a track near Leadville; and the red-light district remained in full operation, day and night. Variety shows were popular at the bars, and arenas were built for athletic events, including wrestling and boxing.

The Arkansas Valley Smelter. The burgeoning mines required additional smelting capacities, and by 1880 nearly twenty such smelters were in operation. That year the Chrysolite Mine, partially owned by Tabor and Marshall Field (of Chicago fame), experienced a labor strike, Leadville's first. It spread to every mine in Colorado, becoming so critical as to require martial law to force the miners' return. It was also the year of the crash for Leadville mining stocks. News had leaked out that the Little Pittsburgh Mine was depleted and that the Chrysolite Mine was overproduced. Some stocks dropped 80 percent. *Colorado Division of State Archives and Public Records*

Colorado. Scenes in the new mining town of Leadville. Miners enjoying a sawdust sleep in a billiard saloon at

"Two Bits" a night. Wood engraving in *Leslie's*, June 7, 1879. *Library of Congress*

A Leadville miner's home, 1875.

The discovery of lead and zinc in 1910 spared Leadville from becoming a ghost town. The Penrose, Mikado, and Wolftone (above) mines remained prosperous until after World War I. Meanwhile molybdenum had been discovered twelve miles away, at Climax. World War II revived the lead-zinc mines up to the 1950s, but by then Climax was the major mining attraction. *Colorado Division of State Archives and Public Records*

The old Healy House, a museum of the silver-mining epoch of the 1880s and the Gay Nineties. It was built in 1878 by August R. Meyer, the founder of the first sampling works in Leadville, and after changing hands several times was bought by Daniel Healy. The museum houses relics of the gold-rush and silver-mining days, and consists of thirteen rooms, all completely furnished with items of the period. The small building on the right is the Dexter Cabin, at one time the "most exclusive private poker club" in Leadville. It was built in 1879 by James V. Dexter, a local mining magnate who became a millionaire. The cabin looks like an ordinary mountain cabin, but the interior is fashioned of the finest materials of the day and is covered with rare wall coverings stamped from hand-cut wood blocks; it has window blinds, Victorian furniture, a Victorian kitchen, and a zinc-lined bathtub. The Healy House and the Dexter Cabin are maintained by the State Historical Society of Colorado and are open to the public, free during the summer. Leadville has preserved among other structures the Dexter Cabin, the Augusta Tabor House, and the Tabor Opera House, and provides a Matchless Mine museum and tours to the mines. *Colorado Department of Public Relations*

OTHER SIGNIFICANT HISTORICAL EVENTS

The Forty-Niners Move On

California

1861: Copperopolis: Lasted six years as a principal copper-producing town. Some of the mines were the Union Copper, Keystone, and Empire. All were abandoned in 1872.

The Fabulous Comstock

More has been written about the Comstock Lode than of any single American mining area. Its history was first recorded in detail by William Wright, writing under the nom de plume of Dan De Quille, in his fantastic *History of the Big Bonanza,* published in 1877. But the flood of material that followed only confused portions of the true history of this fabulous mining area.

It is generally thought that the Comstock Lode is the name of a mine rather than an area in Nevada's Washoe* district that once boasted over sixty major, active, producing mines and at least 400 questionable ones. Nor was the Comstock Lode discovered by H. T. P. Comstock for whom it is named. Often the Comstock Lode is mistaken for a gold-mining project when in fact it was primarily silver that made it famous, notwithstanding the large amounts of gold discovered in the early days. To this day no one knows the exact total value of precious and base metals removed from the lode since 1859 —in all probability less than half a billion dollars. Grant H. Smith's *History of the Comstock Lode, 1850 to 1920* (published by the Nevada State Bureau of Mines and the Mackay School of Mines) accounts for, including production from tailings, about $320 million taken from the Comstock Lode from 1859 to January 1, 1882, approximately 55 percent silver, 45 percent gold.

Misconceptions abound even as to its discovery, often incorrectly credited to the Grosch brothers (sometimes spelled Grosh) who, about two years before the main lode was discovered, found only ore channels.

DISCOVERY

We have to go back to May, 1850. William Prouse, traveling on a wagon train from Salt Lake City, stopped on the banks of the Carson River and panned a few small "colors." Prouse and his party continued, but deep snows in the Sierras delayed them at Carson Valley. Therefore, two men, John Orr and Nick Kelly, returned to Prouse's find. Though panning all the way to the American Fork River, they developed no important amounts of gold

H. T. P. Comstock, who bragged so much that his name remains forever on the Comstock Lode. He was not one of the original discoverers. *From De Quille's* History of the Big Bonanza, *1877*

from their diggings. But in a fit of euphoria, one small nugget prompted them to name the gulch Gold Canyon.

No matter the amount of gold found, exaggerated rumors always brought new hopefuls. Gold Canyon was no exception. For the next four or five years, during some part of the year, about 100 men could be found panning in the canyon. Allen and Hosea Grosch were among them. As the stream became washed out and earnings dropped from about $5 to $2 a day, panning ceased. According to Grant H. Smith, only about $600,000 or less was produced in nine years, and therefore most miners moved to newly discovered placer deposits near Mono Lake.

BLUE STUFF

Many Gold Canyon miners had found that the gravel in their pans was mixed with a heavy bluish sand, which they called "blue stuff." It clogged their rockers and was discarded as a nuisance. It would cause a maelstrom. James Finney (or Fennimore), better known as "Old Virginny" because of his na-

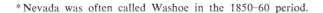

*Nevada was often called Washoe in the 1850–60 period.

tive state, found some placer ground in 1857 near the head of Six Mile Canyon, off Gold Canyon, just below the future lode center, Virginia City. Meanwhile, two others, Peter O'Riley and Patrick McLaughlin, working a little higher up the canyon, dug into a layer of black sand about four feet below the surface. Although they did not know it, this was rich, oxidized silver ore, a concentrate lying on top of the hidden Ophir bonanza, the basis of the rush to the Comstock Lode. Meanwhile, the Grosch brothers, who were probably the first, except for some Mexican peons, to realize that the "blue stuff" was silver, were working along the veins of what is now Silver City. They decided to keep the information secret. But misfortune dogged their luck. Hosea hit his foot with a pick, causing an infection that resulted in his death a short time later. After Hosea's death, Allen was returning to California for additional operating money when he and a companion, crossing the Sierras, were trapped by storms and cold. They were rescued by California deer hunters, but Allen did not survive the experience. He died December 19, 1856, a little over three months after his brother. What the Grosches had found was the Silver City branch of the Comstock Lode, a worthwhile discovery but not connected with Finney's main lode discoveries that followed later.

Three years after Allen's death, on January 8, 1859, Finney, Alec Henderson, Jack Yount, and John Bishop located new claims along the right-hand fork of upper Gold Canyon. They called the new placer diggings Gold Hill. The location notices, which were extremely crude and would be the basis for a great deal of litigation later, were poorly identified. The record books, which contained many erasures and mutilations, were kept by a blacksmith and stored in a saloon.

The Washoe district at this time employed about 100 miners. Most of those who came to look at Gold Hill thought little of its prospects, preferring to work their placer deposits in the canyon three

An artist's conception of Gold Hill as it appeared in *Harper's Magazine* in December, 1860. Note that the most prominent feature of the drawing is the Indication Saloon, originally probably the Vindication Saloon. *New York Public Library Picture Collection*

miles below. However, a few days after the January 8 discovery, L. S. Bowers, Joseph Plato, Henry Comstock, James Rogers, and William Knight staked an adjoining claim. As the miners put the dirt through the rockers, they noticed that the deeper they dug the richer was the ore. At about ten feet they found a rich reddish quartz deposit. They called it Old Red Ledge and though it contained little silver, this was truly the Comstock Lode. Silver was not found in quantity until the main ore bodies were struck later.

Many who scoffed at the property before now rushed to the hill to stake new claims, including both the north and south sides. And only a short time ago, Old Virginny and his friends thought they were finished. Had they dug three feet deeper they would have found the same black sand uncovered by O'Riley and McLaughlin the following June. However, when Old Virginny and his pals in desperation decided to test the sand they found in the water spring, they were astonished to find the bottom of the rockers covered with gold!

COMSTOCK CLAIMS A STAKE

That evening Henry T. P. Comstock came by and after seeing the gold he berated his neighbors for removing gold from land he said he had already staked as a ranch. He also claimed that he and his partner, Emanuel Penrod, owned the spring. Actually it is doubtful that Comstock had staked any claims, but O'Riley and McLaughlin did agree to take in Comstock and Penrod as partners, and Com-

Gold Hill looking north.

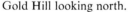

De Quille titled this drawing "Comstock Discovering Silver." On the extreme right is Emanuel Penrod, and holding the horse is Henry T. P. Comstock. The two men with the mining tools are Peter O'Riley and Patrick McLaughlin, the true discoverers of the Ophir. Com-stock and his friend Penrod managed to secure a half-interest in the Ophir Mine when Comstock falsely claimed that he had staked the property as pastureland, resulting in the fourfold partnership. *From De Quille's* History of the Big Bonanza, *1877*

The Comstock Lead at Washoe, 1860. Timbering supports the rock at the entrance. *New York Public Library Picture Collection*

The Ophir Works, the first lode mine of the Comstock Lode. It was mined beginning in 1859, and yielded over $10 million in bullion. It later became part of the Consolidated Virginia group. *Nevada Historical Society*

stock bought Old Virginny's one-tenth interest in the spring for $40 and an old, blind horse. Starting work, the men dug a trench, annoyed at the blue sand that clogged their rockers, not knowing, of course, that it was silver sulfide.

In June, 1859, a miners' code had been drawn up. It prohibited gambling games; set a death penalty for murder; whipping or banishment for robbery; a fine or banishment for assault or battery; and, more important, set placer claims at fifty feet per man and, along the vein, quartz claims at 300 feet per man, and an additional 300 feet for the discoverer. This created a problem for the men. O'Riley and McLaughlin wanted to locate the ground as placer claims, but Penrod insisted that they were quartz veins. They measured 1,500 feet off with a rope, staked each end, and left it at that. That was all they

did to locate the boundaries. This then was the Ophir (named after the fabulous gold center of King Solomon's lost mines), whose location was not even recorded. Penrod claimed a 100-foot strip separate from the Ophir claim and about 200 feet from its south end. He took this plot as a reward for himself and Comstock for locating the ground as a quartz claim as well as for the use of his spring. This became the Mexican Mine. Unfortunately, none of them knew what had been discovered; for two arras-tras and two horses worth about $75 each, they sold a one-third interest in the Ophir.

On June 27 some of the "blue stuff" was assayed at Grass Valley, California. The assayer, B. A. Harrison, established its value at $840 a ton and gave a sample to Judge James Walsh, a prominent miner and mill owner in town, who again had it

177

Local redskins were Digger Indians, a name applied indiscriminately to many tribes throughout the West, and derived from the fact that they dug roots for food, not gold. Digger Indians resented intrusion into their territory by miners, especially by the Chinese, from whom they sometimes collected taxes! *New York Public Library Picture Collection*

analyzed. The second assay proved out to $3,876 a ton—75 percent silver, 25 percent gold. Walsh decided to go to Washoe himself, where he and his partner, Joseph Woodworth, bought Comstock's one-sixth interest in the Ophir, a half interest in the California, and some other Comstock claims for $11,000. They purchased Penrod's one-sixth of the Ophir for $5,500, which gave them a one-third interest in the mine. O'Riley held out the longest, getting about $40,000 for his one-sixth interest from J. O. Earl of San Francisco. George Hearst began the Hearst fortune by buying McLaughlin's one-sixth for $3,000. Penrod sold his half of the Mexican Mine to Gabriel Maldonado, a Mexican, for $3,000, and Comstock received $5,500 for his half interest from Francis J. Hughes. The story went the rounds that Comstock sold his interest in the Mexican Mine for two jackasses, which, based upon what the mines were to produce later, made the jackasses worth about a half million dollars each. With the advent of

Judge Walsh's purchases, the first Washoe gold rush began.

Dan De Quille, who knew Comstock well (he said Comstock was not quite right mentally), wrote that Comstock "made himself so conspicuous on every occasion that he soon came to be considered not only the discoverer but also the father of the lode," which is how "Old Pancake" Comstock's name became attached to the lode despite the fact that he was neither a discoverer at Gold Hill nor of the Ophir.

Probably the saddest and most beloved character was Old (Finney) Virginny, who received the least of any of the "discoverers." It was James Finney who had located the first quartz claim on the Comstock, who had found the placers below the Ophir in 1857, and who had led the discoverers in 1859 up the canyon to locate the placers on Little Gold Hill. He was killed falling from a horse on June 20, 1861.

At some placers in the Washoe, an unusual type of sluice, called a "blanket" sluice, was employed. This was simply a series of sluices side by side, with a single outlet. *From De Quille's* History of the Big Bonanza, *1877*

THE SILVER KINGS EMERGE

Immediately after the Comstock blue stuff—silver-bearing sulfide—became public knowledge, the rush was on to get the former pariah out of the ground. The primitive method, the first and easiest, was to expose as much of the ore body as possible by digging wide trenches. For the deeper ore, to retrieve the sulfides, "wells" were dug—simple round holes big enough for a winch and bucket to remove the ore. Wells were depleted and abandoned for new ones, and in a brief time a rash of empty well holes decorated the countryside. The system hit the lode, but did not follow it. A new method was needed. The Ophir demonstrated the old system's shortcomings. Its ore body was only ten to twelve feet wide at the fifty-foot level, but in 1860, after six months of mining, it had increased to forty or fifty feet wide in places.

In a few years, activity had moved so rapidly that *The Alta California,* a contemporary leading San Francisco newspaper, was reporting that San Francisco showed more interest in Washoe silver mines than in California's gold mines, and that the citizens owned ten times more silver stock than gold. The paper claimed everyone was carrying stock certificates in his pockets. Bankers, merchants, professional men, preachers, craftsmen, shopkeepers, laborers, and just about everyone owned silver-mine shares. Within three years, 2,000 mining companies were incorporated, most mere stock schemes to bilk the public.

Gold Hill in 1868, a rare photo of the site of the original Comstock Lode discovery and later part of Virginia City. Most of the working mines were opened between 1860 and 1863, including the Ophir, Mexican, Gould and Curry, Savage, Chollar-Potosi, Little Gold Hill (twenty mines), Imperial, Yellow Jacket, Belcher, Overman, Utah, Silver Hill, and many others. Comstock's production back in 1859 was a meager $250,000, about $1 million in 1860, $2½ million in 1861, $6 million in 1862, $12,400,000 in 1863, the year the Central Pacific Railway started railroad construction from Sacramento to Virginia City. Though none could approach the production or the profits of the new California or the Consolidated Virginia mines that were still to be developed in the 1870s, of the early mines the Belcher proved the most productive. *University of Oklahoma Library, Division of Manuscripts*

The Gould and Curry patio from A. J. Phillip's *Mining and Metallurgy of Gold and Silver,* 1867. This is believed to be the only patio picture extant. The "patio" process, although not too successful, was developed to ease the problem of grinding or breaking the ore and separating it from the metal. The use of arrastras to grind ore into pulp was a slow process suitable for smaller operations only, so Virginia City tried the "patio" process originally developed in Mexico. This consisted of combining several arrastras on a patio for decomposing the silver sulfides, which allowed for quicker, easier amalgamation. Mixed with quicksilver, salt, and sulfate of copper, pulp from the arrastras was spread over the patio, in the sun, and occasionally turned over by hand shovels. Or, more often, it was placed in the round patio enclosure and trampled by horses, burros, or mules. Thus were the sulfides reduced to chlorides, then to a metallic form that would unite with the quicksilver to form an amalgam. However, pulp conversion was a long process requiring from four to six weeks. *Nevada Historical Society*

The Utah Mine, discovered in 1859, was one of the first in the Comstock District. Despite its early discovery, it never produced any important quantities of ore. *Nevada Historical Society*

Two years of further experimentation with the patio process refined the method to what became the "Washoe process." This consisted of a mechanized combination of arrastra with the patio process, except that instead of relying upon the sun's heat to amalgamate silver and gold, taking weeks, steam-heated pans would speed amalgamation to under six hours. Washoe-process mills, with stamps, replacing arrastras, and steam-heated pans, settling pans, and agitators, were hurriedly built to serve most of the mines. This sketch is of a typical quartz mill and amalgamating room in the Comstock Lode. The ore is brought in at the left and put into the stamps, which crush the ore into a fine powder. As the water and ore become finely powdered, they pass through screens into a sluice or trough that runs to the settling tanks. The ore is shoveled into the amalgamating pans, each holding about 3,000 pounds of pulp. This pulp is then heated and ground for 2½ hours, at which time 300 pounds of quicksilver are put into each pan, which runs for another 2½ hours. Salt and copper sulfate are also added. This material is then run into strainers with the silver amalgamated with the quicksilver. *From De Quille's* History of the Big Bonanza, *1877*

Square setting. Increasing lode mining demanded new methods of economically mining and removing the precious metal. One new technique that revolutionized the mining industry derived from a problem at the Ophir Mine, which in 1860 had reached a depth of 180 feet. At that point the ore body was about 45 feet wide, making it impossible for crosswise timbers to support it. Ordinarily the method had been to erect posts and caps as supporting columns, but it was impossible to secure posts of sufficient length. Nor would they be able to support the great weight and pressure. Philip Deidesheimer, an experienced German miner working in California, was employed to solve the difficulty. After studying the Ophir for several weeks, he devised a timbering plan of "square sets"—framed timbers joined together in the shape of cribs four to six feet in size and piled up to a desired height. Besides providing support, the cribs could be filled in with mining waste, thus reinforcing the supports reaching to the roof of the mine. The square-set system was profitably used throughout the Comstock Lode, and some mines still use it today. *Nevada Historical Society*

Famous Comstock Lode mines during the 1860s. *From De Quille's* History of the Big Bonanza, *1877*

De Quille's *History of the Big Bonanza* contains this picture of the first quartz mill in Nevada, but it is not identified. It is possibly the Gould and Curry Mill, built in 1861, the big year for mill building to process the increasing flow of ore. By 1862 more than 25 mills were pounding and grinding ore, and their 750 stamps could easily have processed twice the amount being mined. In 1862 the Gould and Curry Mine had encountered the largest and richest body of ore thus far found in the Comstock. The Ophir continued to follow the lead of its bonanza, and the Savage extended its workings into a new vein. The 1863 boom had brought more than 25,000 people to Nevada, especially the Washoe District, and Virginia City and Gold Hill soon merged. Over 400 mining companies were operating or selling stock for speculation, but by 1865 only the Ophir, Gould and Curry, and Savage were paying dividends. Most of the others were levying assessments either for increasing or in the hope of starting production. Of course, the Little Gold Hill mines were prosperous, but these were privately held enterprises, until the first, the Empire and the Imperial mines, sold stock, which paid dividends. In the meantime, beginning in 1862, all the new developments created a spectacular rise in mining stocks and led to the formation on September 11, 1862, of the San Francisco Stock Exchange, the first United States Mining Exchange, which soon thrived.

In 1865 these teams of oxen, horses, and mules hauled the ore to the mills near Washoe. *New York Public Library Picture Collection*

The Eureka Mill in the late 1860s. *From De Quille's* History of the Big Bonanza, *1877*

Hoisting cages and cars in the mines of the Comstock Lode. These lowered miners and removed ores from depths of over 1,000 feet. In the early Comstock mines, if a cable broke, there was no possibility of escape. Later, safety devices were devised to prevent the cars from crashing to the bottom. *From De Quille's* History of the Big Bonanza, *1877*

Waste rock, or tailings, dumped all over the Washoe. About $20 million was wasted in the Comstock District before 1866, by which time it had become practical to salvage the tailings. *From De Quille's* History of the Big Bonanza, *1877*

A diagram showing the depth of mines from De Quille's *History of the Big Bonanza.* The small building with the steeple in the lower right-hand corner is a scale drawing of Trinity Church in New York City. Poor ventilation hampered the mines. Air temperatures at the depths often reached 130 degrees. Some mines suffered from lack of pure air, though the contained gases caused most of the deaths in the Comstock. Not until blowers were introduced in 1865 were there any improvements beyond drilling a few ventilation tunnels. Many mines were relieved of the ventilation problem by the development of compressed air drills and blowers a decade later.

Even the legitimate mines had their downs. In 1863 the Gould and Curry began to play out; by 1866 no silver was left. The Ophir, too, had shown signs of failing, at the 300-foot level; 1863 was its last big year. Two years later the Ophir invoked a long series of assessments. To add to their problems, most mines encountered water as they dug deeper. Cornish pumps were introduced in an attempt to keep them dry, or at least workable. As with others, too, both the Sides and the White & Murphy (later joined to the Consolidated Virginia Company) were drained by tunnels, these two by the 2,800-foot Latrobe Tunnel. And the Little Gold Hill mines were tapped by tunnel.

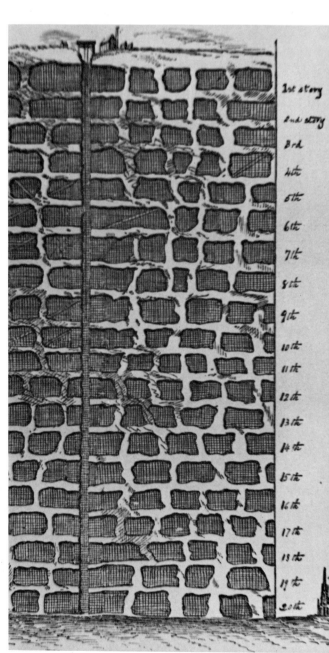

SUTRO'S TUNNEL

The desirability of constructing a tunnel to drain and explore the entire Comstock Lode was the subject of lengthy discussion in 1864. The idea was to build a tunnel from Eagle Valley into Mt. Davidson to hit the Comstock Lode at a depth of 1,650 feet, draining all shafts and tunnels in the lode. The tunnel would also provide ventilation and a means of escape in case of disaster.

At this point, Adolph Heinrich Joseph Sutro, an ancestor of the Wall Street brokerage family, entered the picture. Sutro, who had come to the Comstock in 1860, has been described by many adjectives—quick, shifty, clever, energetic, vain, aggressive, egotistical, offensive, domineering, and shrewd, among others. Disliked or not, he championed the idea for the tunnel, and in February, 1865, secured an exclusive fifty-year franchise from the Nevada Legislature to construct and operate it. He contracted with twenty-three mining companies to pay his company—The Tunnel Company—a royalty of $2 for every ton of ore extracted once the tunnel was successfully draining their operations. The contract included the right to transport men and supplies through the tunnel at stated fees.

With the Comstock in the middle of a depression, Sutro had to secure a necessary $3 million for construction, and he turned East for the money. In the meantime, on July 25, 1866, the United States Congress passed the Sutro Tunnel Act, granting Sutro's company the right to construct the tunnel, and giving Sutro exclusive ownership of all lodes and ledges through which the tunnel passed for a distance of 2,000 feet on each side for a length of seven miles. The act excluded the Comstock Lode, which was intersected about four miles from the entrance.

A year later, Sutro had managed to secure about $600,000 from the local mining companies, but the balance was not forthcoming from the East. He appealed to Congress for funds to complete construction; two bills were put through, both defeated. Two years passed and $50,000 came in, this time from the miner's union inspired by a fire in the Yellow Jacket Mine that killed thirty-seven miners; some

Women and children crowding the Yellowjacket mine area for news of their loved ones. The fire occurred on April 7, 1869, at seven o'clock in the morning, at the 800-foot level. All attempts to rescue the men failed, and the fumes and smoke seeped through the Crown Point and Kentuck shafts. Although the fire was under control by May 18, the fire burned in portions of the mine for over a year. *From De Quille's* History of the Big Bonanza, *1877*

Adolph Sutro (seated) and his party at the Sutro Tunnel. *Mackay School of Mines, University of Nevada*

Artist's view of Sutro Tunnel under construction, finished eleven years later at a cost of $3,500,000. The dream of a German immigrant named Adolph Sutro, who spent thirteen years trying to get government and private support for his project, the tunnel was designed to drain the water from the deep shafts of the Comstock Lode by drawing it laterally from the 1,750-foot level to empty into the adjacent valley below. This was one of the truly remarkable feats of early American mining. *Mackay School of Mines, University of Nevada*

reports cited forty-nine deaths. Sutro had capitalized on the fire, claiming that his tunnel would have spared the men. Construction finally started in October of that year; at the end of 1870 only 1,700 feet had been dug, and it looked as though the project would be abandoned. However, a new discovery, the Crown Point bonanza, saved the project.

Following a further unsuccessful attempt to secure a federal loan, Sutro, in 1871, was able to obtain $650,000 in England by the sale there of 200,000 shares of tunnel stock, plus European subscriptions for $800,000. Sutro's plan included constructing mills at the tunnel's mouth once it was

Inside the Sutro Tunnel, Virginia City. Passenger car for visitors at left. *Mackay School of Mines, University of Nevada*

completed. That way all the ore could be efficiently expedited from tunnel to mill. But fearing the ore bodies might give out, he rushed construction. He again ran out of money and in 1873 returned to London. With a new bond issue of $7.5 million, he resumed work on the tunnel.

In the interim, the Scotch bankers who were to market the $7.5 million withdrew, leaving the McCalmont Brothers and Co., who had secured the original $650,000 and were therefore stockholders, to underwrite a loan at 12 percent interest. That was in 1877. In 1878 the tunnel connected with the Savage Mine; by September, it reached the main shaft, for a grand total length of 20,498 feet.

On completion of the tunnel, the mining companies reneged on the $2 royalty on the claim that the contract had been broken years before. They reached a new agreement in 1879. The mines would pay a royalty of $1 a ton on ore that did not exceed $40 a ton in value and $2 a ton on ore in excess of $40 a ton. But most of the ore bodies by now were depleted.

New ore was discovered occasionally, and although the tunnel automatically drained the Gold Hill mines for fifty years, the operation, as fantastic as it was, failed financially. Sutro resigned, but he had already sold most of his stock and had become a millionaire. The property was foreclosed and sold in 1889. McCalmont recovered about $1 million, all they ever realized on their investment. Sutro returned to San Francisco for other ventures; he was elected mayor in 1894, and he died four years later.

THE PANIC OF 1865

From the time they were first discovered, William C. Ralston, a San Francisco banker, had been interested in the Comstock mines. He was made treasurer of the Ophir and the Gould and Curry in 1860, and ultimately became treasurer of nearly all the leading mines in the Washoe district. In June, 1864, with D. O. Mills as its first president, he organized the Bank of California. Within a month, a branch was opened in Virginia City, and William Sharon became its manager. Sharon freely loaned money for mills and other construction, but at the rate of 2 percent a month, considerably less than the 5 percent charged by others. The market had been falling all year and a depression soon became the panic of 1865, forcing the bank to foreclose on many mills and mining properties. With the revival of activities in 1866, the bank found itself in the mining business. In 1867 it owned seven mills and controlled the Yellow Jacket and Chollar-Potosi mines, two still-valuable properties. Within five years of its founding, the bank controlled most of the leading mines and seventeen mills in the district, and was the largest financial institution in the Far West. They had organized their holdings under the Union Mill and Mining Company; Sharon, Ralston, and Mills, with Alvinza Hayward, who had joined the group in 1867 and owned the famous Eureka Gold Mine at Sutter's Creek, held private ownership of the mills. By 1870, the "Bank Crowd" had outstanding loans of 60 percent of the bank's capital to Comstock enterprises, and it appeared that Comstock would never rise again. The Bank Crowd, or some of it, was saved by

Lithograph by C. L. Smith of a new shaft and hoisting works of the Yellow Jacket Silver Mining Company at Gold Hill. Not long afterward, Comstock production began its fall, from late 1863 to its dismal 1866 performance, and the Comstock seemed finished as a great mining camp. The Ophir and Gould and Curry, of course, were virtually defunct; the Savage ores, mistakenly, seemed exhausted; the Hale and Norcross had not been able to find ore at all; the Chollar and the Potosi, after legal battles extending over four years, had merged; the Gold Hill mines, though still operating, were on the decline; the Yellow Jacket ores appeared, though erroneously, to have given out; the Belcher, the best of the producers, had played out; and 50 other mines within the Lode had closed, while 400 wildcats, formed mostly for the sale of stock, vanished. About 10,000 residents left the Comstock between 1864 and 1865, some for California, others to Idaho and Montana, and a number to Summit City, a new camp. Summit City grew rapidly; about 6,000 people built homes, shops, offices, saloons, and a stock exchange. When they all left in 1866, the city was buried under 25 feet of snow. The few holdouts were able to reach one another only through tunnels dug under the snow. In the spring thaw, even these few cleared out. *New York Public Library Picture Collection*

the Crown Point Mine, but Ralston, who was in serious financial straits, knew nothing of it. Hayward quietly bought up most of the Union Mill stock until in 1871 Ralston and his associates were out and an 1872 market crash deflated Comstock stock by nearly $15 million, another disaster for Ralston, with more to come.

Two years later, Ralston tried to buy control of the Ophir Mine, but by then it was part of John W. MacKay's Consolidated Virginia. Ralston had believed that the Crown Point bonanza ran into the Ophir. Sharon had known otherwise and, anticipating that the news would cause a break in the market, sold, while Ralston was left holding the bag as market values indeed tumbled in a terrible crash. A resultant run on the Bank of California forced it to close, leaving Ralston with debts of nearly $10 million, and, on demand, he resigned from the bank he had organized. His creditors took over all his personal property, and that same day he drowned in San Francisco Bay, accident or suicide undetermined.

No one could foretell that the Comstock Lode had not nearly reached its fulfillment and that it was destined to become the greatest silver discovery in history.

THE COMSTOCK GROWS

At the time of the 1865 panic, nearly $100 million had been extracted from the Comstock Lode, almost the amount spent in developing the mines.

Costs were high: lumber was brought in at great expense from California; wages were at a world high; so, too, milling costs; and mines constantly battled floods. All the while, lawsuits were consuming about 20 percent of the lode's entire production. These suits revolved around the "many-ledge theory" as opposed to the "one-ledge theory"—whether the lode was one great vein or a series of parallel, independent ledges. Under the mining rules, prospectors could locate on one vein only. Parallel or adjoining veins were to remain open to all comers. Since many of the Comstock veins were located as separate mining claims, everyone was suing everyone else. Appointed referee in 1864, John Nugent ruled in favor of one ledge, which the courts accepted. Litigation had been so bitter that a mine involved in fewer than fifteen lawsuits was considered fortunate. Nine companies accounted for 359 cases. Most were practically insoluble because claims had been staked measured from stumps and other transient topography. For the first five years, between $9 and $10 million were spent in lawsuits.

Thus far, litigation was over nothing. As the 1860s waned, few Comstock mines were of major importance, and most showed little profit. The Ophir's only prosperous years were 1862, 1863, and 1864, and while its reputation was great since it was the original Comstock mine, it produced only about $15.5 million, from 1859 to 1939. It paid out under $2 million in dividends but exacted $5.6 million in assessments. The only important profits to come out

"Silver Kings" of the Comstock: Samuel Curtis, J. P. Jones, James G. Fair, William Sharon.   *From De*

Quille's History of the Big Bonanza, *1877*

of the Ophir belonged to E. J. "Lucky" Baldwin who sold 20,000 shares of Ophir stock to William Sharon for $2.7 million in November, 1874. As for the Mexican, it never amounted to much; it paid no dividends, was never listed on the stock exchange, and did not produce even $1 million. The Gould and Curry's assessments exceeded its dividends, and its total production yielded about $16 million. The Savage was somewhat more profitable. Though it yielded only about $8 million in its three good years, beginning in 1866, it paid out $3.4 million in dividends, and although there was heavy speculation in Savage stock in the early 1870s, it, too, was soon played out. The Chollar-Potosi Mine remained in production until 1878 and yielded about $16.5 million; it paid out slightly over $3.5 million in dividends. In profits alone, the Yellow Jacket was the most productive of the mines. It remained in operation through the 1890s, producing over $20 million against assessments of $7 million.

The privately held Gold Hill bonanzas, which in 1876 would mostly merge into the Consolidated Imperial Mine, were profitable for the owners, but of course, most were closed by the end of the 1860s. Gold Hill bonanzas are estimated to have yielded $25 million and payed out $5 million in dividends.

MACKAY GOES TO TOWN

It was time for a change. The tumultuous period from 1865 to the Crown Point revival in 1871 in a sense was a period of consolidation for those mines able to weather the depression years. Future Comstock millionaires were already on the scene. John W. Mackay had come to the Comstock early, was associated with the Union Mine and the failing Caledonia Tunnel and was superintendent of the Milton, later absorbed by the Chollar. In 1863, a J. M. Walker with fifty-five others had incorporated the Bullion, and Walker invited Mackay to join the enterprise. When the Bullion produced no ore, it had passed to a new set of owners who managed to collect $2 million in assessments over fifteen years. Ore was never found. In 1865 Mackay and Walker pooled their limited capital and bought the Kentuck Mine, a small mine participating in only ninety-four feet of the lode. The following January the Kentuck struck ten feet of ore in a new shaft that had been dug, and by 1869 had produced over $3.6 million while paying out nearly $1.2 million in dividends. Sharon, who in the meantime acquired the Chollar-Potosi, Crown Point, and Yellow Jacket mines, now bought the Kentuck from Mackay and Walker.

Sharon also went after the Hale and Norcross

John W. Mackay, born in Ireland, rose to fame as one of the Big Four who ruled the Comstock Lode at its peak. His widow and son founded the Mackay School of Mines in his name. Copper engraving was made about 1912. *Mackay School of Mines, University of Nevada*

Mine despite its poor history. Sharon entered a bitter contest over the stock, driving up its price from $300 to over $7,000 in just over a month. At times it sold as high as $10,000 a share. Sharon got the mine, but by March its shares were selling below $50. However, Mackay, who knew the mine well, was convinced that he could make it pay. Forming a new company with James G. Fair, James C. Flood, and William S. O'Brien, after he agreed again to go after the Kentuck stock he followed up with the Hale and Norcross. Mackay would take a three-eighths interest, Flood and O'Brien would share three-eighths, and Fair would take two-eighths. Flood had been selected to purchase the stock, which would be an easy task as the mine had been levying heavy assessments. Under Mackay the mine paid dividends, and, under his continued leadership, the group was now ready to embark on other ventures, involving hundreds of millions of dollars.

With a great belief in the long-term future of the lode, Mackay and his associates acquired the Virginia and Gold Hill Water Company. This would guarantee an adequate water supply for their operations.

The Yellow Jacket fire exploited by Sutro intruded on Mackay's good fortune. Adjacent to the Yellow Jacket were the Crown Point and Kentuck mines, between the 600- and 900-foot levels, all working in the same ore bodies. The fire broke out at Yellow Jacket's 800-foot level, but heavy doors in the drifts kept everyone in ignorance, until the men were lowered into the shafts the following morning. Under the weight of the roof, the burned timbers of the stopes broke, sending a blast of deadly gas and smoke through all three mines. The shafts were sealed five days after the fire. The three mines, among the most productive of the lode, were ruined. A new ore body was found soon after in the Yellow Jacket north of the fire area, and Mackay's new group uncovered a new lode in the Hale and Norcross.

CON VIRGINIA EMERGES

Nevertheless, Mackay was close to being a millionaire from the operations of the Kentuck and his share of the Hale and Norcross mines. Encouraged by the discovery at Crown Point, he and his associates decided to gamble on finding an ore body deep in a portion of the lode between the Ophir and Gould and Curry mines. Accordingly, on June 7, 1867, they formed the Consolidated Virginia Mining Company, which included the Sides, the White & Murphy, and the old California mines. By 1870 the Con. Virginia, as it was called, had reached the 500-foot level with its new shaft. Drifts were extended in all directions, but nothing of value was found. Without an inkling that the Con. Virginia would become one of the greatest mining ventures the world had ever known, Mackay simply believed that it was a good gamble. Refinanced by several assessments, and with Sharon's permission, they prospected a lode from the 1,167-foot level of the Gould and Curry shaft, following fissures they encountered around the 1,200-foot level. Here they entered a substantial body of ore. That was on February, 1873, the day Con. Virginia stock doubled, from $40 to $80. It was the beginning of the "big bonanza"—1,200 feet below the surface of the heart of Virginia City. By May 20, the stock rose to $100 a share; in October, 1873, when the bonanza was fully penetrated, it reached $240 but dropped to $48 in October, 1873, when the number of shares was increased from 23,600 to 108,000.

Dan De Quille (William Wright), who had followed the mine from its inception and predicted the likelihood and the exact spot of the ore find, was invited to write an on-site report. Using De Quille's report in part and following the drifts, Con. Virginia extended the bonanza at the 1,750-foot level. Production increased rapidly, and, in order to protect their interests, the company acquired the Kinney, Central, and Central Number 2 mines, after which it bought control of the Best and Belcher mines adjacent to the Gould and Curry and adjoining Con. Virginia on the south. In December, the old California and the Kinney were combined with the Central and Central Number 2 into a new California. The

California extended 600 feet north and the Con. Virginia 710 feet south. The purpose of the second company was to create a new mine for the stock market. But all of the bonanza was contained within the two mines.

Increased production required new stamp mills. In a year, the Con. Virginia put in a sixty-stamp mill adjacent to the mine. The mill started operating January, 1875, but within ten months was destroyed by a fire. A new mill was constructed at once. The California also built a mill, with eighty stamps, which went into a separate corporation called the Pacific Mill and Mining Company. O'Brien, Flood, Fair, Mackay, and, a new member, Barron owned this one, and they undertook to process the ore from their mines.

Oddly enough, the Con. Virginia discoveries did not cause a ripple on the stock market. It was William Sharon who started the boom. Seeking a seat in the United States Senate, Sharon sought campaign funds through the acquisition of the Ophir. This was the background of the $2.7 million paid to E. J. "Lucky" Baldwin, the tough trader who held the Ophir. At the outset it would have been necessary for Sharon to buy over 50,000 shares for control, which he started to acquire in August, 1874, when Ophir was selling at $20 a share, Con. Virginia at $80, and California at $40. But within a month the Ophir reached $52, and the market boiled as Sharon desperately tried to secure Baldwin's stock. The figures soared by November. Ophir was $100 a share, Con. Virginia, $160, and California, $90, pulling the entire stock market along. Meanwhile, Baldwin held out. Sharon was forced to pay $135 each for 20,000 shares, and he had control of the Ophir. He manipulated the price of the stock until he was elected senator in January, 1875, by which time the market had gone crazy—Ophir was at $315, Con. Virginia $710, and California $780. Obviously these inflated prices could not last and a panic set in. On January 8, 1875, the bottom fell out of the market. Sharon, of course, had unloaded and, in fact, sold short.

For three months preceding the crash, Con. Virginia and California continued their fantastic successes. In fact, the mines were opened for public inspection. And drifts continued to expose even more valuable ore. Optimistic Dan De Quille, writing in the *Daily Territorial Enterprise,* predicted that California's stock would go to $1,000, though it topped out at $780. Eliot Lord in his United States Geological Survey monographs on *Comstock Mining and Miners,* published in 1883, declared the January 7, 1875, value of thirty-one of the leading mines at

The Consolidated Virginia Mine, America's most fabulous silver mine, yielded over $61 million, and paid almost $43 million in dividends between 1859 and 1882. *From De Quille's* History of the Big Bonanza, *1877*

$262,669,940, but there were sixty-five other stocks unmentioned, perhaps worth another $50 million. On the fateful day after professional speculators began to sell, prices dropped. When the public flocked in, margin accounts were uncovered, and banks and brokers, protecting themselves, unloaded the shares they were holding as security. The stock market would not suffer a comparable decline until the 1929 crash. It continued for over a month, but the solid bonanza stocks held up remarkably well. Con. Virginia fell from $710 to $450, California from $780 to $250, and considerably greater, the Ophir from $315 to $65. Most speculative issues fell correspondingly. When eight months later the bank of California suspended operations, Mackay and his associates (the Bonanza Crowd) and Ralston and his associates (the old Bank Crowd), came under attack by the *San Francisco Bulletin* and the *Call.* The Bonanza Crowd was rumored to have withdrawn their funds from the Bank Crowd, which could have, in fact, been correct since Mackay, Flood, Fair, and O'Brien were organizing the Nevada Bank of San Francisco and establishing a branch in Virginia City directly opposite the Bank of California.

After Ralston's death, Sharon took over and reorganized the bank. Sharon, Mills, Kean, and Baldwin each contributed $1 million, and other sources brought the total to nearly $7.3 million in restored capital. The Bank of California reopened October 2, and two days later, the Nevada Bank opened its doors. Meanwhile, the stock exchanges, which had been closed, reopened October 5. Stocks again climbed —until October 26, a sad day for Virginia City.

In 1878 Frank Leslie, publisher of *Frank Leslie's Illustrated Newspaper,* descended the Consolidated Virginia to the 1,600-foot level. These sketches are his artist's conception of the underground scenes of that trip. *Frank Leslie's Illustrated Newspaper, Western Ways Photo*

A DAY OF HAVOC

A fire broke out at 6 A.M., and within four hours most of Virginia City, including the Con. Virginia and Ophir Hoisting Works, was consumed. All the men in the mines got out safely, but strong winds from Mt. Davidson spread the fire rapidly and explosions of powder created a warlike scene. Piled around the Con. Virginia and Ophir Hoisting Works were thousands of cords of burning wood and lumber, adding havoc as well as fuel to the fire. By noontime the intensity of the fire burned itself out. Included in the wreckage were the new Con. Virginia mill and California's adjoining crushing plant. Two thousand people were left homeless. Fortunately Mackay and Fair had been on hand to supervise the work to keep the fire from reaching the timbered stopes of the mines. They ordered the cages lowered below the surface of the ground, the safety clutches sprung, and dirt and ore piled on top. Similar attempts at the Ophir, its shaft burned 400 feet down, were only partially successful. News of the fire quickly reached San Francisco and started a new market plunge. Con. Virginia fell $100 a share within an hour, and all Comstock issues took similar beatings. The mines were back at work within sixty days, however, and some ore readily was removed from the Con. Virginia through the Gould and Curry shaft for a while.

By 1876 the Con. Virginia and the California resumed full operations. That year proved to be the latter's biggest, though each paid over $1 million in dividends every month. Con. Virginia's 145,466 tons alone topped $15 million, dividends consuming almost $13 million. California's greatest year followed, in 1877, when nearly $18 million was produced, $14 million going for dividends. But it was the beginning of the end. Both mines were near the end of the ore body, and, as the news got around, the bears unmercifully drove market prices down; on January 6, 1877, Con. Virginia stock sold at $36, California at $41.50. Just as in 1864 and 1865, thousands of miners began to leave the Comstock, most going to Bodie, California, where fifty new mines had opened.

The final bit of excitement in the Comstock involved the "Sierra Nevada Deal." It was rumored that the Sierra Nevada Mine, which had been prospected for years but never produced any ore, had a new shaft that looked promising. In June and July, 1878, when its stock started to advance, the San Francisco newspapers and Dan De Quille plugged stories that a new bonanza was in the making. While Sierra Nevada stock had been as low as $45 a share, on September 27, it reached $280.

This is how the Ophir Works appeared just prior to the 1875 Virginia City fire, which destroyed all its surface workings. *Nevada Historical Society*

Almost all Comstock stocks once again began to boom. But not the Con. Virginia or California, the only two that were paying dividends. It was later discovered that Flood and Fair had been buying stock in the Sierra Nevada earlier, thereby to stimulate the public buying surge. However, it was no bonanza, and after September 27 the market fell, capped by yet another panic on November 18 when Sierra Nevada, opening that day at $200, dropped to $65 two days later.

Undoubtedly the Comstock produced a great many millionaires but probably fewer than were generally believed. Most of them made their money in the 1870s. George Hearst, John O. Earl, Robert Morrow, A. E. Head, Andrew B. McCreery, and Charles M. Felton made fortunes, but none were millionaires. The Crown Point-Belcher bonanza did make millionaires out of John P. Jones, Alvinza Hayward, William Sharon, William C. Ralston, and D. O. Mills. However, the greatest fortunes came through the Consolidated Virginia where the follow-

This is not a dairy farm but the Sierra Nevada Mine, circa 1876. It was connected by a large drift with the Ophir, Mexican, and Union mines, later all part of Consolidated Virginia. The mine figured in the famous "Sierra Nevada Deal." *Nevada Historical Society*

ing became millionaires: John W. Mackay, James C. Flood, James G. Fair, William S. O'Brien, General Thomas J. Williams, David Bixler, Robert M. Graves, and Edward Barron. Of course there were E. J. "Lucky" Baldwin who sold his Ophir stock for $2.5 million and Robert Sherwood and John E. Skae who made millions on the Sierra Nevada deal; also Sutro who became wealthy from his tunnel stock, but probably more fortunes were made by the San Francisco stockbrokers than by those engaged in mining.

The naming of Virginia City. According to De Quille, Virginia City received its name in November, 1859. De Quille quotes Comstock: " 'Old Virginny' [James Finney] was out one night with a lot of the 'boys' on a drunk, when he fell down and broke his whisky bottle. On rising he said—'I baptize this ground Virginia.' " *From De Quille's* History of the Big Bonanza, *1877*

HEART OF THE COMSTOCK

The center of Comstock Lode activity was Virginia City, Nevada, where most of the miners lived in wooden shacks of their own construction. If they did not cook for themselves, they left their shacks to sample the restaurants, generally at weekly rates ranging from $8 to $12. Or they could eat at a boardinghouse for about $50 or $60 a month. Virginia City prices fluctuated between bonanza and borrasca, while wages remained consistently high. Early enterprises were saloons and gambling halls, housed in tents. Brick houses and business buildings grew with the town, and utilities were laid. Its International Hotel, originated in 1860 as one story and a basement, in 1862 was rebuilt to provide 100 furnished rooms and an elevator, considered the West's first; after an 1875 fire destroyed the hotel, it was again rebuilt, in 1876. By 1863 Virginia City had filled its streets with fancy restaurants; in addition, three theatres, one seating 1,600 people, did a thriving business.

At the beginning, about 4,000 prospectors trekked across the Sierras from the Pacific to the Washoe, littering the trail with broken wagons and discarded supplies to mix with the mud and snow that had been trampled into a morass by vehicles, animals, and prospectors. Mine owners, superintendents, professional men, and others coalesced into an upper "white-collar" class, living in new homes built on high ground, expanding cultural and social life with their increasing numbers. Common to all Virginia City society, miner or owner, was its participation in horse racing, wrestling and boxing matches, hunting events, and bear, bull, cock, and dog fights, including their various combinations. Music concerts became popular—Walter's Music Hall for lower-class entertainment and Maguire's New Opera House for high-caliber performances. Maguire's had a billiard parlor, smoking room, mahogany bar, and gambling tables to stifle boredom. Humorist Artemus Ward was imported, Julia Dean Hayne presented Shakespeare, Lotta Crabtree,

Virginia City, circa 1866. Reaching its height in the 1870s, Virginia City supported 213 commercial establishments, excluding mines but including 100 saloons, 39 grocery stores, 22 restaurants, 15 butcher shops, 11 dairies, 8 drugstores, 3 undertakers, and a variety of other businesses. *William Culp Darrah Stereo Collection*

sixteen now, sang and danced and was showered with gold and silver. Piper's Opera House, still standing at B and Union streets, later became the elite's favorite, where they were entertained by violinist William Withers, Jr., the musical director fresh from Ford's Theatre where Lincoln was assassinated, Edwin Booth, Lawrence Barrett, Maude Adams' 1877 debut, *Uncle Tom's Cabin,* minstrel shows, lecturers Henry Ward Beecher and Robert Ingersoll, and a variety of entertainment unmatched even in New York.

Compared with most mining towns, Virginia City's gambling was minimal, probably because almost everybody had money invested in mining stock,

In 1870 the mines in the northern part of Virginia City came right up to the town environs. *William Culp Darrah Stereo Collection*

Weighing a load of ore at the scale house at the silver mines in Virginia City, 1873. *New York Public Library Picture Collection*

which was its own vested gambling interest. Women deterred gambling. They managed to force an enactment restricting gambling to private quarters only, which excluded the general public, only to usher in the back or upstairs room! But there was no lack of sites for poker, keno, euchre, faro, roulette, and other games for both high and low society. Gambling legends developed—a "suicide table," immortalized by three successive self-slayers after a bad night's faro; a strange miner who put up his wedding band and later walked out with $86,000, a team of horses, and an interest in a gold mine.

Drinking was another matter. Although whiskey literally flowed like water, it was "ungentlemanly" to appear drunk in public. Wherever drink was served, lunch was free. An 1876 survey indicated 100 retail liquor outlets in Virginia City; Gold Hill alone had thirty-seven outlets, in addition to ten wholesalers and five breweries.

Loose women seemed divided into two classes: taxi dancers who worked in the hurdy-gurdy houses for a drink at the bar, or for "two bits," and those occupying the red-light district. The law did not proscribe prostitution, only its locale; neat rows of cabins, each lavishly furnished, were set up near the Chinese quarter. Virginia City whores took pride in their fancy dress and imported clothing from New York and Paris. They tolerated no unruly behavior in their gaily decorated rooms, whether from miner or millionaire. When the French beauty Julia Bulette, apparently the leader of the brothel contingency, was robbed and murdered by the half-breed John Milleaine, she was given a grand funeral by one of the fire-engine companies. Julia had been an honorary fireman who, beside participating at fires, nursed many firemen injured in the line of duty.

The fire-engine companies were prominent not only in the town's activities, but in its social life as well. Tom Peasley, chief of fire fighting, inspired Mark Twain's fictional Buck Fanshaw. Peasley had divided the town into four fire zones capped by a fire tower where watchmen could overlook the city for the first signs of smoke or flame.

In the early days of the Comstock, "schooners" were drawn by teams of from 10 to 16 mules, each mule carrying a chime of bells. As the teams filled the streets of Virginia City, the whole town rang with music. *From De Quille's* History of the Big Bonanza, *1877*

Cons Virginia — Comstock 1879.

The biggest reception ever given to a visiting dignitary in Nevada occurred on October 27, 1879, when General Ulysses S. Grant spent three days in Virginia City visiting the Comstock mines. He and his party were taken down the California and Consolidated Virginia shaft where the heat ranged as high as 130 degrees. Adolph Sutro entertained the group at his mansion on the same visit. From left to right: John W. Mackay, Mrs. D. Gillette, U. S. Grant, Jr., Mrs. U. S. Grant, General Grant, Mrs. James G. Fair, Governor J. H. Kinkead, and James G. Fair on the extreme right. The person kneeling is unidentified. *Colorado Bureau of Mines*

An 1876 payroll sheet of the North Consolidated Virginia Mining Company. Apparently the miners were not paid weekly, as the number of days worked varied from 6 to 30. The pay scale shown on this payroll indicates that laborers received $3 a day; miners, $4 a day; pump men, $4.50 a day; and mechanics, $6 a day. These were considered high wages at the time. *Mackay School of Mines, University of Nevada*

☞ PAY ROLL ☜
NORTH CONSOLIDATED VIRGINIA MINING CO.

For the Month of September 1876.

NAMES.	OCCUPATION.	Pay Per Day.	No. Days Worked.	Total Amount.	Received in full amounts set opposite our names. 187
Amount Forward				3483 78	
William Jackson	Miner	4	30	120	Wm Jackson
William Downard	"		16	64	William Downard
Nash Underwood	"		10¾	43	Nash Underwood
William Butler	"		14	56	William Butler
O. Madden	"		14	56	O. Madden
William Comsford	"		14	56	Wm Comsford
Pat Brown	"		14	56	P Brown
William Bryant	Pump Man	4½50	30	135	W Bryant
Charles Lewis	Sailor	4	27½	110	Charles Lewis
John Thompson	Laborer	3 00	24	84	John Thompson
James O'Neal	"		15	53 50	James Oneal
Frank Sweet	"		9	31 50	Frank Sweet
Mike Reily	"		22	77	M Reily
J. McGarhen	"		6	21	James McGarhen
T. R. Peters	"	5	30	150 00	R Peters
Wilson Kelder	Sec			100	Wilson Kelder
Ford Hoymes	Miner	4	7	28	Ford Hoymes
O. Stoddard	Mechanic	6	14	84	Orlando Stoddard
Wm Madden	Miner	4	16	64	Wm Madden
				4871 78	

The town's major newspaper was the *Territorial Enterprise,* published for about thirty-five years since its beginning in 1858. Its highly respected owner-editor was Joseph Goodman; its most famous reporter was Dan De Quille, who, when the paper closed, received a $60-a-week pension until death from John W. Mackay.

De Quille was a perpetrator of hoaxes, and fabricated stories for the entertainment of his mining readers, including a story about the invention of a suit to keep one cool in the hottest temperatures. It seemed the inventor went to Death Valley to test it and when he failed to return, a rescue party was sent out, only to find him frozen to death in 117-degree desert temperatures. An eighteen-inch icicle was hanging from his nose.

Another Virginia City newspaperman was Samuel Clemens. After his unsuccessful try at mining, in 1862, the *Territorial Enterprise* took him on at $25 a week. It was while working for the paper that he first used the name Mark Twain, writing humorously about events and people in the Comstock district. Twain sprang into prominence with a story he wrote in 1863 in rebuttal to a *San Francisco Bulletin* article asserting that the Gould and Curry Mine board of directors had engineered a dividend to boost the market price of the stock. Twain wrote about a saloonkeeper who sold his Gould and Curry stock, lost all his money, was forced to murder his redheaded wife and nine of his children, and finally committed suicide. The entire tale was a figment of Twain's imagination, based on a local saloonkeeper, a bachelor. Twain's Washoe experiences are recorded in his book *Roughing It.*

Virginia City was remarkable for its relative freedom from crime. Almost from its inception, the Comstock's social life seemed to have been divided between the mine workers and operators and their operating personnel. Little conflict passed between them, and Virginia City traditionally avoided liars, while humor was a way of life. Profanity, pornography, and the dirty joke were uncommon in the presence of women, and the citizens were courteous and helpful. Spending was rife, and diamonds, gourmet food, and fashionable clothing could be freely purchased.

An exception to its excellent crime-free record was 1863. During the latter half of the year, burglaries, brawls, robberies, thievery, gunfights, and drunkenness were common. Criminals, runaway wives, gamblers, and hookers rushed into town, making it almost impossible for the law to keep order. Two lawmen were killed and one was wounded; two citizens were murdered by red-light women; rivalry erupted between volunteer fire companies, and the courts were derelict—a rioter was slain and his assailant sentenced to a mere two and a half years. Stage robberies were negligible in the immediate Comstock vicinity, although many took place between Placerville, California, and Virginia City. Bank robberies were nonexistent, as were guards, and petty holdups and burglaries were rare.

As for accidents, fainting during the ascent in the mine cages was the most common. The cages descended into the depths of the mine where the high temperatures sometimes reached 130 degrees or more, and as the men ascended to the cooler temperatures many passed out and had to be supported by their fellow workers to prevent their falling into the shaft, as some did. A particularly serious accident struck the Mexican Mine. In 1863 when all of the workings above a depth of 225 feet collapsed, the force was so great that it caused

One of the few fights of the Washoe District occurred on October 3, 1874, at the Waller's Defeat Shaft of the Justice Mine. This drawing, from De Quille, shows the battle at the building containing the hoisting works, where five men were killed fighting for possession of the mine. This was the last mining battle on the Comstock Lode. *From De Quille's* History of the Big Bonanza, *1877*

rock and timber to crash into the adjacent Ophir Mine, wiping out fifty feet of a drift. The pressure created on the second and third levels of the Ophir was so intense that these, too, collapsed, and machinery and surface workings hurtled into the shaft.

In the spring of 1871 a vigilante committee known as the "Six Hundred and One" sprang up in Virginia City. It was a secret organization to execute persons guilty of murder and banish dangerous men. Arthur Perkins Heffernan had shot down a man in cold blood at the bar of a saloon and was found hanged on the timbers

of a mine the following morning with a paper on which the figures "601" were written. Perkins, as shown in these drawings, was taken from the jail and hanged near the Ophir Works. *From De Quille's* History of the Big Bonanza, *1877*

An accident at the Belcher Mine in February, 1874, was caused by a charge of powder that failed to explode on the original blast. When the next shift came to work they presumed that the hole with the remaining charge had not been finished, and started drilling. The concussion of the drill fired the cartridge causing the explosion. *From De Quille's* History of the Big Bonanza, *1877*

Accidents were not rare, despite the installation of safety devices. Eliot Lord in his monograph *Comstock Mining and Miners* tallied 295 fatal and 608 nonfatal accidents from the files of the newspapers from October 16, 1863, to June 19, 1880. This accident occurred at the 1,700-foot level of the Ophir Mine. After setting fuses, the miners rushed to the mine cars and gave the signal to be pulled up. The bell rope, which was 1,700 feet long, had fouled on a timber and failed to register to the hoist operator. Here the miners are seen attempting to climb to safety up the elevator shaft before the fuses set off the blast. No one was killed. *From De Quille's* History of the Big Bonanza, *1877*

Virginia City relics: the old brewery; vintage piano now in the brewery, along with music box; original livery. *Felix A. Peckham*

On to the Rockies

While the Comstock developments were taking place, Idaho was rapidly becoming one of the nation's most important mining centers. Americans began mining in Idaho in October, 1860, around the town of Pierce. Back in the days of Lewis and Clark, white trappers had been trading with the Nez Percé Indians, but fur trading was their principal commodity and they completely discounted gold. Elias Pierce, a Forty-Niner who in 1852 had turned to trading furs with the Nez Percé Indians, wintered on Clearwater River in the village of Nez Percé Indian chief Wislanaeqa. He was convinced the area held rich gold deposits. Had not a man named Martin traveled the Nez Percé Trail in 1856 and panned the river's South Fork? By 1860 others, too, were declaring the existence of gold, this time in the Salmon and Coeur d'Alene rivers.

Also in 1860, Pierce returned, but with a prospecting outfit. Accompanied by Chief Wislanaeqa, he panned gold on the river's North Fork and made his find.

PIERCE AND THE NEZ PERCÉ INDIANS

Now clearly operating as a prospector, he convinced Wislanaeqa to permit him to start a mining enterprise. At this juncture, because other Nez Percé Indian tribes had violently objected to any trespassing on their land, war seemed imminent. Reacting to the fears, settlers around Walla Walla opposed a mining venture on Indian territory. Pierce however had gone ahead, and within six months set off with twelve men on an obscure trail toward Wislanaeqa's territory. It took six weeks of dodging unfriendly Indians to reach the Clearwater. Almost on arrival, at Orofino Creek, Wilbur F. Bassett, a carpenter, had panned some gold in Canal Gulch. Within about a week they were convinced there were ample gold deposits to be mined, and the group returned to Walla Walla over the main Indian trail, ignoring the law and treaty prohibiting their crossing the Indian reservations. In mid-November, a second party of thirty-odd men left for Orofino Creek, arriving December 2, and immediately established the town of Pierce. Word had traveled rapidly throughout the Pacific Northwest and California, but because of the severe winter the inevitable gold rush marked time until spring.

Pierce, in north Idaho at the end of the nineteenth century. The picture was taken about forty years after gold was discovered in 1860 and the rush to the Idaho mines began. Elias D. Pierce's gold find on the North Fork of the Clearwater River on February 20, 1860, opened Idaho. After Pierce's party built eight cabins in which to spend the winter, most of their time was occupied digging ditches, building sluices, and sawing timber for use in the spring. The men organized the Oro Fino District, adopted mining laws, and arranged for claims to be recorded similar to the system used in California camps. Seventy-one claims were staked during January, 1861, and beginning in April, a regular freight service was inaugurated to Walla Walla; in one month some 300 miners staked some 2,000 claims. The end of May, when the snows were cleared and prospecting began, saw 1,000 additional miners, and it appeared the land would not go around for all the claims. In the interim, about two miles from Pierce (where the new town of Oro Fino City was growing), new discoveries were being made at Rhodes Creek. By the end of August, Oro Fino City comprised 400 homes, and about 1,500 men worked the local mines. But in October gold was discovered in nearby Florence, and a rush to that area practically leveled the combined populations of Pierce and Oro Fino. Nevertheless, for the next few years these two camps continued to develop a steady gold production, while Chinese miners gradually began to purchase the claims; by 1866 most such old workings were Chinese-owned. *Idaho Historical Society*

Even into June, the heavy snows plagued the prospectors as 700 claims were laid out, thirty working, averaging a daily $8 to $50 in gold per man. Many claims remained under spring floodwater, delaying the prospectors even further. But except for a few on Rhodes Creek, most of the workable claims were unspectacular. One problem at Orofino was the even land level; claims could not be easily sluiced. More than the placer workings themselves, Pierce and Orofino boomed. Lots were selling from $100 to $200, and log houses for as much as $1,000. At $9 to $10 a day, a carpenter fared better than many a miner. But the best business was a system of ferries that crossed the Snake and Clearwater rivers; it took in about $4,000 a week.

An agreement had been signed on April 10, 1860, with the Nez Percé Indians to keep the miners out of their territory in the South Fork region of Orofino Creek, but the miners summarily violated it. Prospectors spread out from the Pierce and Orofino districts along the South Fork. For several months their exploratory work was nonproductive, but by August, even while Pierce had returned to work the Clearwater area, miners began to find their efforts with rockers and pans worthwhile. A few large nuggets found on the South Fork started a minor rush. Elk City resulted—three shanties in July, twenty log houses in August, and 300 miners working the area. The Nez Percé Indians had become reconciled to the intrusion; in fact, profited from it by the sale of beef and vegetables. Elk City soon added eight stores, six saloons, and a number of other shops, while an estimated 800 to 1,000 miners were at work. However, many miners left during the Florence October gold strike on the Salmon River; fewer than 100 remained in Elk City until the return from Florence of the less fortunate in late 1862.

Getting sufficient water for the mining operations was a major problem; often it was necessary to bring water in from nine miles out. Gradually, hydraulic mining supplanted the old placer workings, and, as new water ditches and sluices were built, production rose through 1864. As with Pierce and Orofino, most of the mines after 1872 were worked by the Chinese, who also were occupied smuggling in opium in tobacco tins.

SALMON RIVER GOLD

Reports of gold along Idaho's Salmon River, dividing north and south Idaho, in August, 1861, permeated the Pacific Coast. Hundreds of miners swept into the area to pan. As with the nearby mining finds, the Nez Percé Indians, on whose territory all the discoveries had been made, were a threat to the miners. But in December, the Indians agreed to permit placer mining. The winter was severe, and prospectors in single file snaked through the difficult trails to Florence and the Salmon River, aided by the Indians with food and shelter. By September of the following year, the Salmon River placers around Florence exceeded all neighboring areas in productivity; in October the influx of men drew off neighboring populations, and by mid-November some 350

prospectors panning with rockers were believed to be taking from $100 to $500 daily. But reports of $2,000 to $3,000 went out. Jacob Weiser's Babboon Gulch reported $20,000 in eight days but, discounting a few big producers, more likely most workings did not exceed $25 to $50 per day per miner. Water was a serious problem, too, as the rivers dried up or froze. What they had was used over and over. As winter advanced, panning became almost impossible. Rockers froze and miners worked under the most adverse conditions. Many froze from exposure just getting to Florence, nearly as many were lost, and all were short of food. Scurvy was rampant among the undernourished miners. Over ten feet of snow fell in February, and in April a further eight feet stopped mining until June. Nevertheless, sluicing had been resumed in March. When the spring waters subsided, water shortages prevented the sluices from operating. By mid-July most workers had gone back to rockers.

Of the 10,000 miners who had come to the Florence area during the 1862 season, probably no more than 3,000 were actively engaged in mining. But production was claimed to run as high as $50,-000 a day.

Mining again was interrupted by weather in October, and at the end of November the 1862 season halted. About a year hence the placers were worked out and only about fifty prospectors remained. Quartz deposits were discovered in 1866, but placer mining remained the principal method of recovery for about thirty years, worked mostly by Chinese miners who slowly filtered into Florence and the surrounding country to salvage some of the old claims.

The Chinese, heartily disliked by the miners, were at first totally excluded from almost all Idaho mining districts. In 1864 the Territorial Legislature encouraged Chinese miners who wanted to work in

Warren, in central Idaho, about 1890. Both quartz and placer mining were important to this camp for many years after its 1862 gold discovery by James Warren. No gold rush followed, but it became the leading mining camp in central Idaho. Warren was especially active when quartz discoveries were made between 1866 and 1868; after 1900 dredges began to work deep into the placer deposits, which continued until the early 1940s. *Idaho Historical Society*

Idaho but placed a tax of $4 a month on them. Many mining areas had become depleted, and disappointed prospectors were now anxious to sell the Chinese their played-out placer sites. Because the Chinese required a much smaller income, they were able to reclaim the thin placer deposits and profit at the lower yields. As for the quartz deposits, by 1896 a fairly large production had been established. All told, Florence's gold at today's values exceeded $18 million.

Lewiston, on the Idaho-Washington border, served as a supply point for the early camps at Pierce, Orofino City, Elk City, Florence, and Warren. Unlike most Idaho mining towns, Lewiston had a crime problem. Here Henry Plummer preceded his Bannack fame as a professional gambler and the secret leader of a robber gang that operated two roadhouses on the highways out of Lewiston, virtually dominating the town. In the highway operation, travelers were forced to give up their pack animals and property for forged bills of sale. Those who refused were murdered. Finally, after the murder of their popular tavern owner, the townspeople drove Plummer off to Florence, before he eventually turned up at Bannack to be hanged by vigilantes. Several Lewiston outlaw diehards were hanged without trial, while others fled.

THE BOISE BASIN RUSH

At the opposite end of Lewiston was Boise Basin where reports from trappers and other mountain pioneers in south and central Idaho had indicated the existence of gold as early as 1844 (originating with a Hudson's Bay Company trapper who first recognized the precious metal). In 1854 members of a Mormon settlement had prospected for copper along the drainage basin of the Lemhi River, but Indian trouble had forced the abandonment of the settlement in 1858 and nothing ever came of the copper venture.

In the summer of 1862, Moses Splawn, a miner with Elk City and Florence experience, with a party of seven prospectors met George Grimes who was working with eight other prospectors. The two gold seekers joined forces and worked their way from Auburn, in eastern Oregon, through the Owyhee (Hawaii misspelled) country, and approached the Basin from the southwest. By August, the new group was prospecting in the Basin, and soon discovered gold. They were subsequently attacked by hostile Indians, Grimes was killed, and the party retreated south toward Snake River.

Word of the new bonanza spread so quickly that within two months Splawn and his group had to hurry back to protect their interests. Their return was followed by a mad rush to stake claims before the winter weather closed in; thousands of prospectors swarmed into the Basin founding various towns. It was simple for early arrivals to locate claims that would one day make them rich, and everyone was ready to fan out in any direction as soon as spring weather arrived. Even before the snow was off the ground, impatient gold seekers searched along the forks of the Boise River, working up the Deadwood, the Bigwood, and the Feather rivers as well as throughout Sawtooth Valley. The Basin developed into Idaho's largest early mining community; more than 16,000 people were working there in less than a year. Some reports put the population at between

A placer mine near Idaho City about 1897. Idaho City became Idaho's leading camp, with Placerville, Hogem, and Centerville running close behind. Almost every known type of gold mining was employed in the basin, not only the pan and rocker, but long toms, sluicing, and especially hydraulic mining, which continued for some twenty years. Jets of high-pressure water from hydraulic monitors undermined the gravel banks and washed the gold-bearing material into long sluices in which the gold was recovered. With water for hydraulicking and other mining in such great demand, private companies had to be set up to carry water for placer operations, often through ditches fifteen miles long. As with the California water companies, Idaho water was sold by the inch. Quartz lodes later were discovered about eighty miles to the south. *Idaho Bureau of Mines and Geology*

Photograph taken before 1886 at Bear Creek above Rocky Bar, showing the Confederate Star and other properties near the Elmore Mine. Other, important, lodes were found at South Boise Basin, some becoming big producers. In June, 1863, four gold and silver quartz lodes had been discovered in the South Boise fields— about eighty miles from Boise Basin—along a rough and rugged trail. During 1864 a steam sawmill was brought into the district, and a five-ton stamp mill was put in operation at Rocky Bar. The South Boise Wagon Road Company completed a toll road into Rocky Bar, relieving transportation problems by year end, and six additional mills went into construction. But the material was low-grade, and outcroppings were soon exhausted; the Elmore Mine was flooded, and most of the South Boise mines were failing. The Victor Mine played out and its stock collapsed, and, as other South Boise mines closed, general disaster swept the area. From 1866 to 1870 the arrastra returned, generally worked by local miners, to keep the Idaho, the Wild West, and the Bonaparte mines in regular operation. Production increased beginning in 1870. The advent of railroad transportation, better mining techniques, and a renewed interest in the South Boise District owing to the Comstock Lode discoveries revived the area. The Bonaparte, Vishnu, Idaho, Eureka, and Wild West mines continued active, and after the flooding problem was solved, the Elmore Mine, operated by the Pittsburgh and Idaho Gold and Silver Mining Company, rapidly became a principal producer. But Rocky Bar still resisted full recovery, and by 1875 mining was again confined to reworking some of the old areas with arrastras and small stamp mills. The vacillating fortunes of the Rocky Bar area continued: the Elmore, Vishnu, Idaho, and Bonaparte mines once more went into production after a new boom in 1884, only to be idle again a year later. *Idaho Historical Society*

In 1886 a British company purchased a number of properties, including the Elmore. The photograph is of a 50-stamp mill, which they built and operated in Rocky Bar under the name of Alturas, Ltd. The mill was successful, and the neighboring mines resumed their former activity—until 1889, when the gold supply of the Alturas holdings was exhausted and many other workings had been closed. Rocky Bar's business area was destroyed by fire in September, 1892, but the town was rebuilt, though large-scale mining was at an end; small mining operations were maintained into the 1960s. *Idaho Historical Society*

Soon a new center was to develop in the South Boise area—Atlanta, seen here as it appeared about 1890 when nearby mining activity was at a low ebb. It began in 1864 when placer deposits were discovered on the Yuba River, eventually creating the towns of Alturas Bar (later changed to Alturas City) and Yuba City. To exploit these findings additional water was required. The result was the construction of a large ditch from the Quartz Gulch mouth to Yuba City and Alturas. A lode of gold and silver was found unexpectedly at Quartz Gulch, which now became Atlanta, after the Battle of Atlanta. The Atlanta Lode developed into one of the most important of the basin's gold discoveries. One of its mines, the Buffalo Mine, remains in operation. The quartz-gold and silver ledge apparently extended for over two miles, its entire length staked out by over 200 claims by the end of 1864. Atlanta was isolated and rocky, making transportation almost impossible. Roads were built from Rocky Bar to Atlanta, but the heavy winter snows blocked their usage during much of the year. In 1867 a stamp mill was put into operation, and tunnels and shafts had been developed to explore the possibilities of the silver lode. Speculation in new stock issues became heavy, and, as in so many western United States areas, included British investors. However, the failure of the Monarch Mine, which had built a 10-stamp mill, dampened investment enthusiasm in the district. In 1869 the Washoe process of silver recovery, developed at the Comstock Lode, was tried. But the local silver ore proved unsuitable for extracting the silver and gold. Except for small arrastras, most operations ceased in a year. *Idaho Historical Society*

25,000 and 40,000. As for the town of Boise, originally called Boise City, it was never a mining camp but a supply center for the Idaho mining districts.

Saloons did a thriving business, especially since they could transform their kegs of alcohol in no time into bourbon and cognac, or any other liquor merely by adding water, burned sugar, caramel, and various chemicals. Saloon owners were the hub of every mining camp and acted as bankers, safety-deposit vaults, arbitrators of disputes and fights, and even assisted those in need of a handout or additional supplies. The saloons were open twenty-four hours a day, and what there was of recreation or enter-

tainment was found mostly in these places. Among the favorite entertainers was John Kelly, a fiddler who performed on a swing high over the drinkers. Kelly so valued his violin that during any gunplay, he would protect it with his body. His adopted Indian boy learned to play as well as he, but at eighteen he died on a visit to Ireland.

During this period of southern Idaho's expansion, vigilante action was not only against those pillaging the mines. Horse thieves took precedence. Many horses were stolen by the Indians who resented the white man's intrusion, but it was almost impossible for the vigilantes to apprehend them be-

The Buffalo Mill, Atlanta, circa 1877. Notwithstanding previous failures, in the mid-1890s speculation in Atlanta gold and silver stocks increased in New York and London markets. In the Monarch Mine a new discovery was made in 1874, which had revived the area; investors from Buffalo and New York brought in new money to finance the Buffalo Mine, its new name. The Last Chance, Big Lode, Tahoma, and others, continued to operate into the mid-1880s. But it was apparent to even the boldest investor that most of the richest ores had been extracted. Between 1885 and 1900 Atlanta was practically a derelict—only the Idaho Gold Mine ore production kept the town alive. After 1900 modern equipment managed to provide a respite for Atlanta, but by 1912 the mines were again shut. *Idaho Historical Society*

Pack train reaching Atlanta during the early spring, while the road from Rocky Bar was still closed by snow, early 1900s. There was poor transportation during the winter months, when roads were subject to constant snowslides and avalanches. Not until 1917, when the St. Joseph Lead Company acquired most of the mining properties in the area, was this problem solved. Then, in the early 1930s, modern methods and amalgamation-flotation concentrators enabled St. Joe to resume production. By 1936 St. Joe's Atlanta operations, after a successful five-year production, closed. Limited mining continues, but production is largely from small, individual operations. *Idaho Historical Society*

cause they ate the evidence. Later, however, the first vigilante committee after forming at Payette turned to the white criminal element and quickly cleaned out a "bogus gold dust" syndicate. Unfortunately, wily outlaws later managed to elect their own sheriff who arrested forty of the vigilantes and sent them to Boise for trial. They were acquitted, and the United States Grand Jury forced the sheriff to resign. A new sheriff was appointed, and was quickly murdered by Fred Patterson, a known Oregonian murderer famous for having stabbed his mistress. Patterson was imprisoned, but mostly to protect him from the vigilantes who threatened to lynch him when they found out his trial would be rigged. True to form, Patterson was acquitted, and murdered soon after, which was credited to the vigilantes; in 1865, an Idaho City vigilante committee in a year and a half left only ten out of 200 men to die a natural death.

From 1860 to 1865, as the Idaho territory gold output rose, so too did shipping costs to the United States Mint in San Francisco. Demands for a federal mint in Idaho grew, and in 1869 Congress appropriated money to erect such a building in Boise. It was completed in 1871 and housed not only a mint but a federal assay office, which began to function about the time the gold placers in Idaho were depleted. When the Coeur d'Alene region was opened in 1883, the office assumed greater importance and continued in operation until 1933, when the building was acquired by the United States Forest Service as headquarters for Boise National Forest.

Boise City's neighbor was Silver City, where, nearby, the Poorman property was located—rich silver-bearing quartz lodes—a disputed tract on which two claims overlapped. Professional gunmen were hired, and actual warfare ensued until they worked out a truce and the property became a joint operation, later sold to a New York group. Silver City was near the height of its second big boom when this picture was taken on September 24, 1895. *Idaho Historical Society*

AN OREGON GOLD INTERLUDE

Coinciding with the rush to Idaho, three gold discoveries between 1861 and 1862 started a stampede into eastern Oregon that threatened to duplicate the California rush twelve years earlier. Discounting the reputed gold discoveries of 1845 in eastern Oregon and that of the 1850s, when a few prospectors supposedly found placer gold in the Burnt and John Day river areas, the first of the three was along Powder River just north of Baker, practically on Idaho's border, at the present Griffin Gulch. A party of prospectors from Portland had been led by Henry Griffin to the site on a Powder River tributary. The second discovery occurred at Upper Town, now Canyon City, some 100 miles southwest of Baker; and the third at Lower Town, now John Day, near Lewiston, Idaho. Auburn, five miles south of Griffin Gulch, became the center for prospecting in that area, and within a year its population was nearly 6,000. The county seat was set up here, and it became the second largest town in the state. But the town was not big enough to overcome its lack of water, handicapping the miners, until the construction of the Auburn Ditch. The ditch provided ample water for the placers, but by 1868 no more gold was to be found and Auburn became a ghost town. The

Auburn Ditch is now part of the Baker City water system.

At the conclusion of the ditch, Wells Fargo had been running from The Dalles to Auburn and Canyon City where about 2,500 miners were working the gold placers at Whiskey Flat—on Canyon Creek along the John Day River. Auburn and Canyon City in turn became the prospectors' takeoff point, spreading throughout eastern Oregon.

About twenty-five miles due west of Auburn is Sumpter, in Oregon's Granite District, named for the old ghost town of Granite, one of the state's earliest settlements. Granite Creek drained the southern part of the area, and it was here that the early mines were found.

Most of the better mines, which were usually well managed and productive, were owned by the rich. Some nonproductive mines were actually "salted" for suckers looking for get-rich-quick stocks, while other mines that began legitimately on seemingly rich deposits fizzled. Considerable speculation resulted in many unwise investments. For example, a 100-ton-per-day smelter was built. Although it operated efficiently, the deficient quantity of ores and concentrates from the mines frequently left it idle.

Portland, 1852. The easiest route to the district was along the Columbia River, and boats running from San Francisco to Portland were sold out weeks in advance. Over 1,000 prospectors came in a single boatload, eventually exposing Portland's 3,000 population to some 82,000 in-transit prospectors in the first three years of the gold rush. Most traveled the Columbia River to The Dalles, a convenient takeoff point for the eastern Oregon mines as well as for the new Idaho mining camps. The Dalles, which connected the Auburn mines by the Oregon Trail, became headquarters for outfitting prospectors who, as they moved east, soon sent their gold west to Portland and San Francisco. *Oregon Historical Society*

Main Street, Sumpter, Baker County, about 1914. Note board construction of street. Sumpter was named by five Confederate deserters who wintered there in 1862–1863 in the shadow of booming mining activity in Idaho and Oregon. Most of the town was built between 1899 and 1900, after gold had been discovered there, and, although it was late in the mine-discovery period, it too turned into typical mining environment. The streets were paved with planks, and wood sidewalks ran for miles. Banks, doctors, lawyers, ministers, brokers, and the usual fast-buck mining promoters helped round out the population. The 100-by-100-foot Sumpter Hotel, a brewery, dairy, cigar factory, undertaking establishment, and several assayers' offices provided many necessities, and an extensive Chinatown added local color. Estimates of total Sumpter-area gold removal reach $11 million, while silver accounts for some $500,000. Many residents left during 1904–1906, and soon only the dredges and the Columbia Mine remained to uphold Sumpter's importance in the mining industry, at least until the Columbia folded in 1916; a disastrous fire the year after completely destroyed the town. *Oregon State Department of Geology and Mineral Industries. Photo by Brooks Hawley*

Buck Gulch, west of Sumpter, 1927. The principal mines in the area were the North Pole, Golconda, Columbia, Red Boy, E and E, Taber Fraction, Buffalo, and the Bonanza. Many others operated but without making any money, and in time dredging became the area's chief mining method, permanently devastating portions of the countryside. *Brooks Hawley*

Inside shaft house of Red Boy Mine, 1925. The gallows frame is a good example of millwright timbering. *Brooks Hawley*

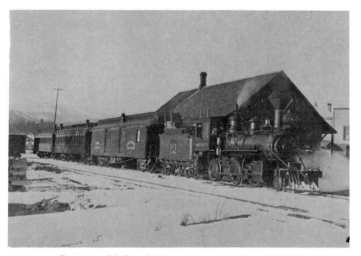

Sumpter Valley R.R. passenger train, 1900. But it was the arrival of the transcontinental railroad at Baker in 1884 that helped the town grow from a small hamlet with a few hundred people into one of 3,500 or more. *Roscoe Doane*

202

Rock-drilling contest, July 4, 1906, Sumpter. Each team drilled 15 minutes, reaching a depth of 30 to 34 inches. First prize was $500. All these buildings burned in 1917. *Brooks Hawley*

The bar of the Gem Saloon, Sumpter, one of at least twenty saloons in that city around 1900. The Gem Saloon was one of the "swankiest" establishments, and featured a lady orchestra. *Oregon Historical Society*

Musick Mine and Mill in the Oregon Bohemia District. It was discovered in 1858 by Dr. W. W. Oglesby and Frank Brass but was named for James Johnson, known as Bohemia Johnson, who with George Ramsey found gold on City Creek in 1863. Within a year over 100 claims had been staked along the creek, and by 1872 a five-stamp mill had been built on the Knott Claim, later to become part of the Champion Mine. An avalanche destroyed the mill in 1877, and mining came to an end. For years the Bohemia District lay dormant. Then, in July, 1889, ore assaying $260 a ton was discovered, and a new boom began. The first lode mine was the Musick, relocated in 1891, and the following year the Noonday was opened. From 1889 to 1910 developments moved at a feverish pace. New deposits were discovered, new tunnels dug, and many other mines opened. Important by-products were copper, lead, and zinc ore. But after World War I, mineowners could no longer compete with increasing costs, and only the Champion continued in operation. In 1936 a mill was constructed at the Champion to recover lead and copper from the gold, but before anything could come of it financial difficulties snuffed it out. Once again the area would be salvaged. The Higgins and Hinsdale Mine, by leases and purchases, acquired most of the Bohemia District mines, and through its development work the area again began to prosper. H and H built a new flotation mill, but during World War II the district again ebbed when the government issued a ban on gold mining. A diamond-drilling program was begun in 1964 by the Federal Resources Corporation of Salt Lake City, involving the Champion, Evening Star, Musick, and other properties. At nearby Cottage Grove an annual celebration is held in mid-July, known as Bohemia Mining Days, a four-day event built entirely around the mining theme, including guided tours and the like. *United States Forest Service*

DIVERSIFIED UTAH

The most diversified group of metals, minerals, and chemicals was being found in Utah. Gold, silver, salt, coal, lead, sulfur, copper, zinc, and borax were but a few of the important elements that were deposited in the rock, soil, and water of the Mormon state.

Even before 1863—officially designated by Utah as its historical beginning in mining—some mining was practiced here. Navajo silversmiths had long used metal from Utah mines and Spanish-Americans were already mining in the 1840s.

On orders from the Secretary of War, United States troops under General Patrick E. Connor had been dispatched to Utah in 1857, remaining at Camp Douglas, overlooking Salt Lake City, until the outbreak of the Civil War. These California and Nevada Volunteers were ostensibly for the protection of the Overland Mail, which faced Indian attacks. But actually it was to prevent any likelihood of the Mormons seceding.

GENERAL CONNOR IN BINGHAM CANYON

A popular subject for discussion at the camp were the outcroppings of ore in Bingham Canyon, a cattle-grazing area found by Thomas and Sanford Bingham in 1848. Because many of Connor's force were former miners, he encouraged them to prospect in the mountains. On September 17, 1863, a prospecting group uncovered silver ore in the Canyon. George B. Ogilvie, who had grazed his cattle there, was among them, and it was he who identified the

ore. Ogilvie brought samples to Connor who had them assayed and then sent Ogilvie to locate the West Jordan Mine. Connor filed a claim in the name of the Jordan Silver Mining Company. Twenty-five people were listed in the notice, including Ogilvie and General Connor. On that same day, Mrs. Robert K. Reid, the camp surgeon's wife, found a vein adjacent to the Jordan claim, and a notice was filed, this time with twenty stockholders, including Mrs. Reid and General Connor's wife. A third claim was filed that day, the Vedette. The three representative groups then met at the Jordan Ward Meetinghouse to organize the West Mountain Quartz Mining District. Though veins discovered by Mormon pioneers and some exploration work had preceded these finds, Bingham Canyon's were the first *recorded* mining claims in the territory.

In 1865, the West Jordan Mining Company incorporated under the laws of California, and tunneling began. Under the general's sponsorship many ore bodies were discovered. Silver was abundant, frequently mixed with lead, copper, and zinc. Financed by General Connor and others, in 1864, smelters and furnaces had been built. By the Civil War's end, the army no longer sponsored mining in Utah. Many of the claims were in the names of Volunteers; in 1866, General Connor himself returned to Stockton to direct his mining interests. Little mining was done during postwar days until the railroads arrived to open the Utah Territory.

This photo, taken by C. W. Carter, an early Utah photographer, is believed to have been in the vicinity of Bingham Creek. Interim explorations of the Canyon created the Galena, Empire, Kingston, Julia Dean, and Silver Hill claims. The Volunteers organized the Wasatch Mountain Mining District, and troops were dispatched as far as southern Idaho, southeastern Nevada, and the Uinta Basin in search of placer mines. Placer mining in Utah was quickly replaced with quartz-lode mining so that photographs of placer operations are rare. *Utah State Historical Society*

The Standard Rex Silver Mine in Little Cottonwood Canyon, 1937, typical of the many mines in the canyons. An important silver-lead discovery, Hidden Treasure Mine, which turned out to be an especially important lead source, occurred at East Canyon. Silver-bearing ore was found in 1864 in Little Cottonwood Canyon, near Salt Lake City; and in that same year in the Oquirrh Mountains the Rush Valley Mining District and the West Mountain District were organized. Within the Rush Valley District, around the city of Stockton —population 400-plus in 1866—over 500 claims were located, and for a decade after 1870, lead and silver mining expanded. Near Salt Lake, in the Little Cottonwood District alone, in a 2½-mile-square area, over 3,500 claims had been staked. Little Cottonwood Canyon activity had spurred discoveries in the Ophir District—around 1870 a number of silver mines were discovered, some producing ores impregnated with chloride of silver that assayed as high as $20,000 a ton. But, like Little Cottonwood, Ophir fizzled. In ten years 2,500 active locations were down to fewer than 150. Nearer to Salt Lake City, and parallel to Little Cottonwood, was Big Cottonwood Canyon, organized in the 1860s as the Mountain Lake Mining District. By 1872 there were more than 700 locations in the canyon, the most famous the Prince of Wales group, developed by the Walker Brothers, primarily a lead-zinc operation with some silver. *United States Forest Service. Photo by W. H. Shaffer*

Tailings (center) from the Chief Consolidated Mining Company are piled high in Eureka. A new district organized in 1870, the Tintic, near the Oquirrh Range, developed three mining camps: Eureka, Silver City, and Diamond City. Deposits were rich in lead, silver, copper, and gold. The important mines were the Sunbeam, Black Dragon, Eureka Hill, and Mammoth. *Arthur Lakes Library, Colorado School of Mines*

THE BINGHAM PIT

Bingham Canyon was a storehouse of rich metal and, of course, the source of General Connor's California Volunteers' 1862 copper find. Thirty-four years later, Thomas Weir and Samuel Newhouse started buying mining claims, the most important being several properties held in the name of the Highland Boy Gold Mining Company. After Newhouse enlisted English capital to finance operations, the Utah Consolidated Gold Mines Ltd. was organized in London, and Newhouse became president and Weir general manager.

In the 1890s, just preceding Standard Oil's takeover of Utah Consolidated, a group had been formed under the leadership of Henry H. Rogers and Leonard Lewisohn to consolidate as much as possible of the lead-smelting operations in the United States. It was called the American Smelting and Refining Company (ASARCO). Asarco had managed to acquire about eighteen companies for the new combine, and by reducing unprofitable operations and closing down smelters that could be served by new plants—which Asarco built—it was hoped to make the combine profitable.

Copper expansion followed in other Utah districts, but mostly as by-products of lead-silver operations. Many discoveries, consolidations, and developments catapulted copper production from nearly 4 million pounds to over 57 million pounds in seven years.

But the farmers were not rejoicing. Farm crops turned yellow and livestock became sickly. Smoke from the smelters was suspected, and a suit was begun in the United States District Court. A court decision on November 13, 1906, outlawed the smelters, and they closed down within two years.

In 1940 mining was still the major activity at Park City, but today it is a fantastic ski resort with ski tows and gondolas rising to the highest peaks (upper right center). By 1879 the permanent town of Park City was well under construction, and by 1888 the mine had paid nearly $9 million in dividends. It continued in full operation until 1897, hanging on until about 1904. West of the Ontario other claims helped elevate Park City to one of the West's richest. Also, the Hearst-Haggin group added to their holdings through an interest in the John J. Daly property, operated by the Daly Mining Company. The United Park City Mining Company, although still accounting for about 250 tons of lead-zinc-silver ore a day, is responsible for the vast recreational summer and winter complex at Treasure Mountain. The gondola ride from Park City, as it goes to the top of the mountain, passes over many of the mine workings and dumps. Alternatively, the top can be reached via a mine train and a shaft, in either direction. *Arthur Lakes Library, Colorado School of Mines*

However, American Smelting and Refining had agreed to compensate the farmers up to $60,000 in return for continued operations.

The mining of sulfide coppers declined as copper producers began to bring out lead. It was about the time that the smelters were closing down that porphyry (rock) mining was introduced, culminating in the development of Kennecott's Bingham Canyon Mine (Utah Copper Division).

The world's largest man-made crater, in Utah, would be clearly visible to an astronaut orbiting the earth. The crater comprises Kennecott Copper's Bingham Pit where more copper ore is mined in a day than is produced in a year at many well-known mines.

The Bingham Smelting Works at Bingham Canyon, 1870s. The first smelter in the canyon was erected at the Utah Mine, but by 1873 it had proved a failure. The Winnamuck Smelter was successfully operated, and although expenses were high, losses were correspondingly low. In the 1860s and 1870s, ores from this Salt Lake area were shipped for smelting to Baltimore, San Francisco, and Swansea (Wales), the period's greatest smelting center in the world. (Estimates of ore shipments from Utah mines to 1880 exceed $45 million, about half in silver, followed by lead and copper equally.) However, as mines developed, local smelters were added, many during the 1870s in the Salt Lake district, surpassing even Swansea. *William Culp Darrah Stereo Collection*

205

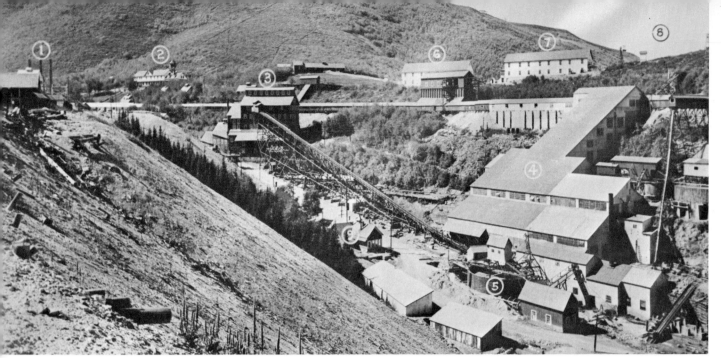

Silver King Coalition Mines Company, Park City: (1) hoist and main shaft 1,300 feet deep, (2) boarding-house, (3) sampler, (4) mill, (5) Dorr tank, (6) sleep-ing quarters Number One, (7) sleeping quarters Number Two, (8) aerial tram to Park City, (9) assay office. *Arthur Lakes Library, Colorado School of Mines*

Upper Bingham Canyon and Copper Hill, 1904, Bingham Canyon, Utah's greatest copper source. In 1870 finds were uncovered in the Lucin District, near the Utah-Nevada border, and large nuggets of native copper were found on the surface at Copper Hill. From 1886 to 1893 the Copper Mountain Mine was worked extensively, and thereafter sold to the Salt Lake Copper Company, adding a smelter near Salt Lake City. All of these copper operations were ultimately purchased by the Lewisohn Brothers of New York City, and operated by them for many years. In the 1870s, following the Lucin discoveries, copper was found in the Tintic District, where the Mammoth and Crimson-Mammoth mines were important early producers. The Beaver Lake District and the Rocky districts produced nearly a million pounds of copper over the next thirty years. Copper Gulch in Beaver County developed the Comet, Cactus, and Copper Chief mines, although they did not produce actively until the mid-1890s, when the Dixie Mine was developed in Washington county and a smelter was added. A smelter had been constructed a decade earlier at Abraham to process its nearby copper production. *Utah Copper Division, Kennecott Copper Corporation*

Old Jordan Mine—U.S. mine road in Bingham Canyon, 1889. The railroads also had made possible the revival, in 1870, of the Jordan and Galena claims, and the Spanish and Winnamuck mines were put into operation by an English company. The area contained sizeable ore bodies of lead carbonate and low-grade argentiferous galena, and as the carbonate zones ran out, sulfide lead ore was uncovered. Lead-silver ore production continued its rise through the decade, while mines changed hands as readily as poker chips—twenty-one mines were producing in the West Mountain District in 1892, among them the Jordan, Brooklyn, Telegraph, Galena, Petro, and Yosemite. *Utah Copper Division, Kennecott Copper Corporation*

206

The complexity of mining in the late 1800s and early 1900s is evident in this picture of the Utah Consolidated Mining Company's operation at Park City. *Arthur Lakes Library, Colorado School of Mines*

End of a shift. Double hoist at the Ontario Mine Number 3, Park City. *Utah State Historical Society*

The Ontario Mine boardinghouse was home to many of the miners. *Utah State Historical Society, courtesy of the Utah Mining Association*

Assay office at the Ontario Mine, Park City, 1900. It was vitally important for every mine to assay its output continuously to determine whether the ore had sufficient metallics to make the operation profitable. The Park City District was one of the most outstanding in Utah, beginning around 1869 with discoveries made by Rufus Walker and Ephraim Hanks. Its first large producer was the Piñon Mine, rich in lead carbonate silver ores. Within two years the Pioneer was located, and a year later Ontario Ledge, the foundation of the vast Hearst fortune. George Hearst, father of William Randolph, together with J. B. Haggin, sent a man to the area to investigate the ore discoveries. The Hearst-Haggin interests purchased the Ontario Ledge claim, and development work began almost immediately. Within four years after its discovery, capitalized at $10 million, the Ontario Mine was producing $14,000 a week, and the balance of the camp was producing about $6,000 and employing over 150 men between the mine and mill. *Utah State Historical Society*

Main Street, Carr Fork, circa 1895. Carr Fork is still the main road leading to the mine located northwest of the Bingham Canyon Mine. Even before 1880 Bingham Canyon had its principal copper mines: What Cheer, Hickman, Murphy, Kingston, and Washington, while other copper derived from lead-silver ores, as a by-product. But the real activity in copper came after 1896 with the development of the cyanide gold-mining process. The process made Samuel Newhouse and Thomas Weir prominent copper men, and attracted to Utah William Rockefeller, Standard Oil, and the Guggenheims. Activity centered upon the construction of four smelters around Salt Lake City, controlled by American Smelting and Refining, United States Smelting, Refining and Mining, and International Smelting and Refining. *Utah Copper Division, Kennecott Copper Corporation*

Lower Bingham, 1909. Freight depot and Utah Consolidated's tramway. While attempting to develop the cyanide method for the extraction of gold, Utah Consolidated's Highland Boy Tunnels Numbers 4 and 5 revealed rich copper ores, and it was soon obvious that mining copper ore would be more profitable than fooling with gold. In three years Newhouse and Weir opened both a smelter for reducing copper ores and a 300-ton-per-day lead-smelting plant, while the company had purchased additional claims in Bingham Canyon totaling nearly 250 acres of mineral land. During this expansion period Standard Oil had been purchasing Utah Consolidated stock, which in May, 1899, put the Rockefeller syndicate in control of the company. The sale involved $12 million, of which Newhouse is believed to have cleared $3 million. Its new smelter had been extremely successful; in the first year it produced about 6½ million pounds of copper, some 93,000 ounces of silver, and 8,250 ounces of gold. In 1903 company headquarters was transferred from London to New York, and a new company, the Utah Consolidated Mining Company, a holding company, was capitalized in New Jersey. It owned the majority of shares in the Highland Boy Gold Mining Company of New Jersey, and thereby title to the Utah properties. *Utah Copper Division, Kennecott Copper Corporation*

The Bingham Canyon Mine of Kennecott's Utah Copper Division, with its amphitheatre-like structure, the largest manmade excavation in the world. The introduction of open-cut copper mining at Bingham was a major milestone in the history of mining. The Bingham porphyries have produced more than 10 million tons of metal, more volume than from any single mine in the world. Bingham Canyon produced one-third of all the copper used by the Allies in World War II. The history of Kennecott's Utah Copper Mine began with Enos A. Wall, from Indiana, in 1887, when he staked out claims in Bingham Canyon. He was unable to finance the development of the property, but managed to hold on to it for sixteen years. Two years after Wall's discovery, Sam Newhouse and Thomas Weir had purchased claims at Bingham and organized the Boston Consolidated Mining Company to develop porphyries. Wall, through the efforts of Daniel C. Jackling, a Missouri farmboy who became a metallurgical engineer, sold his properties to Colorado capitalists whom the Guggenheim family, (which owned the controlling interest in American Smelting and Refining) agreed to finance, including the expansion and development of all of the Bingham properties. *Utah Copper Division, Kennecott Copper Corporation*

Partial view of Kennecott Copper's Utah mine. Trestles at various bench levels bridge gulch in foreground. Three tunnels provide egress from pit for trains loaded with low-grade ore en route to Arthur and Magna concentrators. Traffic density on railroad, controlled by a CTC system, is believed to be the highest of any railroad in the world. About 90,000 tons of ore and 220,-000 tons of waste material were being removed each operating day at time photo was taken. *United States Bureau of Mines*

These loaded 65- to 110-ton capacity trucks haul the overburden to dumps outside the Bingham Mine. Eventually a water-acid solution is percolated through the overburden dumps to dissolve and extract the copper in them. The expansion of copper mining, particularly the development of Kennecott's copper pit, has caused the disappearance of practically all other metal mining in the Canyon. *Utah Copper Division, Kennecott Copper Corporation*

Cuprum, 1909, assembly yards and equipment on High Line above the town. Utah Copper's lines are farther up the mountain. In 1910 the Guggenheims arranged for Newhouse and Weir's original Boston Consolidated to be absorbed by Utah Copper, which rapidly became the largest copper producer in the United States. But the sulfide mines were slowly dying; some were bought or merged—Kennecott Copper (Guggenheim controlled) absorbed Utah Copper. *Utah Copper Division, Kennecott Copper Corporation*

Flotation process at Kennecott's Utah Copper Division's Arthur concentrator. Mineral recovery begins with flotation. In this process copper and other mineral values of the ore are separated from waste material. Every day more than 104,000 tons of waste material (called tailings) flow to a nearby 5,100-acre disposal area. *Utah Copper Division, Kennecott Copper Corporation*

THE COLORADO CANNIBAL

An old Bingham Canyon alumnus was remembered at the University of Colorado in May, 1968. The students demanded that the name of the Roaring Fork Grill, the principal student eating place, be changed to the Packer Grill, claiming that the grill had now attained the high culinary standards of Alferd Packer—a nineteenth-century mining prospector convicted of murder and cannibalism. His gruesome story is based on an elementary motive—survival. And survive he did, by dining on five prospectors.

A drifter who had served a jail sentence for a $23 robbery and who had worked in the Utah copper mines, Packer helped guide a party of twenty-one prospectors from Bingham Canyon, near Salt Lake City, to the goldfields of the Colorado Territory. Also, he had volunteered to care for the horses and to act as general handyman.

Late in January, 1874, after suffering the ravages of a severe, early winter, the party arrived at the camp of Ute Indian Chief Ouray, near Montrose, Colorado. On February 9, 1874, Packer pushed on, leading a party of five companions from Ouray's camp through a shortcut.

Alferd Packer, the Colorado Man-Eater. *Fred and Jo Mazzulla Collection*

On April 16, 1874, Packer arrived alone at the Los Pinos Indian Agency, fresh and healthy-looking, despite the severity of the winter. Questioned about the five missing prospectors, he admitted that they were dead but told a number of conflicting stories about how they died. In his first confession, he said that they had become lost, that one of the men died, but that all of them ate the dead man's flesh. He said that two starved, leaving himself and two others. One then shot the other, and Packer claimed that he had been forced to kill the survivor in self-defense, with a hatchet. Later, however, in his written confession, he claimed that while he was away from camp

Sketch of Packer's victims by John A. Randolph. Harper's Weekly, *October 17, 1874*

searching for gold, one of the men had gone berserk and killed the four others with an axe. On his return to camp, he too was attacked, he claimed, and had to shoot the fifth prospector in self-defense. He said that in order to survive through the severe winter, he had been forced to eat the five dead men, well refrigerated in the icy cold. A search party later discovered the five mutilated and dismembered bodies and buried them at their mountain camp, high on a mountain slope leading to Slumgullion Pass, near Lake City, Colorado.

On August 18, 1874, Packer, who had in the interim been arrested and placed in a dungeon at Saguache awaiting trial, escaped. A reward of $5,000 was posted for his capture. On March 11, 1883, one of the original twenty-one members of the expedition recognized him in Fort Fetterman, Wyoming. He was recaptured, brought to Lake City, and indicted for murder. The trial was held before Judge M. B. Gerry. On April 13, 1883, Packer was found guilty of murder and sentenced to be hanged.

However, on appeal, the Colorado Supreme Court ruled that he had been charged under a territorial law but tried under a state law, and therefore, called for a new trial, which was held in August, 1886, in Gunnison, Colorado. The second jury found Packer guilty of manslaughter on separate counts for each of the five victims, and sentenced him to eight years on each count. He served in the penitentiary from 1886 to 1901 when he was paroled. He died and was buried in Littleton, Colorado, on April 23, 1907. Thousands of tourists have visited his grave, which now lacks a gravestone; on or about July 28, 1968, it was stolen.

Larry Dolan, a barfly who had been in court during Packer's first trial, cadged many free drinks after the trial as payment for an unverified story he related. He claimed that the judge had said, "Stand up, you man-eating s.o.b., stand up! They wuz just seven Demmycrats in Hinsdale County and you et five of 'em. I sentence you to be hanged by the neck until you are dead, dead, dead. Let this be a warning against reducing the Demmycratic population of this state." Although Dolan's story was popular, it was an obvious put-on. Judge Gerry was a learned man, and the district court records show that the judge's sentencing remarks were scholarly, dignified, and somewhat poetic. For years afterward, it was popular to become a member of the Packer Club, whose slogan should be "Have a friend for dinner."

The story of Alferd Packer is well chronicled in a forty-eight-page paperbound book, *Al Packer, A Colorado Cannibal*, by Fred and Jo Mazzulla. The Mazzullas have been collecting material on Packer for more than thirty years.

COPPER-GOLD-COPPER IN ARIZONA

Copper had also been important to Arizona during this time, but nine years after its initial find at Ajo, suddenly gold intruded—at Wickenburg.

Legends surrounding the discovery of gold and other metals are as varied as the mines themselves, and Wickenburg made its contribution, but with a twist, to those attributed to dozens of mine discoveries featuring stubborn burros prodded by the action of a hurled rock; the rock always misses its target and hits another stone, or ledge, and exposes a vein of precious metal. Henry Wickenburg, discoverer of a valuable quartz lode, is supposed to have discovered his mine while following circling vultures, in the hope perhaps of rescuing some prospector in need. The truth is that Wickenburg was an Austrian refugee who came to Arizona in 1862 and prospected at Yuma and La Paz, hoping to catch up with the Peeples group of prospectors that

---

THE MURDERERS' MIRTH

The Supreme Court Says Murder is not a Crime

If Committed Previous to the 28th Day of May, 1881.

Packer will not Hang May 19th, as Ordered.

Packer Free.
Special to Daily-Review Press.

DENVER, Colo., May 11.—The Supreme Court reversed the decision in the Garvey case this morning. It holds that Garvey cannot be tried for murder. This will affect the Packer and also the Brennen case from Gunnison.

Clipping from the *Gunnison Daily Review Press*, May 12, 1883. *Fred and Jo Mazzulla Collection*

When this drawing was first published in 1891, it carried the caption "Finding Gold by Accident." *New York Public Library*

Pouring an $18,000 gold brick at the famed Vulture Mine around 1939 near Wickenburg. Today Wickenburg celebrates the advent of gold mining with "Gold Rush Days," when gold panning contests are held for young and old. *Arizona Department of Library and Archives*

discovered Arizona's richest placer bonanza. But placer mining never assumed real importance because of the early discovery of quartz lodes, Wickenburg being among the first to find such a lode. He had named it the Vulture Mine, which gave the vulture story credence. But Arizona's gold would soon fade into insignificance as copper resumed its role as king in Globe and Miami.

The Vulture Gold Mine near Wickenburg, the most productive of Arizona's early gold mines. The mine produced $2½ million in gold from 118,000 tons of ore during its first six years of operation, and much more later. Wickenburg built an arrastra to crush the quartz gold ore, but he found it impractical to remove the ore from the mine and then to crush it. Instead he permitted others to work his mine while he crushed the ore in his arrastra for a set fee. As with many others before him, the system proved unsatisfactory. More ore was stolen than reached the processing stage, and charges for the use of arrastras were far too low anyway. After three years, Wickenburg sold the mine to the Phillips Company of New York for $85,000, receiving a down payment of $20,000. A dispute with the buyers thereafter foreclosed his ever seeing the balance. The Vulture Mine changed hands many times after that, and developed into Arizona's most successful gold mine. Profits exceeded $17 million. The town of Wickenburg, originally established to serve the mine, in 1866 was one of Arizona's largest towns. *Arizona Department of Library and Archives*

The story of Globe begins in 1864 with the Pinal Mountain gold and silver discovery. The recorded claims by the earliest prospectors were not worked until September, 1873, when new claims were filed on Globe Ledge, and the first ore was produced and shipped to Florence for assay. Along the way, in March, 1875, members of one pack train discovered the elusive Silver King claim. The ore being "packed out" from Globe Ledge assayed at about $121 in silver and $13 in gold. Silver King samples assayed at $4,300 or more per ton! And the scramble to Pinal Mountain country was on.

The Silver King Mine at Silver King in the Globe-Miami Mining District of Arizona. It was first discovered in 1873 and rediscovered in 1875, triggering a rush to the Pinal Mountain country. The country was rugged, and fights with Apache Indians were common. But the spirit of adventure prevailed, and in less than a year after Silver King's founding, at the future village of McMillan, the last large silver claim was made—the Stonewall Jackson Mine. (In 1880 copper replaced silver, nearing exhaustion as a valuable ore.) The mine produced over $6,500,000 in silver by the 1920s. It since has become a ghost town. Approaching Pinal Mountain country today, travelers immediately become aware of vast mining operations. To the east, passing through Globe, asbestos mills and the Old Dominion Copper Mine remains are clearly visible. Huge mounds of tailings near the junction of U.S. Highway 60–70 and the Apache Trail alter the countryside. Some 90 million tons of tailings from the Inspiration Copper Company and the Miami Copper Company resemble distant mountain ranges. *Arizona Department of Library Archives*

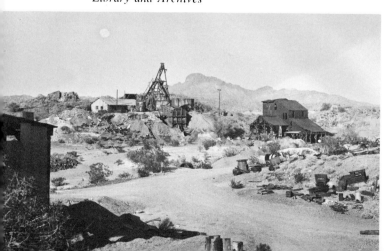

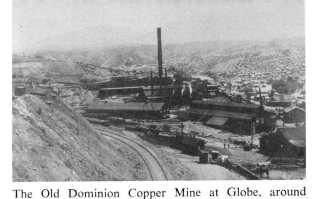

The Old Dominion Copper Mine at Globe, around 1885. The mine was ultimately abandoned when the ore ran out. Down Pinal Creek, four miles from the village, the Old Dominion claim had been staked by prospectors from Virginia, among them, Ben Reagan. After buying out his partners, he, too, sold out, and the Dominion claim developed into the Old Dominion Mining Company. The company experienced financial troubles and changed hands several times. It had even been sold for delinquent taxes at a sheriff's sale. Its final sale placed it with a Guggenheim, who closed it in 1886 because of the low copper prices. With an improved market two years later, an extensive survey and a new shaft, the Interloper Shaft, followed. It shared with the Mooney Tunnel, opening on Pinal Creek, the distinction of sole use of mules or burros in and out of the mine. The Old Dominion became important in the copper industry. The town enjoyed a parallel expansion, including a modern hotel, hospital, and courthouse. In 1906 the Interloper Shaft, now used for ventilation, burned, killing three men and gassing a number of mules. And in November, 1931, down to the 27th level, and failing fast, the prohibitive pumping costs closed the Old Dominion for good. All that remains of one of the world's greatest copper mines, accounting in its day for over seven billion pounds of copper, are Globe's concrete foundations and the Old Dominion Mine and smelter plant. *Arizona Department of Library and Archives*

In 1918 workmen were transported to the mines at Globe and Miami in these specially constructed trucks. Phelps Dodge purchased the United Globe mines in 1892, and in 1903 obtained control of the Old Dominion. Miami Copper was organized in 1907, and a year later Inspiration Copper. These justified extending the railroad from Miami to Globe, and Inspiration accelerated development work. *Inspiration Consolidated Copper Company*

The story of Miami begins with J. Parke Channing, a noted mining engineer, and an uneducated alien with an unpronounceable, unspellable name; the Globe Mine's timekeeper resorted to "New Man Jack," which fellow miners altered to Black Jack to distinguish him from the many Cornish "Jacks" who worked the local mines. Black Jack later modified it to Jack Newman, and even taught himself to write it.

Newman was a first-class mining man who opened new claims adjacent to what would one day be the Inspiration Consolidated Copper property. Some exploration and the sinking of a shaft on the new property was agreed to by the General Development Company. A second shaft reached 200 feet at

From the highway near Miami, extensive copper-mine workings are easily visible. In 1942, while Miami Copper resumed drilling at the Copper Cities ore body, the Castle Dome Mine was initiated and its buildings were moved to Copper Cities when its ore reserves were depleted in 1953. International Smelting built a much needed smelter here, purchased in 1960 by Inspiration, all of which operations are now part of Inspiration Consolidated Copper Company's vast empire, including an underground mine at Christmas, Arizona, forty miles from Miami. *Felix A. Peckham*

In 1912 Inspiration Mines merged with Live Oak, becoming the Inspiration Consolidated Copper Mining Company. The pictures show the new combination raising a 40-foot bent tailing dam in April 1917, and a pile-driver at work in 1918 at Globe, Arizona. *Inspiration Consolidated Copper Company*

213

An electric shovel loading ore into haulage truck at Inspiration's open-pit mine for transport to the mine crusher. For many of the companies, such improved earthmoving equipment and increasing underground mining costs had encouraged them to turn to open-pit mining, the first time in 1948. *Inspiration Consolidated Copper Company*

Possibly the most famous nonexistent gold mine in the West was the Lost Dutchman Mine, which has never been found. Here a prospector crosses the desert after apparently an unsuccessful search for the Lost Dutchman Mine in the Superstition Mountains seen in the background to the north of Globe and Miami. Prospectors have for years searched these rugged mountains, looking for its fabulous gold, but always in vain. One man, Jacob Walz, persisted that he had found ore in the Superstitions. But it was common practice for prospectors to pretend they had discovered rich lodes, disappearing for short times and even coming back with samples of rich ore—probably stolen from some mine. The chances are that Walz had bought his samples from other miners or perhaps had "high graded" it at the Vulture Gold Mine of Henry Wickenberg. *Western Ways Photo*

the same time as the financial panic of 1907, and work stopped. The foreman showed Newman the telegram ordering the stoppage. Newman tore it up and assured the miners, who continued—twenty feet later striking a rich ore that would guarantee the mine's success.

About 100 miles southeast of Globe, new copper areas had also sprung into existence in Greenlee County, which was traversed by Francisco Coronado in his sixteenth-century search for the Seven Cities of Cíbola. Here are the towns of Clifton, Metcalf, and Morenci, whose mining history began in 1864 when Henry Clifton and a group of prospectors from Silver City, New Mexico, encouraged by evidence of early mining—by Mexican explorers—uncovered rich copper carbonate ore. Clifton, sitting practically on New Mexico's border, is the county seat and probably the oldest continuously producing copper-mining camp in the southwest. But its gems and rocks, especially turquoise, all types of agates, and

azurite, are equally well known. Dealers and rock hounds throughout the country come here to gather the semiprecious gem stones. Clifton owes its existence to prospectors Isaac Stephens, Bob Metcalf, and six others who in 1872 located the first mining claims and founded the town named for Henry Clifton.

Clifton, Arizona, 1885. *Phelps Dodge Corporation*

Within a year after Clifton's founding, a copper furnace was built and the Longfellow Copper Company organized. The reason for this assemblage at the Old Longfellow Mine in 1900 is not known. Perhaps the miners were on the verge of a strike or maybe they just came to have their picture taken, as the camera can be seen in the foreground. *Greenlee County, Arizona, Chamber of Commerce*

Apache Indians, circa 1890. The figure on the right is believed to be Geronimo. Shootings, outlaw raids, and Indian attacks enlivened Metcalf's early-day diggings, with the old Coronado Railroad hauling the rich copper ore over a nine-mile track from the Arizona Copper Company to Clifton. Metcalf was a parallel discovery, of gold, about five miles north of Clifton. Its suddenly arrived 2,000 inhabitants were intent on claiming a share of the wealth, but when the gold played out and the price of copper fell, Metcalf went the familiar mining-town route—a derelict filled with stark, roofless walls, weed-covered foundations, and dust. *Phelps Dodge Corporation*

Arizona Copper's smelter, near Clifton. Almost simultaneous with the Morenci discoveries, the Copper Queen Mine changed the Phelps Dodge business from a merchant trading company to an important factor in the copper-mining and refining business. Originally a combination of two merchant firms from the 1830s, Phelps Dodge turned from exporting, importing, and merchandising to a major manufacturer in Connecticut's Naugatuck Valley, which was, and still is, the copper/brass industry center of the United States. Phelps and Dodge built a small mill around Waterbury, and soon produced metal products in other areas of the valley, including such items as brass and copper kettles, rivets, tubing, sheet metal, buttons, clocks, wire, and other products. While most of its metal was imported from England, as the Morenci and Copper Queen properties came into production in the 1880s, domestic sources for Phelps Dodge operations provided for increased expansion, and copper was sold on the open market. Phelps Dodge continued its expansion with the acquisition of the Arizona Copper Company, in 1921, which, from 1880 to 1921, had produced 460 million pounds of copper. *Phelps Dodge Corporation*

Anson Greene Phelps (1781–1853), co-founder of Phelps Dodge. *Phelps Dodge Corporation*

The old Copper Head locomotive in Clifton, still a tourist's attraction as it sits in front of the old jail in the heart of town. Copper ore was originally hauled by wagons from Metcalf to the smelter at Clifton. Marauding Indians made this a risky operation, so a 20-inch narrow-gauge railway track was constructed. At first the ore cars rolled to the smelter by gravity and were hauled back by mules, but in 1878 the first locomotive arrived from La Juanta, Colorado—towed by oxen for 600 miles! *Greenlee County, Arizona, Chamber of Commerce*

William Earl Dodge (1805–1883), co-founder of Phelps Dodge. *Phelps Dodge Corporation*

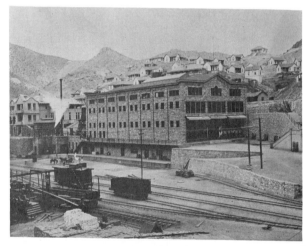

Morenci about 1900. Morenci was different. Its "Copper Mountain" made it famous. William Church's Detroit Copper Mining Company, organized in 1874, built a smelter six years later, on the San Francisco River, three miles below Clifton. A year later a narrow-gauge (20-inch) railroad was constructed; it carried Arizona's first locomotive, known as the Copper Head. It proudly sits alongside Clifton's main street today. *Greenlee County, Arizona, Chamber of Commerce*

Morenci (circa 1890), showing the company store and the narrow-gauge railroad where the famous Copper Head engine worked. Originally called Joy's Camp, Morenci was named after Morenci, Michigan, by an official of the Detroit Copper Company. Phelps Dodge acquired a half-interest in the Detroit in 1882, becoming the Morenci Branch of the Phelps Dodge Corporation in 1917. With the smelters and concentrators that had been built, Morenci became a major copper district. *Greenlee County, Arizona, Chamber of Commerce*

A railroad connected the Morenci mines with the reduction works. *Phelps Dodge Corporation*

The flotation section of the Morenci concentrator. Here the crushed and ground ore, mixed with water, air, and chemical reagents, is agitated to cause copper particles to float to the top and overflow in the froth. This process separates the copper minerals from waste rock. *Phelps Dodge Corporation*

The Morenci Hotel, once the center for social activities in the copper town. *Greenlee County, Arizona, Chamber of Commerce*

The Morenci pits of the Phelps Dodge Corporation in this 1940 photograph are the second largest copper-producing properties in the United States. More than 800 million tons of material have been removed from this pit, transforming what was once a mountain into a hole 1½ miles in diameter and a ¼ mile deep. *Greenlee County, Arizona, Chamber of Commerce*

LAW COMES TO MONTANA

On May 26, 1863, six haggard prospectors camped near an alder-banked stream in the Tobacco Root Mountains, roughly seventy-five miles from Bannack, Montana. The party had just been freed after having been captured and threatened with death by the Crow Indians if they continued their search for gold in Indian territory. Their capture turned out to be fortunate indeed—they had fled to a gold-laden area soon to become known as Alder Gulch. While a camp was being set up in the shadows of the alder trees, two of the prospectors saw some promising-looking gravel and panned it out. The residue contained $5 worth of gold. Bill Fairweather, Henry Edgar, Tom Cover, Barney Hughes, Harry Rogers, and Mike Sweeney had truly struck it rich. They sent Hughes back to civilization for additional supplies. So conspicuously supplied was he, that during his return to camp, 300 to 400 men were right behind, anxious to discover his secret. Astutely confronting them along the trail, he asked for a meeting, and explained that his party had found less than $200 in gold, and he described what they might hope to find if they ever got to the site. But he steadfastly refused to go one inch further unless the stampeders, as they were called, guaranteed to each of the six discovers 200 feet of any ground they staked as claims, never to be jumped or confiscated. The crowd agreed and retired to draw up a mining code. That night, with several friends from among the stampeders, Hughes sneaked off so as to arrive first and stake new claims as near to the original discovery as possible. When the bulk of the stampeders arrived later, they were furious, but they were able to stake out some good claims. Days later an accidental grass fire burned out part of the gulch, including the prospectors' supplies. Those who suffered no damages from the fire shared their goods until new supplies arrived.

The day the stragglers arrived the town site had been staked out and dubbed Virginia City. Without proper building supplies, the men lived in makeshift outdoor shelters—wagons, dugouts, and so on. Neighborhood lumber however was plentiful, and there was no need to rely on the nearest sawmill at Bannack. The first building was a bakery.

In 1864, for the seventeen miles along the gulch, between 10,000 and 15,000 men were working both sides of the snakelike creek, including the streambed and the hillside. Despite the number of prospectors, no noteworthy discoveries were made, but some 1,000 claims were reasonably profitable. According to William S. Greever's *The Bonanza West,* the first lode was discovered in January, 1864, the first water-powered stamp mill was started in October, and in December the first steam mill went into operation. Greever says, "Perhaps by 1865, certainly by 1868, they had extracted $30,000,000 in gold from all the gulch, and by 1900, the total yield was over $85,000,000. Gold dust was bought by dealers in Virginia City and Bannack at $19 or $19.50 per ounce; they usually resold it for $22." This was indeed a considerable amount of gold, without benefit of a major lode discovery.

In the meantime, Henry Plummer, on an excursion from Bannack, had transferred his criminal activities to Virginia City. At this juncture, Plummer, a former inmate of San Quentin Prison, was still bossing a gang of road agents; three, Buck Stinson, Charley Forbes, and Hayes Lyons, were busy robbing travelers en route to Virginia City from Bannack. D. R. Dillingham, a deputy sheriff, refused to join them and forewarned travelers. The three men shot Dillingham in Virginia City in front of a miners' court, which was in session, in view of about 100 citizens. The three men immediately were seized. Stinson and Lyons were unanimously found guilty, and sentenced to hang. Forbes, glibber than his companions, was acquitted, whereupon his friends cried for mercy, and a second vote was taken. Stinson and Lyons were freed on that vote. However, the conviction later of another Plummer subordinate at Nevada City led to the formation of the Montana Vigilantes in Virginia City, Nevada City, Helena, and other locations. Between December, 1863, and January, 1864, the vigilantes, the same that hanged Plummer, hanged at least twenty-one men. In December, 1864, in Virginia City, H. L. Hosmer, appointed Chief Justice of the Montana Territory by

Virginia City, Montana, about 1865. *New York Public Library Picture Collection*

The ever-present rocker in Alder Gulch, in 1871. *Montana Historical Society; W. H. Jackson photo, Hayden Survey*

Hydraulic mining in Alder Gulch, near Virginia City, 1871. Note the sluice boxes throughout an area that was devastated by earlier placer workings. *Montana Historical Society; W. H. Jackson photo, Hayden Survey*

Chinese miners in Montana were permitted only to rework the old properties during the 1860s and 1870s. This is a view of Chinese miners examining a sluice box in Alder Gulch in 1871. *Montana Historical Society; W. H. Jackson photo, Hayden Survey*

Stark wooden markers at Boot Hill Cemetery, near Virginia City, mute testimony to the lawlessness of vigilante days in that rip-roaring mining community. These are graves of gangsters hanged in 1864. *Montana Highway Commission*

Robbers' Roost, near Virginia City, a hangout for hold-up gangs during the early gold-rush days when stagecoaches were making regular runs between Bannack and Virginia City. *Montana Highway Commission*

President Lincoln, in the interest of law and order urged the disbandment of the vigilantes in favor of the courts. By year's end, none remained.

Congress had established the Idaho Territory in March, 1863, which included the present State of Montana. Pleadings by Sydney Edgerton, a chief justice assigned to the Montana Judicial District, resulted in President Lincoln's authorizing a separate Montana Territory in May, 1864, with Edgerton as its first governor. Bannack was its first capitol, replaced in 1865 by Virginia City and in 1867 by Helena. With the formation of the Montana Territory, the principles written into the Montana miners' courts were now officially enacted into law.

Virginia City grew rapidly as a supply point for the surrounding mining areas, though its homes probably were exceeded by its numerous saloons. The town was wide open, and for $1 women could easily be procured. Its first theatre was the Montana, opened in December, 1864, when prizefighting became popular. Two lumber mills were in production since 1863, and in August, 1864, *The Montana Post,* its first newspaper, was published. Its editor was Thomas J. Dimsdale, the author of *The Vigilantes of Montana* and a popular resident who conducted teaching classes. Some 10,000 people lived in Virginia City at its height, many supported by placer mining.

In the winter of 1864–1865, with fifteen-foot snowdrifts in the passes, food became scarce. Hoarding was common, and a committee had to search the town, particularly for flour. During the search, over 125 bags were seized, paid for, and distributed—twelve pounds per person.

A mile up Alder Gulch, Nevada City was following Virginia City. Three of the Plummer gang— George Ives, John Franck, and George Hilderman— were charged with the murder of Nicholas Thiebalt. Shortly after Thiebalt's frozen body was found, the men were arrested and taken to Nevada City for trial. They were defended by Plummer's lawyers. A jury of twenty-four men was convened, twelve from Nevada City, twelve from Junction. It was no ordinary court: 1,000 citizens watched the outdoor proceedings. For every questionable point raised, the evidence was put to a vote by the 1,000 spectators. Franck, known as "Long John," confessed to witnessing the murder, and was discharged. Ives was sentenced to hang; Hilderman was banished. This was the famous trial that created a vigilante committee on the spot, as well as arrests, captures, and hangings, some without trial. In its wooden markers, famous Boot Hill Cemetery, just above town, still bears witness to the proceedings.

Prospectors and hopefuls of all nationalities had converged on the territory. Indians were already there, but, aside from treaties permitting mineral tracts, they were not involved to any extent in mining. But about 800 Chinese were in the Montana Territory by 1869. Restricted and permitted to work abandoned claims only, or those no one else wanted, many opened restaurants and laundries, all heavily taxed.

BUTTE AND THE COPPER BARONS

The earlier Montana gold-mining towns were but steppingstones toward the foundation of a copper empire and the "world's greatest mining town" —Butte. Butte evolved from gold to silver to copper —the richest find in the world.

In 1864, miners from Virginia City prospected in every direction before finding gold in a valley at Silver Bow. From here, the placer miners worked

Walkerville was a silver camp north of Butte. This 1880 scene shows Walkerville and the three mines adjoining it: the Alice Mine, background left; the Lexington Mine, extreme right; and the Valdemere and Magna Charta mines, foreground. *C. Owen Smithers Collection, Montana Bureau of Mines and Geology*

An 1879 woodcut of the Alice Mine owned by Marcus Daly. The feud between Daly and William A. Clark began, in part, when Clark mined at a higher level than the Alice Mine so that the water leaked into the Alice, forcing Daly to pay the cost of pumping it out. *C. Owen Smithers Collection, Montana Bureau of Mines and Geology*

their further claims toward a resultant Butte. Within three years, the shallow deposits vanished, Butte almost with them. Silver was found by a few prospectors, but it was difficult to separate the silver from the gold and not much was done about it even though an 1865 silver discovery by Hector Horton at Philipsburg had already been followed up with a processing mill.

Butte's revival was kicked off in 1875. A William A. Clark foreclosed on a William L. Farland's unprofitable smelter, built to separate gold from silver. Clark had loaned Farland $30,000 for its construction, and just after Clark took over the failing operation, the lode began to produce. Twelve years and five mills (with nearly 300 stamps) later, the Butte area could not have looked rosier, but it wilted in the silver panic of 1893.

Clark, who had mined in Colorado, owed his fortune not to mining but to trading in merchandise at Bannack back in 1863. He invested his profits in Butte mines, making loans and buying claims. This was three years before he acquired Farland's smelter. He had also leased a number of claims with options to buy. Meanwhile, a Marcus Daly had come to Butte representing a group of mine financiers interested in the Alice Silver Mine, near Walkerville, which Daly bought jointly with the Walker brothers. He also acquired the Anaconda Mine in cooperation with James B. Haggin, George Hearst, and Lloyd Tevis. The latter three owned the Homestake Mine in the Black Hills of South Dakota.

Clark and Daly were to become protagonists in a bitter feud. Because of Daly's success with the Alice Mine, in 1872 Clark started to develop the

Teams of horses and mules used to haul copper ore from the mines at Butte to the Colorado smelter. *C.*

Owen Smithers Collection, Montana Bureau of Mines and Geology

Moulton Mine, shrewdly setting it up at a higher ground level so that its water runoff might flood the Alice. Daly had to endure the cost of pumping it out.

Clark possessed the touch of Midas. The superintendent at his Mayflower Mine had twice been ordered to suspend work, and had twice disobeyed. His first refusal resulted in finding a $2 million ore body and the second a $2.5 million deposit. Clark's luck was even a match for the 1893 silver panic. Demands for copper had been increasing some time earlier and Clark had begun to develop copper mines. In 1873, with Nathanial P. Hill and Richard Pearce, he had formed the Colorado and Montana Smelting Company. The smelting plant they had built at Butte served the district as a local market for the constantly increasing production of copper. In the summer of 1878, rumors spread about an impending wage cut in the mines. To protect themselves from Clark, Daly, and the other owners, the men organized a union. In 1883 it became the first local of the Western Federation of Miners. By 1900, about 8,000 Butte miners were members. They were guaranteed $3.50 per day for underground mining, and union hospital care, sick benefits, and payments to their widows and families.

One of the first copper mines in the Butte district, the James A. Murray Mine. Though the date of the photo is unknown, it was probably taken in the late 1870s. *Montana Bureau of Mines and Geology*

THE FOUNDING OF ANACONDA

Marcus Daly's juncture with Haggin, Hearst, and Tevis derived from Daly's 1881 option on a piece of property that had been staked six years before and mined for silver. Daly, Haggin, Tevis, and Hearst picked up the option and divided it equally, developing and expanding its silver operation. But they found copper, and within two years silver was secondary, with copper assaying 55 percent being shipped to Swansea for refining. They dropped Swansea, as it was costly, in favor of refining their copper at Clark's Colorado and Montana Smelting Company where they tried to burn the ore between layers of logs and ore. They were unprepared for the acidly sulfurous fumes that spread throughout Butte, killing fifteen people. An injunction prohibited further smelting in the city, so Daly and his partners built a smelter about twenty-five miles west of Butte, at Anaconda; the 500-ton-per-day-capacity plant opened in 1884. Though it was the best technology could provide, its smoke permeated the local ranchlands, and after a series of lawsuits and compensations in 1903, a new system was installed that would purify the fumes through flues and stacks.

The partners incorporated into the Anaconda Mining Company in 1894, and a year later, after Hearst sold out to the Rothschilds, it was reorganized as the Anaconda Copper Mining Company. In 1899 Henry H. Rogers and the Standard Oil Trust purchased the company, retaining Daly as its nominal head. By then owning the world's largest copper producer, the Standard Oil group formed Amalgamated Copper—a holding company for the mine and its additional properties, including a railroad, coal and lumber interests, a newspaper, various utilities, and Butte's Montana Hotel.

After floating a stock issue of $75 million, priced at $100 a share, and manipulating the price down to $75, they bought back as much as possible. Two years and two companies later—the Boston and

Montana and Butte and Boston Consolidated Mining (digested by Amalgamated)—plus manipulations, the value of the stock exceeded $150 million, at which point shares were selling at $130. The group then sold as much stock as the public could absorb, then cut the dividend and watched the price fall to $33 a share, after which Amalgamated again bought as much stock as possible. In 1910, even the wily William A. Clark sold his three copper mines and smelter to Amalgamated, for $5 million, a fraction of their worth. He had believed the mines were about played out.

Throughout this period, Amalgamated's chief rival in the Montana copper business was F. Augustus Heinze, a shrewd and expert geologist. Heinze was more than a geologist and successful mine operator; he was a brain, scoundrel, and thief. When he first came to Butte, he had leased a copper mine under an agreement to pay a 50 percent royalty on ore containing at least 15 percent copper. Heinze avoided any payments by mixing dirt and rock with the ore until it was below the standard 15 percent minimum. It was easy for Heinze because he had rented a mine presumed to be exhausted but in which he uncovered new deposits that eventually financed his own smelter, at Meaderville, near Butte. He then transferred his activities to Canada, finally selling out to the Canadian Pacific Railway for over $1 million. Returning to Butte, he became involved with Anaconda in an estimated 133 lawsuits, requiring 37 lawyers. And Clark and Daly were involved in a major political battle. The political feud between the two men began with the 1888 elections, which had been rigged. Later, civil and criminal suits were begun; the Republicans and Democrats became very much involved; a battle to become the capital of Montana ensued between the towns of Anaconda and Helena; bribery suits were started and finished; Clark was elected to the United States Senate and forced to resign; was reappointed to fill his own vacancy by the lieutenant governor, whose act was revoked by the governor. It finally ended when Clark was re-elected to the United States Senate.

Heinze, with Clark's support, got two judges, William Clancy and Edward W. Harney, elected to state office. Both continually rendered verdicts favoring Heinze, who became a constant irritant to Amalgamated Copper. Shortly after returning from Canada, he had bought the Rarus Mine adjacent to the Michael Davitt Mine, owned by the Boston and Montana. This caused a series of lawsuits. Heinze claimed infringements by the Boston and Montana onto what he said was the apex of the deposit. Montana law held that whoever owned the apex owned

the deposit! Amalgamated, meanwhile, had purchased the Boston and Montana after the first jury trial, which had awarded the Davitt property to Heinze. On appeal, an injunction was issued prohibiting either side from mining the property. Heinze therefore started a new company, the Johnstown Company, theorizing that the court order applied only to the Davitt Mine. Heinze connected the Davitt Mine with the Rarus Mine, secretly removing Davitt ore through Rarus hoists. He also sealed off Amalgamated's Pennsylvania Mine from the Davitt. When Amalgamated learned of Heinze's machinations, underground and surface fighting broke out, and two miners were killed. Nevertheless, Heinze managed to remove about $1 million worth of ore before the United States Supreme Court ruled that he was not

An idea of the huge amount of timber formerly used for underground mine support can be obtained from this photograph of the Stewert (copper) Mine in Butte. *Montana Bureau of Mines and Geology*

Miners about to descend mine shaft near Butte. *Montana Bureau of Mines and Geology*

The Berkeley copper pit of the Anaconda Company. It is one of the largest in the world, and is worked for low-grade copper ore—only 12 pounds of copper are extracted from every ton. This amounts to less than $4 for drilling, blasting, loading, hauling, and smelting 6,000 pounds of ore, made possible only by the most modern and economical methods of mine operation.

Nearly 40,000 tons of material are removed from the pit each day when operations are at maximum, excluding almost twice as much waste material that is also removed from the pit. In all, Butte mines have produced more nonferrous metals than any other district in the world. Today's production is principally copper and zinc. *Bill Browning, Montana Chamber of Commerce*

entitled to the property. Heinze caused further trouble by securing a minute piece of property, less than one-hundreth of an acre, between Amalgamated's Anaconda, Saint Lawrence, and Neversweat mines, and had Judge Clancy issue an injunction preventing operation of the three mines until the lawsuit could be decided to determine whether Heinze's little piece of property was the apex of the mineral land. But Amalgamated retaliated by shutting down the mines, putting 3,000 miners out of work, and advising the men that Judge Clancy's injunction, which was nothing more than an attempt to steal the mines, was the cause. The miners threatened to hang Clancy, and the next day he revoked the injunction. Amalgamated then tried to purchase all of Heinze's interests in Montana, but he had moved to New York to speculate in the United Copper Company. These altercations, annoyances, and lawsuits, climaxed by another injunction issued by Judge Clancy preventing the Boston and Montana from paying dividends to Amalgamated, completely shut down all Amalgamated's operations in Montana, throwing more than 20,000 men out of work. That was in October, 1903. It was Amalgamated's purpose to force passage of a "fair trial law" permitting one party in a lawsuit to obtain a "change of venue" if it believed the trial judge was prejudiced. It took only three weeks for the Montana Superior Court to reverse Clancy's judgment and to get the statute on the books. As for Heinze's properties, shares were at $60 in 1907,

when Amalgamated drove the price down to $10, virtually bankrupting Heinze and ending his forages against them.

After 1907, with the development of Butte as an important copper center, and with the ending of the Daly-Clark feud and the Heinze-Amalgamated fiascos, Butte was able to settle down to some real mining.

Anaconda now has underground workings in Butte that include more than 40 miles of vertical shafts and about 2,600 miles of underground passageways and tunnels. All told, with stope excavations, the total underground length is about 10,000 miles.

An Anaconda ore train several thousand feet below Butte. *Bill Browning, Montana Chamber of Commerce*

Above, at the Berkeley Pit, the copper waste remaining in the mine is reclaimed. *Bill Browning, Montana Chamber of Commerce*

Granite, the deserted "Silver Queen," in about a decade poured out $45,000,000 from the Granite Mountain Mine in southwestern Montana, near Philipsburg. Granite is one of the best Montana ghost towns remaining today. *Montana Highway Commission*

Fraternity Hall in long-deserted Elkhorn, a ghost town. *Montana Highway Commission*

WORLD'S GREATEST MINING TOWN

Butte was a city of contrasts. Only New York City would ever comprise the variety of races, creeds, and colors of Butte's pioneer copper-mining days. Protestants, Catholics, and Jews lived peacefully together, their respective clergy addressing jointly assembled flocks on Tolerance Day; Lent nearly halved business; a rabbi killed Sabbath chickens in front of his Main Street store; merchants closed on both Jewish and Christian holidays; a leading early Jewish expressman owned a horse named "Jesus Christ"; East Park Street's Jewish clothing dealers rivaled New York's (one filled his shop with fire-damaged merchandise for every fire within a half mile and another displayed a "closing out, going out of business" sign for five prosperous, uninterrupted years). Nationalities included Irish, Finn, Serbian, Greek, Afghan, Turk, Austrian, French Canadian, Indian, Egyptian, Pole, Syrian, Spaniard, Mexican, Cornish, and, inevitably, Chinese.

The Chinese, as in other camps, followed others and reworked old placers, panning what gold might have been overlooked, living from the remnants of former operations. But Butte was not much of a gold camp, and since only a few Chinese reworked the old gold mines, Butte's Oriental population remained insubstantial until the early 1880s. Most Chinese at this time worked at chopping wood for the white contractors who supplied the smelters. This eventually led to skirmishes with the French Canadians in town, who had monopolized all wood-chopping jobs. Violence continued for several weeks, and many Orientals were slaughtered in these bloody battles. Finally, there was no recourse for the Chinese but to return to their laundries ("washey-washey" houses) or open a restaurant; some peddled vegetables, others opened gambling houses and opium dens. It was now 1882 and several hundred pig-tailed, costumed, Chinese called Butte home. Chinatown was fast becoming a tourist attraction filled with Oriental stores, gambling joints, and shops selling drugs, herbs, and souvenirs. A joss house was constructed, and the first floor reserved for tong meetings, the second for religious meetings. Reports of trading in slave girls constantly appeared in the news, but even these were understated! Crime was highly organized. Chinese blackmailing, protection insurance, and "rolling" were infamous. The police were powerless to stop the opium dens, where a single pipeful sold for $10 to $20, and gambling dives featuring birdcage, fantan, and chuck-a-luck flourished, patronized by the Chinese as well as disreputable white underworld characters and assorted pimps, gamblers, and prostitutes. Lotteries were a favorite Chinese pastime, and drawings were held several times an hour. The laundries in particular, some employing several dozen washers, seemed to be profitable businesses. Some Chinese families lived near their laundries and restaurants, outside the Chinatown area.

The Chinese seemed to be excluded from the general tolerance between ethnic groups (even the closely related Koreans fought with them) and were restricted to just these two occupations. But no one discriminated against their food, only against those who prepared it. Chop suey, chow mein, and noodles became Butte's most popular foods. Deliveries were made regularly to the white gambling joints and the brothels of the red-light district.

By 1900 Chinatown had become quieter, its inhabitants more Americanized. Some even cut their pigtails. Suddenly, in February, 1922, tong wars broke out and a half dozen Chinese were killed. For a while it looked as though the entire town might be embroiled, but a truce was arranged and the city returned to normalcy.

Indians on the other hand, even with fairly large numbers prior to 1890, were never a problem. That year, hundreds of Cree and Chippewa camped south of the city, spawning a colony that would exist some twenty years. During Indian festival days, huge celebrations were held at the old Marcus Daly Racetrack. A dollar admission and virtually 100 percent Butte attendance at the races and festivities for years assured the Indians sufficient funds to live through the winters.

The Finns, bringing with them their custom of sauna (baths), flocked into camp around 1900, and soon there were nearly 3,000. Many of them became expert miners, and all were popular.

The Cornish, with their wholesome, outgoing personalities and expert mining abilities, always were a welcome addition, and played an important part in Butte's mining life.

Butte was also a city of homes. Most early-day miners built their homes along the hills and gulches, or near "the Hill" to be close to the mines. Many original miners' homes were still occupied in the 1920s and 1930s, some even beyond.

Butte had 10,000 horses and mules, which posed not only a sanitation problem but required ample stables and food for their proper care. Just catering to these animals was an important industry. About another 3,000 worked in the mines and were cared for in huge underground stables. These specially harnessed animals were blindfolded and lowered from 1,000 to 3,000 feet into the mine shafts. Gen-

A mule wrapped in canvas, tied and ready to be put into a cage to be lowered into the depths of the North Star Mine, which had a 3,200-foot vertical shaft. By turning the photo sideways, the mule's head can be seen protruding from the top of the sack. *Grass Valley Chamber of Commerce*

erally, once a mule or horse entered a mine it rarely saw daylight again, although a few favorite pets were given an occasional vacation above ground. Every mine horse or mule pulled six cars loaded with about a ton of ore each, from the point of extraction to the shaft for hoisting to the surface. Underground animals were carefully tended and learned quickly: as a car was loaded, the animals moved up the track exactly one car length; they knew when six cars were full. And none could be persuaded to pull more; they knew without instructions from their mule skinners to take off for the hoisting station as soon as the sixth and final car was full.

Working so closely with horses, horse racing was a natural popular attraction. Marcus Daly ran a stable of some 100 racehorses, some generally running every holiday, including Saint Patrick's Day, Saint George's Day, Miners' Union Day, and others not usually celebrated elsewhere.

Butte's prostitutes and mademoiselles, as in other towns, somehow managed to appear within days of the mining camp's establishment. Butte's red-light district centered around Galena Street, known as the "line," which soon became one of the wildest, wide-open red-light districts in the United States. The Casino was the prized whorehouse, a combination saloon, dance hall, brothel, theatre, and prizefight arena, open twenty-four hours a day, seven days a week, and the scene of many gunfights and killings. Active prostitutes earned as much as $60 for an evening's work. On one side of Galena Street more than 100 girls worked in a series of small rooms, or compartments, called "cribs," each decorated with a sign, or "nom de crib." All Butte's nationalities and races were represented. Descriptive names such as Blondetta, French Erma, Austrian Annie, Jew Jess, and Mexican Maria left no doubts in the minds of nationalistic clients. Many whorehouse visitors as well as drunks were rolled, and petty thievery and pickpocketing were common crimes. The district was well patrolled by the police, but often they were in cahoots with the girls.

For the elite and the millionaire copper kings, there were the richly furnished "parlor houses" served by Chinese servants and well-groomed girls. Here the wealthy might spend several thousand dollars in a single evening. One of the most pretentious of all the brothels was Lou Harpell's Place, openly advertised in the theatre and racetrack programs. Other ornate establishments were those of

Belle Rhodes, Mabel Loy, and Molly De Murska.

Butte's first recorded theatrical performance was in 1875, featuring John McGuire, a strolling Irish minstrel. As mining increased, many theatres opened—Owsley's Hall, Renshaw Hall, Sutton's Union Family Theatre, Speck's Hall, Gordon's Comique Theatre, McGuire's Grand Opera House, the Lyceum, and others. Some of America's famous entertainers who appeared in Butte were Eddie Foy, William A. Brady, Rose Osborn, and Maude Adams.

Aside from horse racing and boxing, and an occasional "bootlegged" bull and bear fight, were the regularly held drilling contests for prize money donated by the mining companies. Several different kinds of contests were held, and betting was heavy. "Double-hand" and "single-hand" contests were the favorites. Double-hand called for two men, one to strike the drill and the other to hold and turn it after each blow. In the single-hand, one man held, struck, and turned the drill. Some expert drillers could strike ninety blows a minute without missing. Drilling contests also were held for nonprofessionals, and betting was equally heavy. Butte's most popular drilling attraction was an exhibition by Harry Rodda and Mike Davei, two blind miners who lost their sight in a mine explosion. They were so adept that they even appeared in Madison Square Garden in New York.

Coursing was a popular sport, especially among the Cornishmen. Today, coursing is commonly known as dog-track racing, with stuffed mechanical rabbits for the dogs to chase. But at the West Side Coursing Track, where 6,000 people attended an afternoon's racing, live rabbits were used. The Cornishmen were also great wrestlers, and big wagers were placed on the most popular.

Boxing and horse racing, however, remained

Butte's famous opera house. *Montana Historical Society, Helena*

Bathing in necktie and petticoat. Columbia Gardens, about 1889. It was built by William A. Clark for Butte's recreational use. *Montana Historical Society, Helena*

The Middleweight Championship of the World, McCoy versus McDonald, Butte, May 18, 1884. *Montana Historical Society, Helena*

the kings. Boxing attracted the world's leading participants, including John L. Sullivan and Jack Dempsey. Kid McCoy, Stanley Ketchell, James Jeffreys, Jack Johnson, Battling Nelson, and hundreds of others boxed in Butte, many born there.

Although the bull and bear fights soon faded in popularity, cockfights boomed. They were easy to hold clandestinely in small places. Fighting cocks were sometimes imported from Ireland and Scotland, but most were bred in the Carolinas and Tennessee. Bookmakers accepted bets on cockfighting as readily as they did on horse racing. Dogfights also were held in fight arenas, and, once, in 1891, a wolf was pitched against two greyhounds and a bulldog. The wolf was finally put to flight and disappeared in a cloud of dust.

Foreign games were popular among the ethnic groups. The Italians loved boccie, similar to an English bowling game, and the Irish practiced their curling whenever possible.

Turkey shoots were held. Live turkeys were placed in boxes constructed to permit the head to stick through holes in the top; the object was to shoot it off. A similar attraction was "pogrom in a hen coop." For this unwholesome diversion, a chicken was buried in the dirt with only its head exposed. Horsemen would gallop by, attempting to wring the fowl's neck off or to pull the entire chicken from the ground. This was to be accomplished without falling from the saddle, but often as many men as chickens were injured.

And there were the disasters. Many were mining accidents—the first major calamity the Anaconda Mine shaft fire on November 23, 1889. Fortunately, the fire broke out between shifts; six miners were

killed and two injured. In 1893 a fire in the Silver Bowl Mine killed nine miners, and in 1900 the Parrot Mine was destroyed by flames, but there were no deaths. In 1911 there were a series of mine accidents. In April, a mine cage carrying fourteen men fell 1,500 feet into a shaft. Five men on the lower deck were killed but nine on the upper deck, all seriously injured, managed to survive. In September, disaster struck at the Black Rock Mine. School-age boys, "tool-boys" (or "nippers"), had been employed to pick up dulled or damaged drills and tools for repairs. Although they were forbidden to ride the cages, ten of them nevertheless rode a cage containing a load of dull tools and steel, which somehow became loosened from the bottom of the cage. Rushed to the surface at high speed, the cage was torn apart by the protruding tools and drills. Eight tool-boys were ground to pieces; the two who survived were horribly mutilated. And in 1915 an explosion at the Granite Mountain Mine blew up twelve cases of dynamite, scattering the remnants of sixteen men over a mile.

There also were town fires. The worst occurred in January, 1895, at a flour warehouse, which quickly spread to an adjacent hardware concern stocked with 350 boxes of dynamite. A mighty blast blew up the structure, killing all but three firemen and a horse. Bodies hurtled 300 yards into the air and parts of bodies were found more than a mile away; a railroad car wheel was found eight blocks off. While rescuers were removing the wounded to hospitals and first-aid stations, a second explosion occurred, and a third. Timbers, steel girders, and debris became like straws in a wind. All resources,

Time out for the Walkerville Fire Department banquet, Butte. *Montana Historical Society, Helena*

private homes, hotels, and lodging houses, were pressed into service for temporary hospital care. Almost every family had someone injured or killed. The exact number will never be known, but at least sixty people were believed killed in the holocaust.

A fire occurred in March, 1898, at the Hale House, the largest miners' boardinghouse in town. The miners were asleep when it started, and within five minutes the building was a blazing inferno. More than fifty were injured; about twenty were killed by the fire or from jumping out of the upper stories. Seven years later on September 24, 1905, Symon's Department Store fire burned out a block of the city, causing nine injuries but no deaths.

Today Butte is a modern city but still a mining camp, nurtured by copper ores of the Anaconda and other company pits.

MONTANA GOLD

Increasingly more mining towns were laid out in Montana. In the early 1860s, prospectors had spread through what is now Yellowstone National Park, fruitlessly searching for gold, yet with remarkably few reports about the scenic wonders of the Yellowstone area. They finally discovered gold in 1864 at Emigrant Gulch, where Virginia City was located, and that same year, three deserters from the Confederate Army discovered gold at Confederate Gulch, in the Big Belt Mountains, which produced $10 million, and at Diamond City—population 10,000 by the 1870s. So much waste was produced by the placer workings that Confederate Gulch became almost filled with tailings, and, to avoid being buried, some of the houses had to be raised on stilts. By 1870 the gold was exhausted. Flooding devastated the entire area, ruining the placers, which were pretty well petered out anyway, and only the Chinese stayed to pick over the remains; but by 1878 they, too, departed.

But "the richest half-acre of ground in the world" was Montana Bar. When four discouraged prospectors found gold there in the spring of 1864, their first pan yielded $40 in gold. By nightfall, they reputedly recovered dust and nuggets worth $21,000. The next day they staked their claims, and keeping

This abandoned mill formerly was used for extracting gold in Marysville, Montana, a few miles north of Helena, off U.S. Route 91. Marysville is not quite deserted, and some mining still goes on, but at one time its 2,000 residents had known it as the town where Irishman Tommy Cruse's magnificent Drumlummon Mine poured out $50 million before its desertion in the early 1900s. Marysville had boasted other productive mines, in the 1880s, including Bald Mountain, Empire, West Belmont, Bell Boy, Penobscot, and Shannon. Marysville, a winter ski center, retains many excellent relics of its mining days, including the old Drumlummon mill. *Bill Browning, Montana Chamber of Commerce*

An early picture of the Taylor-Thompson Diggings at Helena, Montana. Notice the sluice box in the gulch, and piles of tailings. A month following this Emigrant Gulch find, three prospectors, John Cowan, Robert Stanley, and Cabe Johnson, discovered promising placer deposits at Last Chance Gulch. They formed the settlement of Helena, and drew up a set of miners' rules that served as the legal structure for all mining in the area until June, 1872, when the United States Land Office issued title to the townsite of Helena. Three years after its founding, Helena's local government structure was complete, by which time perhaps 4,000 people were living there. Placer operations were even conducted along the main street. Coinciding with the discovery at Last Chance Gulch were those lode mines and fruitful deposits found in the surrounding areas at New York Gulch, First Chance Gulch, and Montana Bar. In addition, gold operations were established at the nearby towns of Jefferson City, Boulder, and Trout Creek. Helena was hit particularly hard by fire—nine, from 1865 to 1876—causing several million dollars in damage. But it did not prevent an estimated more than $30 million in gold from being taken out of the immediate Helena vicinity. *Montana Historical Society*

the location secret, worked till winter to remove three and a half tons of gold worth over $1 million, which they hid under their log cabin. Removing the gold was a problem, solved by obtaining a covered freight wagon, a team of four horses, and enough empty nail kegs to hold the gold, which they took to Fort Benton. There they built a flatboat and floated it and the gold down the Missouri River to St. Joseph. After they left their half-acre, stampeders rushed in and extracted another $3 million or so.

LOST CABIN

Stories of lost mines are as abundant as spring flowers, but one that has endured, with some validity, is the story of the Lost Cabin Mine, near Casper, Wyoming.

In 1865, seven prospectors from the Dakota Black Hills entered the Big Horn Mountain region. Five were killed by Indians and two escaped, with $7,000 in coarse gold. Ever since, groups of all sizes have tried to find the Lost Cabin Mine's rich placer deposits, where the ground is believed to be gold-strewn. As for the two survivors, they turned over their gold to Charles Gray, a Wyoming pioneer, who put it in the safe at the Post Trader's Store at Fort

Type of cage used to remove ore cars from the mines. Note that the base of the cage has railroad tracks so that the ore car can be rolled directly into the cage. *Montana Historical Society*

Laramie. Gray has given testimony how earlier, in October, 1865, the two men had reached old Fort Reno in a weak and exhausted condition to tell of their experience; they said that all seven had come to a heavily timbered area that was bisected by a mountain stream, which joined a larger stream a few hundred yards below. Here they found signs of the yellow metal and, digging to a depth of three or four feet, struck bedrock where seams of gold were easily visible. They camped at this spot, and in three days built a flume and a log cabin. On that third day they were attacked by a band of Indians who killed five of them instantly. The survivors reached the cabin, held the Indians at bay until nightfall, and escaped in the darkness, taking nothing but gold, guns, and food. Traveling by night and hiding by day, they reached Fort Reno three days later. Apparently their story had not been believed. They were arrested as deserters by the commanding officer and taken to Fort Fetterman for trial. There, examination showed that they were completely innocent, and they were discharged and their gold returned, after which they arrived at Fort Laramie.

The two men, Swedes, were unfamiliar with local names, including the area where they had discovered the gold, but they were determined to return and had no difficulty recruiting a new group to follow their old trail. Their party of about twelve was ambushed and killed by Indians, leaving no trace of the location of the gold discovery. Meanwhile, on the Swede's information, Colonel Bullock, the post trader at Fort Laramie, formed an expedition of 150 men to find the Lost Cabin claims, unaware of the Indian slaughter. But the commanding officer, on learning of his plans and fearing it would culminate in an extensive Indian war, stopped him. It was nearly fifteen years before one could safely travel into the region and prospect, and though many now have, the site of the Lost Cabin remains a mystery.

Two interesting "finds" occurred in the 1920s. In 1922 Lost Cabin hopefuls found an aged, weather-beaten Mexican saddle—an unverified claim connecting it with Spanish explorers from New Mexico—and some mine drifts in Big Canyon Creek, and in 1927 an excited herder arrived at Casper claiming that he had found the mine. He had no trouble attracting a party for a prospecting trip to the area he described, and a complete expedition equipped with dynamite, wrapped in bedding for protection, set out to locate the promised lands. The group located an intersection of two streams and found an old cabin, but it proved to be an ancient shooting cover used by Indians. There was no evidence of any gold. Rather than carry back their dynamite the frustrated prospectors inserted it in a large drilled boulder, which, when exploded, was found to contain a quantity of gold the size of a pinhead. Further research disclosed an old Indian battleground with rifle pits and the skulls of thirty horses and an ancient Indian banquet ground covered with deposits of meat bones.

CROWN PRINCE SILVER

While copper ruled in Bingham Canyon, gold was being crowned king—and silver, crown prince—in the Colorado San Juan region. The Colorado San Juan region extends from northern Durango, on the border of New Mexico, for about fifty miles along both sides of Route 550, and includes historic mining areas of the Continental Divide, the Uncompahgre, Needle, and San Juan mountains, and the land lying to the west. Such famous places as Ouray, Camp Bird, Sneffels, Telluride, Ironton, the Red Mountain District, Howardsville, and Silverton are located here.

Actually, from a mining viewpoint, comparatively less has been written about the fabulous San Juans than any other mining area in Colorado. Yet,

Burros packed for hauling timber to the mines in the Colorado Mountains, around 1885. The timbers were cut extra long to allow for wear as they were dragged along the rough mountain trails. *Colorado Division of State Archives and Public Records*

Dangerous confrontation between Indians and a prospector in the San Juan Mountains in the 1870s. *Duane A. Smith*

from 1870, the San Juan region was one of the country's leading producers of silver—dug from land that a few years before belonged to the Ute Indians and their chiefs Ouray and Ignacio. Some San Juan gold had been reported earlier, preceding the Civil War, but it was minimal; a Charles Baker with his exploring parties had found gold far to the west after enduring many hardships just to reach the territory—moving wagons by rope along steep inclines and escaping a mutinous crew, near Eureka. Baker later returned to Denver, and in 1871 he appeared around Silverton, where he was killed by Indians a short time later.

But by 1870 exploring parties had worked their way west from the Continental Divide's east side. Prospecting spread north; exploration work extended along the Rico River as gold seekers moved in from the southeast as well as from Leadville and other famous areas lying to the northeast. And the search for gold turned from placer deposits to lode prospecting.

The entire area was Ute territory, often unsafe for prospectors until the Brunot Treaty was signed with the Utes in 1873. Thereafter, the land was thrown open for mining and prospecting, even though six months before the Brunot Treaty was signed, Chief Ouray had received $1,000,000 for 3 million acres of land.

H. A. W. Tabor, of Denver fame, operated here, but he lost out in the San Juans when, according to stories, he offered a check in payment for a mine and was turned down because the seller refused to endorse it unless he was first given the money!

Within five years, many claims were operating in Rico-Silverton; one, the Grand View, sold out in 1879 to Jones and McKay of Virginia City (both of Comstock fame), and that year ore samples from a claim on Nigger Baby Hill arrived at Ouray for assay, the combination of which precipitated a new stampede, this time out of Ouray and Silverton to Rico.

For revelry, there was Silverton's Blair Street. Its notorious gambling houses included the Diamond, National, Mikado, Bon Ton, and Sage Hen, and its brothels were all named for their star performers or purveyors—Lola's, Big Mollie, Diamond Tooth Lil's, and Diamond Kate among them. Some 300 girls worked them, and a dozen or more worked the dance halls. Many of these Blair Street buildings are still intact and have appeared in a number of movies.

San Juan's biggest town, Ouray, was perhaps saved from extinction (made imminent by the 1893 silver collapse) by the famous Camp Bird Mine at Sneffels, which had been worked for silver from

Silverton's main street, late 1890s. Mrs. Marvin Gregory's (she furnished many of the Ouray-Silverton photographs), grandfather moved into Silverton in 1894, and was a freighter and mule skinner, as were two of his sons who are still living. Silverton, about fifty miles northeast of Rico, was San Juan region's principal town, founded in 1874, when more than 4,000 claims had been staked out. An important producer was the Silver Lake Mine, as was the nearby Sunnyside, Shenandoah, and Gold King mines. Silver Lake's owner, Stroiber, ultimately sold out to the Guggenheims for $2,500,000. Silverton continued to grow with the construction of the Martha Rose Smelter in 1881, later purchased by Thomas Walsh whose mining operations in Animas Forks were extensive; profits from his smelting operations bought him the Camp Bird Mine at Sneffels. Silverton was noted for its aerial trams that carried gold, silver, copper, lead, zinc, and other ores from the mines to the mills or railroads. The highest mines were the Gold Prince (13,000 feet), Sunnyside (15,600), Iowa Tiger (14,400), Silver Lake (13,700), Mogul (10,000), Shenandoah (10,000), and Kittemac (10,000). *Marvin and Ruth Gregory Historical Collection*

All was not work at Silverton. These miners and their families are preparing for a day's outing. *Marvin and Ruth Gregory Historical Collection*

about 1870. Named for the mountain jays that stole the camp food, Camp Bird had ceased its silver operations a dozen years before, but in 1896 Thomas F. Walsh bought the mine for $20,000 with the expectation that he could develop its gold veins. The mine was modernized and tramways were built. Walsh was successful, and the Camp Bird Mine yielded $3 to $4 million in gold from 1896 to 1902 when he sold out to a British syndicate for some $5 million. Walsh had become a fabulously wealthy Wall Street financier. It was his daughter, Evelyn Walsh McLean, a newspaper publisher in Washington, D.C., who inherited the famous Hope Diamond at her mother's death. Walsh's residence in Animas Forks still stands, although badly in need of restoration.

A boardinghouse miner's dining room in the San Juan region. *Colorado State Historical Society Library*

The Camp Bird Mill and Mine was a village in itself. Camp Bird, purchased by its present owners in 1963, continues to operate, while new explorations are being developed by the Federal Resources Corporation of Salt Lake City, Utah. *United States Forest Service*

The "Black Kid," lynched at Silverton on August 21, 1881, for participation in the shooting of Clayton Ogsbury, the local marshal. Three others participated in the shooting; one was lynched ten days later, when he was captured. *Marvin and Ruth Gregory Historical Collection*

The Sunnyside Mill in Eureka around 1915. Mrs. Gregory lived in the residence at the base of the mill where her grandmother cooked for the millworkers. The mill was the principal operation; by 1917 it had been enlarged to handle 1,000 tons of ore per day. Most of the town consisted of company housing for the mill's 400 employees. In 1919 a raging fire destroyed most of the mine buildings, but they were quickly rebuilt. Mining continued actively until the end of 1921, when operations ceased because of a metal market drop, and the following year work resumed until 1930, when the mine again closed. It reopened in 1937 for about eighteen months, after which Eureka became a ghost town. The song "There'll be a Hot Time in the Old Town Tonight" originated here. Notwithstanding, crime was at a minimum, and the law was strictly obeyed. A number of ghost towns are close by. Nearby was where Charles Baker almost met death by mutineers. *Marvin and Ruth Gregory Historical Collection*

The Silverton, Gladstone, and Northerly Railroad, which served the mining district in 1898. Narrow-gauge railroads were constructed for traveling the narrow passes and sharp curves. One mine, the North Star on King Solomon Mountain, was 13,300 feet above sea level, unique even for Colorado. Many of the mines, as well as the towns, were often bombarded by avalanches. In 1882 the Denver and Rio Grande Western Railroad built a forty-five-mile line connecting Silverton and Durango, which joined Durango's main line. The first train to Silverton arrived on July 4, 1882, and the line became vital for getting the ore to the reduction plants in Durango. It continued in operation until after World War I, operating today as a passenger railroad taking visitors to the wonderful scenery along the gorge of the Los Animas River from Durango to Silverton. *Marvin and Ruth Gregory Historical Collection*

Stagecoaches picked their way carefully along the old Mears Toll Road near Ouray, Colorado, in 1883. The rugged Colorado terrain also required some system of transportation between the rapidly developing mining camps and the larger towns. Originally, only burro trails were the connecting links, but as mining developed, toll-road companies were organized. Colorado's foremost toll-road builder was Otto Mears who developed nearly five hundred miles of roads over dozens of mountain passes. Perhaps his greatest accomplishment was the toll road he built from Ouray to Silverton, a precarious engineering job often cut into rock 1,000 feet above the canyon that ran between the cities. From Silverton, Mears's road was expanded to Red Mountain, and in 1885 he began the Silverton Railroad, a three-foot narrow-gauge track that was completed in 1889. It opened shipments of ores from Red Mountain and Ironton, another Walsh mine site. The present Million Dollar Highway, one of Colorado's most spectacular automobile rides, follows the old Mears Toll Road where it is not occupied by the Denver and Rio Grande Railroad. *Marvin and Ruth Gregory Historical Collection*

The Denver and Rio Grande Railroad runs on part of what was once the Mears Toll Road. *Felix A. Peckham*

The main street of Ouray in the early 1880s. Note the flagpole in the middle of the street. The mountain in the background is Mount Hayden. *Marvin and Ruth Gregory Historical Collection*

Pictured in this 1878 street scene of Ouray is George Ripley, in the center of the photograph with his hand on the burro's back. Ripley was the publisher of Ouray's first newspaper, whose first edition came out on June 17, 1877. The town remains a beehive of activity. Ouray, or the Uncompahgre District of the San Juans, was first developed in 1875 when gold-bearing lodes were discovered in the rocks of the canyon walls at Mineral Farm, just outside of what was to become a town. A little later, to the south, silver-lead deposits were found in the limestone. It was not long before in-rushing prospectors founded Ouray between the two sites; most of the productive deposits fell within a radius of three and a half miles of Ouray, which grew into the San Juans's most important town, even supporting three newspapers. In 1889 rich gold ore had been found at the American Nettie Mine, and adjacent properties had been rapidly developed. Ouray (around twenty-five miles north of Silverton) eventually became freight center for the entire San Juan area. *Marvin and Ruth Gregory Historical Collection*

Thousands of burros were constantly traveling between the various districts. Burros were an important part of mining operations in the 1880s. This scene on Second Street, Ouray, shows burros in front of the J. Donald Stables loaded with timber for mining operations. On the left is the Beaumont Blacksmith Shop. *Marvin and Ruth Gregory Historical Collection*

One of the earliest mines in the Ouray area was the Mineral Farm Mine seen in this 1910 photograph. *Denver Public Library Western Collection*

The Batchelor Mine, four or five miles north of Ouray on Dexter Creek. By 1892, the famous Batchelor quartz site had been discovered; by 1895 the Batchelor was chief among all the producers. *Marvin and Ruth Gregory Historical Collection*

Women often helped in the arduous tasks of mining. The two women are the cook and her helper at the Hidden Treasure Mine. *Marvin and Ruth Gregory Historical Collection*

The Ruby Trust Mine in the Yankee Boy Basin on the south side of Mount Sneffels in 1895. *Marvin and Ruth Gregory Historical Collection*

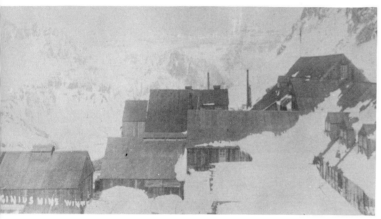

The Virginius Mine at an elevation of nearly 13,000 feet in the Humboldt Basin, just below the Saint Sophia Ridge between Ouray and Telluride. But of all the San Juan areas, the Telluride and Sneffels districts have remained productive the longest. When the Smuggler Union at Telluride closed in 1928, after producing for fifty-two years, the mines incorporated and reorganized as the Telluride Mines, Incorporated. Included were the Tomboy mines and many of the others. However, the most famous of the Sneffels district mines was Camp Bird. Some of the period's well-known silver-lead producers included the Virginius, Humboldt, Terrible, and Atlas mines. *Marvin and Ruth Gregory Historical Collection*

A pack train on the main street of Telluride, Colorado, about 1880. Telluride was founded in 1876, about fifteen miles north of Silverton. When the railroad arrived in 1890, the town became one of the principal mining camps of Colorado, with a population of 5,000. Gold, silver, lead, and copper were taken from Silverton and Telluride mines in the 1890s, some of which are still in operation. The old Sunnyside Mine at nearby Eureka and other properties in the area are now operated by Standard Metals Company of New York City. *Marvin and Ruth Gregory Historical Collection*

Prospector on Mount Sneffels, 14,000 feet above sea level, in the San Juans, about 1870. *Colorado State Historical Society Library*

The famous Ophir Mine on the highway south of Telluride. *Marvin and Ruth Gregory Historical Collection*

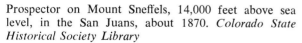

The main street of Ironton, in the Red Mountain Mining District, a busy place in the 1880s. Ironton is at the top of Uncompahgre Gorge, seven miles south of Ouray on the old toll road between Ouray and Silverton. The Red Mountain Mining District was one of the most inaccessible and spectacular sections of the San Juans, where ore was discovered in 1881. It comprised Mineral Creek, a tributary of the Animas River, and the Red Mountain Ridge and Cement Creek. Red Mountain's principal production came from the Red Mountain Creek valley near the old town of Red Mountain, where altitudes range from 9,600 feet near Ironton to 13,000 feet on the surrounding mountains. Such famous mines as the Yankee Girl, Guston, Genesis, Vanderbilt, National Belle, Congress, Barstow, and Kentucky Giant provided the bulk of production from this area. Most mining activity ceased in 1896. *Marvin and Ruth Gregory Historical Collection*

The Gold King Mine in Silverton is in the foreground. The large building in the background is the boarding-house where the miners lived in 1906. Among the smaller ghost towns around the San Juan region is Alta's one-mine camp, started in 1870 with the discovery of The Gold King Mine. Its remains, juxtaposed against the many modern homes in the vicinity, include cabins, a boardinghouse, a school, and a tram operator's office. The mine tunnel entrance, called the Black Hawk Portal, runs nearly 9,000 feet into the gold veins, from which nearly $20 million worth of gold was extracted. *Marvin and Ruth Gregory Historical Collection*

Guston in the Red Mountains in 1895. *Marvin and Ruth Gregory Historical Collection*

The Idarado Mine at the east portal of the Treasury Tunnel. The mine currently produces ores of copper, lead, zinc, gold, and silver. Of all the Red Mountain mines, the Idarado Mine was and still is the greatest. It once produced some of the largest silver and gold values in Colorado. Today the Idarado is considered the second largest underground metal mine in Colorado, exceeded only by the Climax Mine in production. A subsidiary of the Newmont Mining Corporation of New York, the mine now has miles of tunnels, drifts, and shafts between Red Mountain and Telluride; one tunnel is over six miles long. Over twenty-five miles of tunnels run through such old mines as the Tomboy and the Smuggler, which Idarado now owns. *United States Forest Service*

Stephen Venard, after killing three bandits who held up and robbed the North San Juan coach. He was awarded $3,000 and a handsome Henry rifle engraved with a drawing of the exploit and the inscription " . . ." for his gallant conduct May 16, 1866. . . ." *Wells Fargo Bank History Room*

235

OTHER SIGNIFICANT HISTORICAL EVENTS

On to the Rockies

Idaho

1862: Idaho City (Bannack), Placerville, Hogem, Pioneerville, Centerville, Buena Vista founded.

1860s: Newsom Creek claims staked; Clearwater Station became its supply depot, which grew larger than Newsom.

1863: Auburn, south of Griffon Gulch, became the center of prospecting in that area. Productive placer mines were Canyon, Dixie Creek, Granite, Susanville; and eastern Oregon's Grant and Baker counties, where quartz mines also opened up.

Utah

1840s: Silver and gold mines were found near Cedar City and Kamas.

1847: Salt was mined in Utah; at Cedar City it was coal and iron, and coal alone at Wales, Sanpete County, and Coalville, plus minor lead and sulfur operations before 1863.

1854: Gold discovered in Bullion County.

1867: Alta founded as mining camp along Mount Baldy; Emma Mine founded.

1875: Horn Silver Mines discovered in the San Francisco Mountains.

1878: Deer Trail Mine discovered near Marysvale, which still operates, yielding gold, silver, lead, copper.

1888: Kimberly founded with gold discovery of Annie Laurie group of mines, operating until 1930s.

1890s: Bingham Copper Gold Mining Company incorporated in New Jersey, and developed two commercial mines—the Vernard Tunnel and the Old Hickory—and built a smelter in Midvale.

1899: Bingham purchased Eagle and Blue Bell Mining Company.

1901: Bingham Copper Gold Mining Company purchased Dalton and Lark property at Bingham and reorganized as Bingham Consolidated Mining and Smelting Company, Inc.

1899–
1905: Smaller companies started: Tintic Mining and Development Company; Utah-Apex Mining Company.

1902: United States Mining Company started.

1909: Utah Metal Mining Company began.

Montana

1870–
1890: Elk Horn thrived, both mine and town.

Colorado (San Juan Region)

1869: Pioneer Mine staked.

1872: Little Giant Gold Mine found. Rico established, center of mining activities.

1873: Parrott City began with find along La Plata River.

1878: Atlantic Cable, Grand View, Phoenix, Yellowjacket claims became operational in Rico-Silverton area.

The Field Broadens

Gold, silver, and copper in the West did not stop new development of an older American industry—iron. The use of iron from eastern deposits was increasing, and the need for far larger deposits was foremost in the minds of eastern industrialists. The end result was the discovery and development of one of the world's greatest iron-ore areas.

THE VERMILION AND MESABI RANGES

It was not unusual in the 1800s for gold rushes to precede discoveries of other important mining deposits—as in Minnesota. Although in the 1850s, iron-ore specimens had been found, nothing was done about it until 1865 when Henry H. Eames, the state geologist, surveyed the iron region known as the Vermilion Range. In Eames's report, published in 1866, the iron discoveries were mentioned along with gold deposits, and a Vermilion gold rush was on, while the iron seemed to have been completely ignored. The Vermilion gold, however, proved of little value, and interest quickly subsided.

Ten years following the survey, Charlemagne Tower, a Pennsylvania industrialist, sent Professor Albert H. Chester to report on the Vermilion and Mesabi ranges' iron deposits. Chester, who had seen only the fringes of the Mesabi Range, favored Vermilion in his recommendations to Tower. Five years passed before Tower started to buy Vermilion land, but, in 1882, with 20,000 acres of land, he incorporated the Minnesota Iron Company. A year later Tower brought in a number of Cornish and Swedish families and about thirty unattached workmen to dig ore. It was the founding of Tower, the town.

Tower almost immediately started building the Duluth and Iron Range Railroad to link his mine, at the edge of Vermilion Lake, with Two Harbors on Lake Superior. The sixty-five-mile railroad was completed in 1884, after an investment of a million dollars and 1,400 men on round-the-clock shifts. On July 31, the first trainload of ore started down the track to Two Harbors, carrying 220 tons. It reached the lake one hour before a midnight deadline established by contract for the railroad's completion.

Professor Chester, in choosing Vermilion, over-

Before working a new open pit at Eveleth, Minnesota, the topsoil is removed. *Standard Oil Company of New Jersey*

A partial view of Missabe Mountain Open Pit Mine at Virginia, Minnesota. This pit ships about 7,000 tons of iron ore a day. The oldest and deepest iron mine in Minnesota, operated from 1884 to 1963, and producing over 16 million tons of high-grade iron ore, was Tower's Soudan Mine. Here the ore was taken from seven open pits. Today its shafts extend 2,500 feet down, with drifts and tunnels running three-quarters of a mile from the shaft. Its peak production year was 1892; nearly 575,000 tons of ore were shipped and 1,800 men were employed. The State of Minnesota acquired the mine as a historic site, together with 1,000 acres of land donated by the United States Steel Corporation in 1963. *Standard Oil Company of New Jersey*

looked the world's largest iron-ore deposit, the Mesabi Range, where the Mountain Iron Mine was discovered on Iron Mountain fifteen years later by the Merritts. For the next seventy-five years or so, over 2 billion Mesabi tons were shipped to Amer-

Gondola cars being loaded from the Susquehanna Mine in the Mesabi Range. *Inland Steel Company*

The 34-ton, 400 horsepower diesel trucks carry the iron ore to the central dump at the open-pit mining operations of the Oliver Iron Mining Company in Virginia, Minnesota. This mine began when John D. Rockefeller gained control of the Lake Superior Consolidated Iron Mines Company property that encompassed the Mountain Iron Mine. Rockefeller spent huge amounts of money developing the Mesabi Range, and in 1901 he exchanged his Lake Superior Consolidated stocks for $80 million in shares of a new combine—United States Steel Corporation. United States Steel's Oliver Iron Mining Division operated the Mountain Iron Mine until 1956, when it was closed. *Standard Oil Company of New Jersey*

ica's steel mills, accounting for more than half of the nation's iron ore.

Christian Wieland, geologist Eames's guide, had been mainly interested in gold, but he did not overlook the iron deposits near Babbitt. He discussed them with a group of mining men from Ontonagon, Michigan, who formed a syndicate and sent Peter Mitchell, a man of great mining experience, to explore the Mesabi Range. In 1871 Mitchell put down a test pit, which revealed what he thought was rich iron ore but in reality was taconite, a low-grade material that would await the mid-1900s for utilization. It was during Wieland's tenure that iron-ore samples were brought to Duluth by Louis H. Merritt who for sixteen years with his four sons and their four cousins searched the Mesabi Range until, in 1890, they made their strike, subsequently hiring a mining expert, J. A. Nichols—the beginning of the Mountain Iron Mine. The Merritt brothers also discovered other rich mines. In 1891, together with other investors, they incorporated the Duluth, Missabe and Northern Railway Company to lay forty-five miles of track from the Mountain Iron Mine to

A close-up of the central dump. *Standard Oil Company of New Jersey*

The Hull-Rust-Mahoning Open Pit Iron Ore Mine, the largest iron-ore mine in the world. This pit has a total area of 1,275 acres, with 55 miles of track in the pit. Development of this pit began in 1895. Although the Mountain Iron Mine was the first developed, it was not the largest, being exceeded by the Hull-Rust-Mahoning Open Pit, near Hibbing—a combination of 9 open pits combined in a single hole 1½ miles wide, 3 miles long, and over 540 feet deep. The material removed from

this pit exceeds that excavated to create the Panama Canal. Since operations were begun here in 1895, more than 500 million tons have been removed. Hibbing, Virginia, Eveleth, Mountain Iron, and Biwabik, all within a 15-mile stretch of U.S. Route 169, are the great Mesabi Range towns. The last of the three ranges that make Minnesota a great iron state is the Cuyuna. Its ore was first shipped in 1911. *Standard Oil Company of New Jersey*

a point near Duluth. During the 1890s, Mesabi ore, because it occurred near the surface of the ground and could not be mined by underground methods, was ideal for open-pit mining, but, without further improvement in steelmaking techniques, not so ideal for the steelmakers' furnaces.

When the 1893 depression occurred, stimulated by the silver panic, the Merritts were involved in extending their railroad into Duluth and building ore docks to avoid transhipping their ore to the mills by still other railroads. But the times and the heavy financial burden cost them their railroad and ore property. It was acquired by John D. Rockefeller.

Today an important part of Minnesota's iron-ore industry is taconite mining. It is a low-iron-content hard-rock ore, and because modern smelting methods can easily handle it, it is used extensively. Some $500-odd million has been invested, though recent explorations in Lake and St. Louis counties indicate that within a few years copper-nickel might rival taconite mining.

Early underground lead-zinc mining in Tri-State area. Missouri's lead-zinc area overlaps into Kansas and Oklahoma, and is known as the Tri-State District, formerly the Joplin District. Zinc mining operations here were on a larger scale than they are today; the greatest quantities of zinc now come from New York, New Jersey, and Tennessee. Between 1850 and 1870, zinc from the Tri-State District was discarded because the mining operations were for lead only. Before 1910 most Tri-State zinc mining was restricted to Missouri, but since 1915 the Oklahoma-Kansas Eagle-Picher Industries operations at Picher, Oklahoma, comprise the bulk of the district's zinc output. *Eagle-Picher Industries, Inc.*

TRI-STATE LEAD AND ZINC

Like iron, the demand for lead and zinc was increasing, and known deposits were running out. It was time for the nation's largest lead deposits to be discovered—in the tri-state area of Missouri-Kansas-Oklahoma. Lead was common in the populated areas of the United States almost from its earliest days. Like zinc, often it is associated with other metals, easily extracted, as technology advanced, from gold, silver, copper, and the other deposits in which it is frequently found.

Lead mining operation at the 300-foot level at Tri-State lead-zinc operations. During most of the nineteenth century, these shallow mines of the Upper Mississippi valley served as important lead sources until the southeast Missouri discovery in 1867 developed into one of the most productive lead regions in the world. Southeastern Missouri remained the leading lead-producing mining district in the United States (excepting 1962 when Idaho took the lead because of a long strike at the St. Joseph Lead Company). From 1801 to around 1810 only about 1,000 tons a year had been produced in the United States. By 1840 it had increased to about 13,000 tons a year. As the railroads stretched across the country, beginning in 1869, prospectors were helping to develop lead deposits at Eureka, Nevada; Bingham Canyon, Park City, and Big and Little Cottonwood canyons, Utah; Lead, Colorado; Cerro Gordo, California; and the Coeur d'Alene region of Idaho. None, however, exceeded Missouri's Bonne Terre and Joplin deposits. Notwithstanding early uses in the east, about 96 percent of today's domestic output comes from west of the Mississippi River, particularly from Idaho, Utah, Colorado, Washington, Montana, Arizona, California, and Missouri, its southeastern lead district being the leading United States producer. *Eagle-Picher Industries, Inc.*

Trip into a lead mine. *Bureau of Mines*

Typical hand mining of tiff, 1941. Note primitive rocker to shake off dirt. Pile of tiff in foreground. A family of this size digs about $1.75 worth of ore per day in the Potosi District of Clark National Forest. Barite is locally known as "tiff," a mineral calcite that resembles calcite in form, color, and cleavage. All barite and tiff production in Missouri comes from the east-central district, primarily Washington County, and all tiff mining is by open-pit operation. Barite is relatively common in Missouri, found at several locations, and the state leads the nation in the production of this material used primarily in the production of drilling mud for the petroleum industry, with some use in paint manufacture and related industries. *United States Forest Service*

A cut at the "Sucker Flats" area reveals the character of the zinc and lead ore. The deposit extends 65 feet deep from the truck level and the overburden 65 feet over the truck level. *Cooley Bros.*

Hard Luck Mine, south of Joplin, Missouri, circa 1900, a somewhat more elaborate version of the Wandering Jew Mine. The finer material, called "chat" by local people (in the right-hand part of this glass negative), is an indication of better processing methods. It contrasts sharply with the coarse material in the background. *Missouri, Division of Geological Survey and Water Resources*

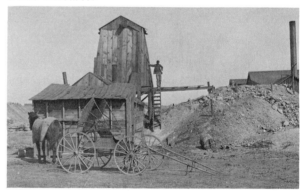

Empire City, now a part of Galena, Kansas, once a thriving mining town in the center of lead and zinc deposits discovered in 1877. The proverbial saloon predominates in this early photo. *Kansas State Historical Society.*

Typical Tri-State mine road. The Tri-State zinc-lead area is also known for its non-metallic mining. Among the products mined here are shale, fire clay, limestone, building stone and concrete aggregate, and gravel and sand for use in glass manufacture. *Eagle-Picher Industries, Inc.*

The entrance to the shale mine of the Diamond Paving Brick Works, circa 1900. *Missouri Division of Geological Survey and Water Resources*

Known as Wapanucke limestone, these blocks of oolitic limestone were taken from the old Galbreath Quarry near Bromide, Oklahoma. This limestone is soft, white, and massive. *Oklahoma Geological Survey*

TWO-TON BONANZA!

Phosphate was developed in 1867, when two tons were mined in South Carolina. From that unpropitious beginning until 1894, South Carolina remained the largest producer.

In 1889, phosphate was discovered in Florida, and a year later the following appeared in the *Florida Times-Union:*

> BULLETIN—Leesburg, Fla., January 20, 1890 —Two hunters, while engaged in a wild and thrilling pursuit of a ferocious manatee through the primeval forest of Pasco County, came upon an immense deposit of phosphate containing the remains of 9 ichthyossuri, 4 megatherii, 11 mastodons, 6 troglydons, and 2 parellelopipedons. Gosh! Ain't they rich.

This phosphate discovery started a boom that year in Jacksonville, a boom in some ways equal to those of the gold-rush days. Everybody was discovering phosphate, and every backyard resembled a phosphate mine. Prospectors were all over the central part of the peninsula, and land agents, miners, and chemists dogged their footsteps. Instant towns sprouted, replete with dance-hall girls, swindlers, gamblers, and gunmen, and everyone who found a fossil, of which there were many, thought that he had struck it phosphate rich. The newspapers had reported the phosphate beds to be "the petrified remains of countless millions of animals whose existence dates back into the grey dawn of time. . . . But in carrying out God's plan, these huge monsters . . .

Working the phosphate pits in the early Florida (Ocala) days, 1890. Florida accounts for 70 percent of domestic production, which began in 1888, followed by Tennessee in 1894 and the western states in 1906. From 1900 to 1912 Arkansas did some phosphate mining, as did Kentucky from 1919 to 1926. And from 1937 to 1948, phosphate concentrates also were being produced in Virginia. Production in the West originated in Idaho in 1906, with limited production in Wyoming and Utah in 1907; Montana entered the picture in 1923. *Historical Archives, Florida Publishing Company*

buried through all these millions of forgotten ages, again came forth in other forms to give luxuriance and fertility to the plant life which feeds a hungry people." All of which proved nothing but that phosphate is a good source of fertilizer and other chemicals.

Several companies had actually bought land and developed phosphate operations before 1890; it was no secret that phosphate was plentiful in central Florida. But since virtually no one bothered to mine it in any quantity before 1890, it was questionable which came first, the phosphate boom or the land boom. Land that had gone begging for $1.25 an acre or less, was now being sold for $1,000 an acre. Most of the action centered at the town of Dunnellon; even its streets were pure phosphate.

Hand-mining phosphate in Tennessee. *Tennessee State Library and Archives*

In one bite, this dragline will take more than 900 cubic feet of phosphate ore from the Florida mine of International Minerals and Chemical Corporation. The 2,200-horsepower dragline has a total lifting capacity of 82½ tons. *International Minerals & Chemical Corporation*

Surfaced mined area immediately following completion. *Florida Phosphate Council*

Draglines (of 72 cubic yards and 19 cubic yards) working the pit at Texas Gulf's Lee Creek Mine, North Carolina. North Carolina may become the big phosphate-producing state thanks to Texas Gulf Sulphur's new plant, including a $50 million fertilizer complex on 700 acres along the Pamlico River, which runs into Pamlico Sound, protected by Cape Hatteras. The plant is known as Lee Creek and is completely integrated, from mining to processing—the largest operation of its kind in the United States. *Texas Gulf Sulphur Company*

"Cat" pushing phosphate ore onto sifter grating. *United States Forest Service. Photo by B. W. Muir*

The same mined area after land reclamation. *Florida Phosphate Council*

THE MOLLY MAGUIRES

While even from the beginning the very rugged-ness of mining was conducive to violence, violence became organized in the late 1860s.

A most remarkable episode (well documented in literature and movies) belongs to the Molly Maguires, named for both Connor Maguire (a seventeenth-century Irish conspirator) and for the fact that members of the original group were known to dress in women's clothing—for reasons of security.

The Pennsylvania coalfields were worked by large numbers of Irishmen—immigrated to the United States during the Irish potato famine—some, former members of this Irish secret society that had been formed in 1845 to combat the so-called evils of Irish landowners.

Conditions in the Pennsylvania mining communities were at least as bad as those the men had combatted in Ireland—primitive and with little, if any, protective legislation for safety, working conditions, or labor. Housing, sanitary facilities, hours of labor, low pay, and high accident rates all contributed to the miners' unrest. Rent, groceries, and other living expenses were high for $35 in weekly wages, and expenses were usually under the control of the mine operators. High accident rates made working hazardous. In one seven-year period, over 550 miners had been killed, nearly 1,600 maimed

Conditions around the mines, as well as the living quarters, were a sordid combination of coal dust and decay. Harper's Monthly, *1882.*

or crippled, and, around 1870, 5,000 out of 22,000 were under sixteen years of age.

During the Civil War many miners, mostly foreigners, had been physically forced to enter the army, some taken directly from their homes, tied to horses, and pulled to the induction centers. After the war, the recession caused many miners to be laid off, while returning veterans were given preference over foreign workers.

All of these conditions spurred the miners to strike in January, 1868, and to form a coal union, the Workmen's Benevolent Association. The strike was settled quickly, but another occurred in January, 1871, now backed by the union and a coalition of northern and southern Pennsylvania miners. Meanwhile the Molly Maguires were becoming secretly active, operating without regard for law and order. Their methods called for vandalism and threats of murder, often followed by actual killings, robberies, and assaults.

The strike in the coal mines. Meeting of "Molly Maguire" men. Wood engraving in *Harper's,* January 31, 1874, after Frenzeny & Tavernier. *Library of Congress*

These Harlan wives are holding copies of *Bloody Harlan,* a booklet exposing the mines and the courts for jailing their miner-unionist husbands. United Mine Workers

The Pinkerton Agency was employed by the mine operators to break up the secret organization. Allan Pinkerton believed that the only way to accomplish this successfully was from the inside, and he gave one of his detectives, James McParland, a twenty-nine-year-old Irish immigrant, the task of infiltrating the Molly Maguires. Posing as James McKenna, a fugitive from a Buffalo murder charge, McParland arrived at the Pennsylvania coalfields in October, 1873. Moving from town to town as a happy-go-lucky tramp, McParland's Irish personality soon made him a favorite of the Irish mine workers. A good singer, drinker, dancer, and gambler, his popularity grew, and he obtained a job in the mines. His fabricated background and his ability to fight, drink, and spend money enhanced his popularity with the criminal element, and he soon became a member of the Molly Maguires, working his way up to secretary of the clandestine society.

The fires of discontent were smoldering. In September, 1873, the *Miners Journal,* the newspaper of Mahanoy City, Pennsylvania, reported that 300 pistols were sold. Franklin Benjamin Gowen, a lawyer who had become president of the Reading Railroad in 1870, had purchased large tracts of coal land and managed to have the governor of Pennsylvania sign bills that made the Reading a monopoly in the coalfields, making Gowen a virtual czar of the industry. He controlled the Workmen's Benevolent Association (WBA) and now was forcing the

Headquarters for the Amalgamated Association, 1882, one of the groups that grew out of discontent with industry conditions.

Mahanoy City miners cheer return to work. *Schuylkill County, Pennsylvania, Historical Society*

union to submit to his demands, and in concert with other operations, he fixed the price of coal at $5 a ton, a scheme that obviously would reduce wages and break the union. Tensions in Mahanoy City grew when a fire broke out, followed by a fight in which an official was killed. A Molly Maguire was charged with the murder, and the violence increased. Rumors of an impending strike spread. By January, 1875, almost all the mines were forced to close as the "long strike" began. This was the Molly Maguire signal for sabotage acts, which were all carefully chronicled by McParland. The saboteurs planned to dynamite bridges, and managed to cut loose a railroad car loaded with iron, which almost crashed into a passenger train.

As the strike ran on into May, 1875, the situation became critical for the mine workers whose money was now running out and whose credit was no longer being honored. The mine owners announced plans to reopen the mines despite the strike, and on June 1 the first mine to reopen was the West Shenandoah Colliery. Hard-pressed miners rushed to work, thus ending the strike. But the Mollys would

not be pacified and agitated a raid against the Shenandoah, joined by miners they coerced from the Hazleton mines. The mobs were so large that troops were rushed in to restore calm. The power of the union was broken but that of the Mollys increased. During all this time, McParland, ostensibly active in the Molly organization, continued to send in detailed reports of their activities.

McParland, in constant danger of being discovered, had to be careful indeed, as discovery would surely end his life. On July 5, 1875, the Mollys killed Benjamin Yost in a street fight, the details of which McParland also reported. Tension continued to grow with additional killings in Mahanoy City, Shenandoah, and Girardville, and McParland continued to gather evidence against the murderers. Particularly singled out for death by the Mollys were the mine bosses, and McParland was assigned the job of the next killing. Jimmy Kerrigan, the killer of Yost, became impatient with McParland's stalling, and without waiting killed the intended victim at the Tamaqua railroad station. Kerrigan and two of his accomplices were captured.

The Mollys had suspected that there was an informer in their midst, so at McParland's suggestion the Pinkertons talked about forming a vigilante group to fight the Maguires. (McParland had given the Pinkertons a list of about 375 Molly members and their crimes.) Actually, the Pinkertons were not known to be involved in such action, but rumors of vigilante reprisals increased the Mollys' suspicions that there was an informer among them.

On September 3, 1875, Jimmy Kerrigan, Mike Doyle, and other Mollys were put on trial for the murder of the mine superintendent. Doyle was sentenced to be hanged, but Jim Kerrigan turned informer and named each of the Mollys. The Pinkerton men formed posses to bring in the men he accused. Finally the Molly Maguires realized that McParland was indeed a detective, and he found himself being stalked by gunmen, whom he eluded.

Many Molly Maguires went on trial for various killings based upon the testimony of Kerrigan, but McParland's testimony was needed to convict the balance of the murderers.

On May 6, 1876, in a trial held in Pottsville, McParland appeared on the stand as a state's witness. As the trial continued, one by one the Molly Maguire gunmen were found guilty and sentenced to die. By June, 1877, nineteen of the Mollys had been sent to the gallows, ten executed simultaneously. Other trials were held at Mauch Chunk and Bloomsburg, and with the death of their leaders the Molly Maguire reign of terror was squashed.

Certificate of membership in the United Mine Workers of America, with nine scenes of work in the mines. Lithograph by Kurz and Allison, 1899. *Library of Congress*

Sulfur "vats." Before 1912, vats were broken down by hand. *Texas Gulf Sulphur Company*

THE YELLOW STONE THAT BURNS

Sulfur is one of the oldest, most interesting, and unusual elements known to man. The Egyptians in 2000 B.C. used it to bleach linen textiles and in 1550 B.C. as a medication to treat granulated eyelids, an infection that still occurs today. The yellow "stone that burns" (coal is also "the stone that burns") is the brimstone of the Bible, and an ingredient, with saltpeter and charcoal, in China's gunpowder discovery in A.D. 1200.

Sulfur is found in four types of deposits: salt dome, volcanic, sedimentary, and pyrite. Sulfur-contained salt domes extend from east Alabama, at the McIntosh Salt Dome, westward through Mississippi, Louisiana, and Texas to about the Rio Grande River. Deposits lie in a belt 75 miles to 300 miles inland from the Gulf Coast as well as offshore. These domes are generally a solid vertical column of salt, usually circular in form and extending horizontally from a few yards to over two miles. A salt dome is often distinguished by its flatness, by a characteristic series of minerals that appear on or near the surface known as the "cap." Not all salt domes contain sulfur; in fact, few warrant development for sulfur recovery. Nevertheless, most native sulfur is taken from salt-dome deposits, with about thirty domes producing some 150 million tons.

Volcanic sulfur deposits, the second type, are found in most volcanic regions of the world, many originating from thermal-springs precipitation. Such deposits are mined at the Cuprite and Rabbit Hole mines in Nevada, at the Sulfur Bank Mine in California, at the Cave Creek Mine in Utah, and at mines in Wyoming, particularly near Cody and Thermopolis. Sedimentary sulfur is the third type of deposit, and is generally not found in the United States. And last, accounting for about 40 percent of all sulfur, is that produced from metal sulfides, called "pyrites," occurring in pyrite veins.

The exact date of the discovery of sulfur in the United States is not known but there are pre-Revolutionary War references.

It was the early days of the oil boom, around 1870, and wildcat drillers had discovered a salt dome in a Louisiana swamp with a 100-foot-thick vein of sulfur running through the cap rock. The first attempt to tap this sulfur source was a test-drilling to 1,230 feet, which showed 400 feet of clay and gravel, then quicksand, followed by a 600-foot layer of sulfur-impregnated limestone. Though for twenty years thereafter various companies tried to open the deposit by conventional mining methods, the sulfurous water, quicksand, and noxious hydrogen-sulfide

As prepared sulfur piles are depleted, tracks are shifted to new vat areas. *Texas Gulf Sulphur Company*

gas made it impossible. In 1890, five workers were asphyxiated and the mine was abandoned.

In 1890, while that first mine in a Louisiana dump was being abandoned, Dr. Herman Frasch, a German petroleum chemist, conceived an idea that would revolutionize the sulfur industry by making possible the tapping of salt-dome resources. Frasch knew that sulfur liquifies at the low temperature of 235 degrees Fahrenheit, and he toyed with the thought of melting the sulfur underground, treating it as oil, and pumping it to the surface through wells. He worked out a method and secured his first patent in 1891—to the ridicule of cynics who perhaps thought he was crazy. But Frasch went to work on the salt domes on an island in Louisiana. Drilling to the cap rock, he and his crew then boiled water in four old boilers and pumped it down the hole for twenty-four uninterrupted hours. Hardly daring to believe his idea would work, Frasch opened a valve to start the pumping engine. In a few moments, from a depth of 600 feet, a stream of golden-brown liquid sulfur gushed out. Though it took another nine years to perfect the process commercially, the Frasch method is the one most widely used in the United States today.

247

The Frasch method of sulfur mining utilizes a well, superheated water, and concentric pipes. Injected into the formation through the upper set of holes, the hot water melts the sulfur, which, being heavier than water, sinks to the bottom. Pressures in the well force the melted sulfur into the lower set of holes and up an inner pipe. A third pipe, carrying compressed air, helps to raise the column of liquid sulfur to the surface. *Texas Gulf Sulphur Company*

Bagging the sulfur, 1924. *Texas Gulf Sulphur Company*

The first sulfur vats at Gulf, July 15, 1919. Ten Frasch-process mines, operated by four companies in Louisiana and Texas, provide most of the United States production. Some small deposits are found in California (the Anaconda Company operates the Leviathan Mine), Colorado, Nevada (the Western Sulphur Corporation operates the Rabbit Hole and Humble House mines in Nevada), New Mexico, Utah, and Wyoming, but these are consumed locally. By far the two giants are Freeport Sulphur Company and Texas Gulf Sulphur, which also recovers sulfur from sour gas (a natural gas with a hydrogen sulfide odor, which, when removed, produces sulfur in the process but which is a chemical rather than a mining process). Texas Gulf had entered sulfur mining just six years after Frasch's mining process went into commercial operation. For about ten years after its formation, TGS acquired and explored deposits in Matagorda County, Texas, and then production got under way. The company's four Frasch mines in Texas produce over 2 million tons of sulfur a year, not counting two sour-gas-recovery plants in Canada and one in Wyoming. (TGS also produces potash from a 15,000-acre reserve in Utah, phosphate rock from North Carolina, zinc, copper, and silver ores in Canada, and soda ash from the Green River region of Wyoming.) *Texas Gulf Sulphur Company*

The Bryanmound Mine, 1912, site of Freeport Sulphur's first sulfur production five months after it was chartered on July 12, 1912, as the Freeport Texas Company, a holding company for Freeport Sulphur, which assumed its present name in December, 1936. This fantastic operation endured until October, 1935, producing 5 million tons of sulfur. In 1933, when it appeared that Bryanmound would be depleted, Freeport acquired the sulfur rights to the salt-dome properties at Grande Ecaille (Port Sulphur), Louisiana, which today is the second-largest producing sulfur mine in the world. In the meantime, in 1923, the Hoskins Mine, Hoskins, Texas, had been opened. This produced nearly 11 million tons of sulfur before it was depleted in 1955. Other Freeport plants in operation are at Bay Sainte Elaine (a saltwater operation thirty-five miles south of Houma, Louisiana), and at Grand Island Bay, acquired in 1953. In 1968, a new plant opened, operated by the Duval Corporation, the third-largest producer, operating plants in Texas and elsewhere, with a capacity of 300,000 tons a year; a new mine will add about 300,000 tons more to the company's capacity. Its largest facility is a mine in Culberson County, Texas, which produces about 2½ million tons a year. *Freeport Sulphur Company*

Freeport, 1912: The Tarpon Inn. *Freeport Sulphur Company*

What appears to be horseplay is the setting of a pole at Grande Port, Louisiana, 1933, in conjunction with a sulfur operation. *Freeport Sulphur Company*

Mining sulfur at Fishlake National Forest, Utah, 1920. Some of its hundreds of uses contribute to cellulose products, chemicals, dyes, fertilizers, iron and steel, pharmaceuticals, rubber, water-treatment procedures, and other fields, plus diverse applications to keep up with technology as new markets are developed every year. About half of all sulfur goes to the fertilizer industry, the demand at times exceeding production. *United States Forest Service*

Beaumont Terminal, Texas, the hub of the world's greatest sulfur distribution complex. At the docks are a dry cargo vessel and two new oceangoing tankers that went into service in 1964. Highly mechanized loading facilities speed shipments of both solid and liquid sulfur in ocean vessels, river barges, and railroad cars. *Texas Gulf Sulphur Company*

Bay Sainte Elaine. *Freeport Sulphur Company*

ARIZONA COPPER

Coincidental with the rise of Ray in 1873, two soldiers were building a wagon road between Superior and Globe, Arizona, when one, known only as Sullivan, struck chloride of silver rocks. But he did nothing about it. A year later, Charles Mason and three companions found it and quickly organized the Silver King Mine. They built a stamping mill and other facilities for silver reclamation, which became the foundation of a large mining camp.

Meanwhile, in 1875, Hugh Jones, prospecting in Arizona's Mule Mountains, discovered copper. However, Jones was looking for silver, and in his disappointment he did not file a claim for the copper deposits. Jack Dunn, an American Army scout, filed two years later (obscuring Hugh Jones, George Warren, and two others) on the great Copper Queen deposit.

As miners arrived, a typical mining camp emerged. In 1879, a San Francisco brokerage firm, Bisbee (for whom the town was named), Williams and Company, sponsored a new company to operate the Copper Queen. A year or two later, James Douglas came to Bisbee, obtained an option on the Atlantic Claim next to the Copper Queen, and in 1883 found a great body of copper ore. Through mergers, these became the Copper Queen Consolidated Company, eventually absorbed by Phelps Dodge.

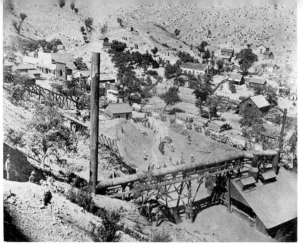

By the end of the 1880s, Bisbee had become a busy mining town. The streets were filled with teams of horses and mules transporting the ore as it was removed from the mine. *Western Ways Features and Arizona Pioneers Historical Society*

George Warren who with three others located the Copper Queen Mines in 1878, where Bisbee now stands. Warren lost his ownership in the mines in a footrace won by G. W. Atkinson. *Western Ways Features*

Main Street, Bisbee, 1886. Copper Queen office is at right. In time lead and zinc were produced, and by 1917 Copper Queen Consolidated was absorbed by the Phelps Dodge Corporation. Meanwhile, two other mines had prospered, the Shattuck and Denn mines, merging in 1925 into the Shattuck-Denn Mining Company. In 1947 they sold out to Phelps Dodge, which today maintains the huge operation at its Lavender Pit Mine begun in 1954. Estimates for the Lavender Pit exceed 32 million tons of ore yearly. Between 1954 and 1961 it had converted ore into 500 million pounds of copper. *Phelps Dodge Corporation*

The well-planned community of Superior, Arizona, a copper town owned by the Magma Copper Company. The Magma Mine seen in the background is a high-grade copper producer in operation since 1910. In 1880, the Lake Superior and Arizona Mining Company had developed their Gold Eagle Mine, and increasing silver production soon made this area an important center. But by 1889 most of the silver was exhausted. In 1910 (with the formation of the Magma Copper Company) the Magma District again assumed importance. The Silver King and Silver Queen properties were revitalized with the discovery of copper, and in 1914 Magma constructed a 200-ton-per-day concentrator to process the new ore, which in two years reached 300 tons a day, including some zinc and lead ores. By 1922 the concentrator was processing 600 tons, and construction of a new, 500-ton-per-day copper smelter was begun. Around 1923 the Belmont and the Gold Eagle mines' new gold and copper production added considerably to the Magma-Superior District's importance, as did the Magma Mine by 1943, when it had become the largest zinc producer in Arizona. In fact, most of the property in the area is now held by the Magma Copper Company, which in turn is largely owned by the Newmont Mining Company. Also part of Magma's operations is the nearby San Manuel Copper Corporation. Mining continues actively in the district. *Magma Copper Company*

The local saloon at Bisbee, 1910. *Phelps Dodge Corporation*

Staking a claim (scribbled) by placing it in a tin can on a stake at one of the corner markers. The prospector will then go to town and file it to make it legal. *Western Ways Features*

Sacramento Hill, behind Bisbee, 1928. *Phelps Dodge Corporation*

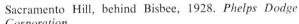

The company store, Copper Queen, 1873. *Phelps Dodge Corporation*

THE MINES THAT DROWNED

While the coppers were being developed, the criminal element was running rampant at Tombstone. Tombstone is famous for Wyatt Earp, from Dodge City. In 1878, he was sent as an armed guard for Wells Fargo to Tombstone, then booming with 7,000 miners, gamblers, and gunmen, a few law-abiding citizens among them. The town was the site of the much-publicized O.K. Corral gunfight, when Wyatt Earp, with his brothers, Virgil and Morgan, and a friend, Doc Holliday, fought the Clanton gang.

Ed Schieffelin, discoverer of the famous Tombstone mines. *University of Oklahoma Library, Division of Manuscripts*

Ore train moving out of Bisbee, 1870. *Phelps Dodge Corporation*

Prospectors striking out from Tombstone to make their fortunes, 1890. Three years after these men arrived at Tombstone, the mines were closed, but attempts were made to reopen them. In 1903 a company was formed to sink a drainage shaft and tunnel to pump out the entire district in an effort to lower the water table. The operation was fairly successful and continued for about four years, until breakdowns refilled the shafts and the project finally was abandoned. In 1914 the Phelps Dodge Corporation took over most of the mining properties, and though activity has been spasmodic, Phelps Dodge continues to mine it. Tombstone has been partially restored as a historic site. *Phelps Dodge Corporation*

Whether Earp's group had killed a gang of criminals or were themselves thieves and murderers has never been proved. (It took a rancher-turned-sheriff, John Slaughter, to clean up the town.) From Tombstone, Earp moved from mining camp to mining camp, opening saloons in San Diego, Nome, and Tonopah.

Tombstone's mining story begins in the summer of 1877 with Ed Schieffelin. Schieffelin arrived from Fort Huachuca with a party of soldiers sent to guard against marauding Apache Indians. With his two prospecting partners, he soon struck silver, two years later founding the Lucky Cuss Mine, the first of three the group ultimately owned.

The name Tombstone has two origins, the popular, which derives from Ed Schieffelin's comment that all he would find would be his tombstone, and the more probable, that the rock outcroppings resembled tombstones. Its popular tourist attraction, Boot Hill Cemetery, containing gravestones with colorful epitaphs from those rough pioneer days, is probably its best justification.

Tombstone's high elevation (4,500 feet) notwithstanding, its water table was quite high, but the demands of increasing numbers of miners who stormed into town would result in disaster. Dams were built along the San Pedro River to supply water for the mills around Tombstone, but they proved ruinous for the mines. The deep shafts of the Lucky Cuss, Grand Central, Contention, Silver Thread, and Emerald mines began to fill with water from the high water table, raised further by the dams. In all the shafts, expensive Cornish pumps were installed that could tip the balance between profit and loss. Unfortunately, exceptionally heavy rains fell for two years, and by 1888 it was evident that the pumps could not do the job. Now with the price of silver continually falling, the mines began to close. By 1893 the town was virtually deserted, but oddly enough over $80 million in silver had been taken out of the district.

The water problem spawned new towns. The San Pedro River, nine miles west, was easy to dam in several places. One result was Charleston, built almost overnight as a company town to mill the rich Tombstone silver ores. Charleston's mills ran day and night, while its saloons and brothels kept pace. The town was as rough and as wild as Tombstone.

Johnny Ringo, the Clanton Gang, Wyatt Earp and brothers, Doc Holliday, and Curly Bill Brocious often were seen in Charleston as well as neighboring Millville, across the river. Most towns in the area died when mining ceased at Tombstone, though Charleston briefly came to life again in 1943, when troops from Fort Huachuca rebuilt some of the adobe buildings to practice street fighting in preparation for the invasions of World War II. But these buildings were later torn down.

THE WAY OF JEROME

Tombstone was literally a "washout" as a mining town, but Jerome, practically at the other end of Arizona, was a huge success, as long as it lasted. Just outside Jerome, on Highway 89A, a marker proclaims the town's population—15,000, 10,000, 5,000, 1,000, and "Ghost City," all but the last with a line run through.

Jerome originally was precariously anchored athwart Mingus Mountain, with a 1,500-foot vertical separation between upper and lower housing. Its main streets were, and still are, switchback roads that snake over the mountain. But Jerome's "ups

The road marker indicates the decline of Jerome from its heyday as a mining center. *Jerome Historical Society; photo by J. Weidenborner*

Thirty-six-horse team hauling boilers to a mine near Tombstone, about the 1880s. *University of Oklahoma Library Division of Manuscripts*

and downs" were not confined to its steep streets. Fire and the vagaries of copper prices plagued it.

Jerome's history begins in 1876 with Al Sieber, a scout with General Cook, who staked a claim. It aroused little interest, but claims staked by M. A. Ruffner and Angus McKinnon (John Ruffner and August McKinnon) the same year created a stir. The prospectors dug a shaft forty-five feet deep, naming their workings the Eureka and the Wade Hampton. They brought in Phelps Dodge's Dr. James A. Douglas, Sr., to examine the area. But because of the 175-mile wagon haul to the Santa Fe Railroad, Douglas would not recommend mining exploitation. He showed poor judgment because Jerome mines ultimately produced some $800 million in copper.

Ruffner and McKinnon leased their claim to Governor Tritle of the Territory of Arizona. Tritle inveigled James A. MacDonald and Eugene Jerome of New York into forming a company. Jerome agreed to put up the money, but the mining camp was to bear his name. The result was the formation in 1882 of the United Verde Company. Senator William A. Clark and his Montana Mine superintendent, Joseph L. Giroux, bought all but 71,000 of United Verde's outstanding 300,000 shares. After an investment of $60 million, United Verde became the richest individually owned copper mine in the world.

Senator Clark moved to Jerome and built the

Montana House—it could house 1,000 men—the largest stone structure in Arizona. But it was later lost in one of the fires. Jerome swelled, with people living in tents and wooden shacks, not to mention the poorly constructed restaurants and saloons, which all contributed to devastating fires between 1897 and 1899. A Prescott, Arizona, newspaper showed its scorn in one of its headlines: "Jerome Burns Again! Entire business district of 24 saloons and 14 cheap restaurants destroyed." Omitted from mention were the gambling houses and the red-light district.

Now it was Douglas, Jr.'s turn to visit the area. "Rawhide Jimmie," as he was called, bought the

In the left background are the stack and workings of the Clarkdale smelter. In the center, the Little Daisy Hotel and, to the right, the home of James S. Douglas, with the workings of the Little Daisy Mine in between. The foreground shows the 1919 buildings of Jerome. When Clark built the smelter in 1894 he also constructed a 27-mile narrow-gauge railway to connect to the Santa Fe running south from Ash Fork to Prescott. *Jerome State Historic Park*

An old sketch of the original claims that became the United Verde Copper Company. The hillside appears to be fairly well timbered compared to later pictures that show the hill completely barren. The trees were quickly cut for firewood and mine timbers. In 1884 United Verde was owned by the Jeromes of New York who bought the Eureka Mine from Logan and Lenig of Philadelphia, for whom Dr. James Douglas examined the claims in 1880, advising their purchase. A year after its founding (1882), United Verde Copper had a new type of blast furnace, fed by coal from New Mexico, which made the mine a paying proposition. Just the gold and silver, extracted as a by-product, were enough to pay expenses. Suddenly, the price of copper dropped—from 19 cents to 11 cents a pound—and the mine was forced to close, though the town carried on. *Jerome State Historic Park*

Little Daisy claim formed ten years earlier. Geological studies by the shrewd young man convinced him that about 600 feet of lava and limestone covered huge deposits of copper on the Little Daisy territory. His calculations were correct. The town had been built on a geological fault; in ancient times the Verde Fault had slipped about a half mile down Cleopatra Mountain. In 1916, at 1,400 feet, Douglas found 15 percent ore; at 1,500 feet, increased to 45 percent. Clark's United Verde had overlooked some $125 million in ore!

In the 1920s, triggered by dynamite blasts, the area's geological instability caused a section of Jerome to slip downhill, and many buildings had to be shored up or wired with steel cables; after the city jail skidded 100 feet down the mountain it became known as the "traveling jail."

Meanwhile Senator Clark was having his troubles at United Verde. A new fire (one had been burning now for twenty years) at the 400-foot level had spread through other parts of the mine. Behind these fires were 10 million tons of ore, which could not be taken out by the tunnel-and-shaft method. Clark therefore decided to pull off the overburden and make an open-pit operation of it, at the same time extinguishing the fires. But the smelter was directly in the middle of where the pit should be and would have to be removed before the operation could succeed. Reconstruction started in 1912, and by its completion in 1915, there stood Clarkdale, a model town with a fine water supply, modern plumbing, landscaping, paved streets, brick houses, a town square, a company-owned-and-built business block, churches, schools, a bandstand, and a community center. Jerome is restored to life, but as a tourist attraction, designated a state park in 1965, with its rickety but supported frame buildings, and two museums.

Main Street, Jerome, 1905. The brick structure with arched windows is the Bartlett Building. *Phelps Dodge Corporation, United Verde Branch and Jerome Historical Society*

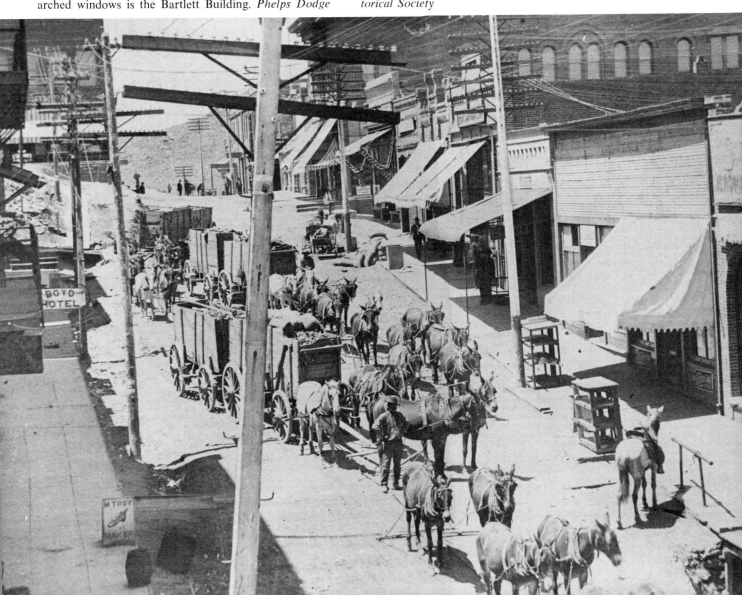

An overall view of Jerome in 1920, perched on the side of a mountain. Clarkdale stirred Jerome to improvement, and some of its hastily built frame houses were replaced by brick or concrete structures. Both towns prospered. By 1929 Jerome housed 15,000 people; nearly 2,500 of them were miners. But it was the year of the Depression; the bottom again fell out of the copper market, with prices down so drastically the mines could not operate. *Jerome State Historic Park*

United Verde mine pit at Jerome, circa 1920. In 1930 Verde Central closed. The following year United Verde bought it. In 1932, with copper at five cents a pound, United Verde closed, and Jerome dwindled to fewer than 5,000. In 1935, Phelps Dodge reentered the area and purchased the mine for about $21 million. This time Phelps Dodge had been wiser. They netted over $40 million by the time they began closing the mine in 1950, finally completing the job in March, 1953, for a total production of over 2¾ billion pounds of copper. *Arizona Department of Library and Archives*

Pouring copper in the new Verde smelter, a manual job in 1900. *Phelps Dodge Corporation, United Verde Branch and Jerome Historical Society*

In the 1940s, the Hopewell Haulage train operated at the 1,000-foot level of the United Verde Copper Company through a tunnel 9,100 feet long. *Phelps Dodge Corporation, United Verde Branch, and Jerome Historical Society, Inc.*

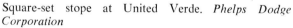

Square-set stope at United Verde. *Phelps Dodge Corporation*

256

The remnants of the old Bartlett Building, a three-story structure that housed a hotel on its upper floor and business places on the other two floors. In the 1950s it was sold for $125 for salvage. *Jerome Historical Society. Photo by J. Weidenborner*

Air view of the copper precipitating plant for "on-site" copper leaching at Kennecott Copper's plant in Ray, Arizona. In the background can be seen the train-loading bins and the No. 2 mine hoisting shaft. In the far background is the little town of Ray between Superior and Winkelman. Copper continued to predominate in Arizona although when the Mineral Creek Mining Company was formed in 1873, silver was mined there but, like many silver mines, copper ultimately became the bonanza. In 1883 the Ray Copper Company was organized, and copper mining now began in earnest. By the turn of the century, Ray Copper, acquired by a London company, had expanded its plant; by the early 1900s, Ray witnessed much growth, many consolidations, and new companies: Calumet Copper, Gila Copper, Arizona Hercules, and others. In 1907 the London company sold out, and by 1910 companies began to consolidate; by 1927 most were under the umbrella of Nevada Consolidated. In 1933 the properties were acquired by Kennecott Copper, which continues its operations today. *Bureau of Mines*

The Mineral Park Mine and concentrator of the Duval Corporation at Kingman, Arizona. *Bureau of Mines*

The Pima Mining Company's open-pit copper mine and concentrator can be seen in the upper left. The Mission Unit of the American Smelting and Refining Company is on the lower right. Note, on the right side of the upper left-hand pit, a line that is the conveyor leading out of the pit, seen in close-up in the following photograph. *Bureau of Mines*

A closeup view of the 22-ton incline skip on the north side of the Pima Open Pit Copper Mine. Notice that the conveyor runs underneath the bench roads of the pit, permitting continued operation of both the conveyor and trucks riding the bench. *Bureau of Mines*

A GRAND CANYON SPIN-OFF

Just as skiing developed from gold in Aspen, so, too, did tourism in Arizona, this time from Grand Canyon gold—or the lack of it. While unsuccessfully prospecting for gold and other metals in the Arizona Grand Canyon area around 1880, John Hance concluded that there might be more profit catering to tourists than to continue mining, and he began the first Grand Canyon tourist center—complete with mule tours and primitive overnight facilities—by improving the old Indian trails that led into the canyon. In 1890, William Bass, a miner, in competition with Hance, built a trail to the Colorado River and started a tourist business. Two years later, stagecoaches were carrying tourists from Flagstaff, and a hotel was built at Grandview Point. It would seem that Grand Canyon National Park owes its origin to mining.

CUSTER'S FIRST STAND

From Arizona the scene shifts to the Dakota Territory where gold rumors, though rarely fol-

lowed up, had persisted for years before the first find. Most prospectors instead were eager to reach Montana, preferring to take their chances on known gold deposits rather than to speculate on possibilities.

But Horatio N. Ross changed all this at French Creek, near Custer, South Dakota. Ross, a prospector, had been traveling with General George A. Custer's military expedition of 1,000 men sent to explore the Dakota Territory during the summer of 1874. On August 2, 1875, he stumbled on gold, which threw the entire camp into a frenzy. Of course, Custer's exhilarating telegram to the War Department, plus the news disseminated by expedition reporters, soon had hopefuls rushing in from coast to coast. Among the first to arrive was a Sioux City group, who built a stockade for protection against the Indians. But it seemed they had trespassed on Indian lands. By winter's end, they were arrested and taken to Cheyenne. However, it did not discourage the horde of fortune seekers who by then were resisting not only the Indians but the United States Army. The Sioux went on the warpath for two years, killing prospectors and troops without distinction. During one of their battles in this Sioux War of 1876, Custer and 250 of his men were annihilated at Little Big Horn.

In the meantime, 10,000 gold seekers were laying out mining claims and town sites on ground to which they had no title. Technically, they were all outlaws, and they behaved thus. Six-shooters rather than peace officers enforced the laws, which favored the best marksmen. Court decisions were replaced by a length of rope or a round of bullets, and lynchings, shootings, and robberies became common. Out of these came such names as Wild Bill Hickok, Calamity Jane, Lame Johnny, Fly Specked Billy, Jack McCall, Poker Alice, and Deadwood Dick.

It was during these few hectic years that most of the mining towns were established. In 1875 a group of prospectors had built a camp called Stonewall, but the army drove them out. But when the army withdrew, the men returned and laid out the town of Custer, Dakota's first boom town, which quickly reached a population of 5,000. It plummeted to 100 when new mines were discovered the next year at Deadwood. Deadwood derived from Deadwood Gulch, a canyon named for its fire-gutted trees, and its fortunes waxed and waned as its nearby gold and silver mines started or faltered. It was a rough city; Wild Bill Hickok was murdered here in its first year —Jack McCall shot him in the back. A miner's court freed McCall but the federal government hanged him for the crime later.

Main Street, Deadwood, 1876. *Deadwood, South Dakota, Chamber of Commerce*

Deadwood today is a modern city and the home of the Broken Boot Gold Mine, a tourist attraction, only three miles from the Homestake Gold Mine. Antedating Deadwood, and coinciding with Custer, Golden City's placer mining camp sprang up along Spring Creek, but its name was soon changed to Sheridan. Sheridan preceded Rapid City as the county seat, and became an important station on the Denver-Deadwood Stage Line. But the railroad killed the stage business, and the town died with it, finally coming to rest under Sheridan Lake, created by a 1938 dam. Coinciding with Deadwood's gold find, nearby Hill City claimed a find along Spring Creek. Unfortunately, Hill City lost out to Deadwood; and it was not until 1883, when prospectors found tin in the vicinity, that an English group, the Harney Peak Consolidated Tin Company, bought up the claims, stirring up the town for a few years, at least until 1892. They abandoned the area, and Hill City went downhill. *Felix A. Peckham*

Rarely used was the plunger type of stamper, which was a large, heavy metal barrel, weighing about 1,000 pounds, that was dropped onto the confined ore below. These barrels, used in South Dakota in 1870, broke the ore into pieces sufficiently small to be put into whatever stamping mill was available. *South Dakota State Historical Society*

259

One of the most picturesque and best-known characters of the Black Hills was merry Johnny Perrett who worked the gulches on Iron Creek and Potato Creek, tributaries of Spearfish Creek. Here he found the largest nugget ever found in the northern Black Hills—a single nugget worth several hundred dollars. A replica of this nugget is on display at the Adams Memorial Museum. Known as Potato Creek Johnny, Perrett took his name from the stream on which he placered. He was born in Wales and came to the Black Hills in 1883, prospecting for gold until he died in February, 1943. He is buried beside Wild Bill Hickok in Mount Moriah Cemetery. *Deadwood, South Dakota, Chamber of Commerce*

WELLS FARGO—A NEW TYPE OF GOLD MINE

Beginning in 1875, while prospectors throughout the west were hauling rich metals from the ground, a lone bandit was pursuing his own brand of gold mining—lifting gold shipments from the coaches of Wells Fargo. Black Bart, a mild-mannered man, began his career of crime when past middle age, but it was no satisfaction to Wells Fargo, which he plagued for years—for a grand record of twenty-seven successful robberies. When working, Bart wore a flour bag over his head (he peered through peepholes). Though he worked alone, he often succeeded in making his victims believe he was part of a gang. He stopped his first Wells Fargo stage in the middle of the road. Pointing to what appeared to be seven or eight gun barrels protruding from the surrounding rocks, he told the driver that if he resisted he would be riddled with bullets. The driver, believing he was surrounded, followed instructions and threw the treasure boxes to the ground. Bart then opened them with a hatchet and examined their contents. Assured of plenty of loot, he ordered the driver to move on. When alone and quite secure, he calmly emptied the boxes of money, gold, and valuables. That night, when the driver arrived at Milton, he reported that a band of robbers had held up the stage, but, on investigation the next day, the guns jutting from the rocks proved to be only sticks. About five months later, Bart robbed his second Wells Fargo coach, bound from San Juan to Marysville, California, and five months later, his third, near Oregon, the Yreka-Roseburg stage.

Bart's reputation grew, deservedly, as Wells Fargo's might have gone down. The bandit never robbed a passenger, even returning purses to those who voluntarily threw them down to him. His only interest was the Wells Fargo treasure boxes.

Black Bart, gentleman bandit and poet. *Wells Fargo Bank History Room*

REWARD!

WELLS, FARGO & CO.'S EXPRESS BOX, CON

taining $160 in Gold Notes, was robbed this morning, by one man, on the route from Sono to Milton, near top of the Hill, between the river and Copperopolis.

$250

And one-fourth of any money recovered, will be pai

for arrest and conviction of the robber.

San Francisco, July 27, 1875.   **JOHN J. VALENTINE,** General Sup't

First reward poster (July 27, 1875) for the capture of Black Bart, whose name at the time was unknown. *Wells Fargo Bank History Room*

A poster put up by J. B. Hume, Wells Fargo's special officer, quoting the poetry of Black Bart and offering a reward for his capture. *Wells Fargo Bank History Room*

Wells Fargo assigned its police department chief, James B. Hume, to the case. Hume employed a private detective from San Francisco as a helper and also assigned one of his own policemen to work on the case. In the meantime, reward posters for his capture covered the West. But the bandit remained a mystery. No one knew his name, where he came from, or what he looked like. Catching him seemed a hopeless task. And he always seemed to know which Wells Fargo shipment carried gold and other treasure. Stranger still, Bart usually worked without a horse, lugging gun, blankets, equipment, and stolen treasure over deserts and mountains. How he covered the ground he did was a mystery to everyone,

since he often traveled some twenty-five miles a day with his heavy loads. In the beginning, he had also carried a valise, which was found, apparently abandoned, near the site of one of his robberies.

Bart seemed to have become bolder by the summer of his second year. He began leaving poetry behind. One otherwise-empty express box contained this poem:

> I've labored long and hard for bread—
> For honor and for riches—
> But on my corns too long you've tred,
> You fine haired sons of bitches.

He signed this beautiful verse, and those that followed, "Black Bart, the Po 8" (poet). At least Wells Fargo now had a name for him.

Legends about him grew, and despite his being horseless, he managed to rob two stagecoaches, thirty miles apart, within twenty-four hours, traversing rough mountain country. Eight years of plaguing Wells Fargo passed, and always he wrote his verses.

But then he made his first mistake. When he held up a stage from Sonora, containing a treasure box of $4,100 in amalgam and $500 in cash, one passenger had gotten off shortly before to look for game. Bart had stopped the coach as usual, ordering the box, this time fastened securely to the stage floor, to be tossed down. The driver unhitched the team as ordered, and Black Bart began to chop open the box with his hatchet. Just then the passenger returned, and began shooting, scaring Bart who scampered off into the hills. But in his haste, he left behind a hat, a magnifying glass, a field-glass case, and a handkerchief, with the laundry mark "F.X.O.7." When detective Hume got Bart's possessions from the driver, he began tracing the laundry mark, which led to San Francisco. After visits to ninety-one laundries, it was identified as belonging to a C. E. Bolton who lived on Second Street. Bart was arrested during a stakeout in the laundry without a fight or any resistance. It was a surprise to everyone in town. Bolton had been a very respectable daily visitor at a bakery where police officers often ate, sometimes even sharing a table with them. It is possible that Black Bart learned of gold shipments inadvertently from these officers.

It turned out that his real name was Charles E. Boles; that he had come from New York; and that in San Francisco he had lived under the name of Charles E. Bolton. It was learned that he had a wife in Hannibal, Missouri. For all his twenty-eight holdups, Black Bart was sentenced to only six years, at the age of fifty-five. He was released in January, 1888, and disappeared.

SOAPY SMITH—A SLIPPERY CRIMINAL

While Black Bart was operating in California, a far more sinister character, Soapy Smith, was swindling the miners in Creede, Colorado.

By the end of 1891, Creede's second year, and a year before Smith's arrival, a branch of the Rio Grande Railroad had reached town, and trains ran regularly several times daily. Each trip meant another 200 to 300 people added to the already overcrowded camps. On the return, the train carried rich ore bound for the smelters. It was common for Pullman cars to be left on the tracks for those who had no place to sleep. The few hotels were no more than board shanties with a blanket for a door and forty or fifty cots to a room. But the town had electric power—a big floodlight was placed high on the sheer cliff to mark the entrance to the canyon, down which steep road thundered a ten-ton load of ore every few minutes. The drivers, to avoid getting stuck, had to pound the horses to keep them moving.

A rare and early view looking down Willow Creek Canyon between Creede and Upper Creede. The story of the town of Creede begins in 1889 and revolves around six camps, all in the booming Creede District. As its population grew, spreading beyond the cliffs guarding the entrance to the canyon, a second town evolved, variously called Jimtown, Gintown, Creedemoor, and Amethyst. Some of the overflow spread up the gulch to become Upper or North Creede, the third of the mining-camp town. After a disastrous 1892 Jimtown fire, Bachelor—the fourth town—was built, high on a hill above Jimtown. Sunnyside Camp, just over the hill from Bachelor, and Weaver, built in the West Willow Creek gulch, became towns five and six. There was a "Creede" post office in the upper gulch and an "Amethyst" post office down on level Jimtown. *John La Font*

Lower Creede in the early 1890s. Gold and silver mining started in the Creede District in 1876, when the Alpha Mine was hauling ore for about twenty-five miles to South Fork. Within two years the mining area included the Sunnyside District, about three miles from Creede. *Denver Public Library, Western Collection*

Upper Creede in the early 1890s. *Denver Public Library, Western Collection*

Bachelor in 1910. Most people had left by then. The last person lived here in about 1940. Just two old shacks now remain. *Alfred E. Birdsey*

Sometimes a load would get away from the drivers and smash with tremendous force, often breaking the horses' legs. Burros loaded with ore trotted over one of the zaniest bridges ever built—planked, narrow, zigzagging down the length of the stream, partially crossing it here and there as it meandered down the canyon.

This raw, wild town featured a weekly newspaper, soon after changed to a daily. One issue noted that "at night there are no policemen to interfere with the vested right of each citizen to raise as much Cain as he sees fit—and three-fourths of the population are of that kind that does see fit."

Bob Ford lived here, the man who, assisted by his brother Charles, had shot Jesse James in the back on April 3, 1882, in Missouri. He had collected a $10,000 reward offered by Missouri Governor Thomas T. Crittenden for the capture of any of the James brothers, dead or alive. Since Ford's arrival in Creede, he traded on his dubious reputation, insinuating himself as a sort of town boss. Ford's Exchange, a saloon and dance hall, was his personal property.

This was the background for the emergence of Soapy Smith, a suspicious confidence man who arrived in Creede fully expecting to take over the town. Back in Denver he had been a gambling and shell-game operator and had employed Bat Masterson as a faro dealer. Soapy now sent for Masterson and some of his more trusted lieutenants, and together they offered to maintain law and order in Creede. It was a ploy he had used before and would use again in Skagway, Alaska. He installed his brother-in-law, John Light, as town marshall. Bat Masterson became Light's deputy. Masterson, then thirty-eight, was a quiet, mild-mannered dead shot who loved to wear lavender corduroy suits. He had

The old Hall's Restaurant at Bachelor above Creede in the early 1900s. *John La Font*

Looking south over Creede from the cliffs at the northeast corner of the town in 1900. Although some mines continued operating into the 1900s, by 1894 the boom days were gone. In the 1930s, there was some resumption of mining, and lead and zinc were produced as well as silver. The Homestake Mining Company was rumored to have discovered a new silver lode in 1968, and a big development program is expected. Homestake responded with a 300-ton-a-day mill, on the slopes below the Old Bulldog Mine where the new strike is presumed to have been found. *John La Font*

The Officer and Gaughran Grocery Store in Creede on the day before Christmas, 1892. Note the birds hanging on the left side of the door, either turkeys or chickens. *John La Font*

West Willow Creek. This rickety burro bridge wandered back and forth across the creek in Willow Creek Canyon. The burros carried ore from the Amethyst Mine to Creede. The year 1889 saw the discovery of a promising mine at the head of West Willow Creek, seen here, named the Holy Moses by its discoverers Nicholas C. Creede and George L. Smith. In less than a year they sold the property for $70,000, while other prospectors found two other mines, the Ridge and the Solomon, which were finally sold to Senator Thomas M. Bowen. This generated an unbridled excitement that was further agitated when a young man named Renneca, grubstaked by the local butcher, discovered high-grade ore on Campbell Mountain, the two naming their claim Last Chance. Meanwhile, Nicholas Creede, continuing to prospect while working for the men who bought his first discovery, found the Amethyst Mine, near the Last Chance, both turning into extremely rich producers; $6 million in silver was removed the first year. Gold suddenly began to occur in increasing amounts, and soon every foot of land for more than six miles in West Willow Gulch was staked. The prospectors had spared none of the land in the narrow canyon for housing, so to validate their claims they constructed houses on poles out over the stream. (A house built on the property legalized a claim.) It was a mad rush. New arrivals stacked their goods on the creek ice; claims staked in the morning were often jumped before night. It required planting one's feet on firm land and readying a loaded gun to hang onto a claim long enough for any sort of structure resembling a house to be built. *John La Font*

A crew of miners at the Commodore Mine at Creede, about 1891. Note the hobnails in the miners' boots and the candles that were used for light inside the mine. *John La Font*

Commodore Mine No. 3 in 1900 shows how horses and mules hauled the ore from underground. *Alfred E. Birdsey*

privately hoped his shooting days were over, but his reputation as the twenty-two-year-old Dodge City sheriff preceded him, and he was treated accordingly.

Though they never came to a showdown, Soapy Smith and Bob Ford had little love for each other. Ford was a small man and wore big hats and carried big guns. He lived with his common-law wife, Nell Watson, in rooms that today are a section of the Creede Hotel. Soapy is remembered as a pleasant, public-spirited rascal. And though the town was wide open, under Soapy Smith's control there was less violence than might have been expected from the motley collection of gamblers, bartenders, pimps, fancy women, and tinhorns. But Bob Ford lived in constant dread of the revenge he knew Jesse's death

This 1895 photograph of the devastation of Creede by fire shows how completely the old mining towns were ravaged by these destructive holocausts. This was the second of five major fires in Creede. The first, in 1892, started in a saloon, and burned most of the business section; an 1895 fire destroyed most of the town; in 1902, twenty houses and two hotels in Upper Creede went up in flames; and in 1936 a third of the business section was again wiped out. *University of Oklahoma Library, N. H. Rose Collection*

would bring. He carefully observed any mirror around him and kept his back to the wall, fearful that sooner or later some member of Jesse's gang would shoot him in the back.

A man named Ed O'Kelly, who probably was a member of the James gang, arrived in town one day and soon was singing a song about "the dirty little coward who shot Mr. Howard and laid Jesse James in his grave." (Howard was James' nom de plume.) Some claimed O'Kelly and Ford once had been rivals for the affections of a dance-hall girl.

O'Kelly was proving a troublemaker and Soapy and Bat Masterson ordered him to leave town. Instead he went gunning for Ford, ready for him as he entered his saloon (The Leadville) with Nell on his arm. O'Kelly opened up with a shotgun, emptying both barrels into his neck, killing him instantly. Far from the congratulations he expected, the Creede citizenry was ready to lynch him, mostly for substituting the approved weapon, a six-shooter, for a shotgun. But Soapy withstood them, and O'Kelly was tried and sentenced to life imprisonment, later commuted to a shorter term, and, still later, to a full pardon. Pressure from members of the old James gang was believed to have been behind his lenient treatment. Bob Ford was buried in Creede's Boot Hill Cemetery, and his grave marked with a wooden headboard. Though the marker is still there, Ford's remains were taken back to Missouri by his faithful gal Nell.

As for Soapy, who often used his influence for good, his good was not good enough. There were frequent killings and suicides, especially among the

This is the unimposing Leadville Saloon, the old bar of Bob Ford, slayer of Jesse James. It was here that Ford was killed. *John La Font*

"girls on the row." One was Lillian Shields who had killed a former lover. Soapy got her acquitted. Poker Alice, Calamity Jane, and Killarney Kate—three notorious female gamblers—smoked their big stogie cigars while gambling at Creede's joints. Six-foot-tall Rose Vastin, known as "Timberline," shot herself, but recovered. Lulu Slain and the Mormon Queen, two unsavory Smith friends, were inseparable morphine addicts who lived in a log cabin in Upper Creede, until Lulu took an overdose. Creede Lily's claim to fame is that she and Bob Ford bowed out on the same day. When a preacher, Reverend Paddock, arrived in town, to the outcries of "some s.o.b. is always trying to save Creede," he found a defender in Soapy Smith. Soapy raised $1,500 in just a few hours after the reverend's plea for subscriptions to build a church produced no donors. Soapy gave visiting Reverend Joseph Gadston of Ouray a faro table to stand on while preaching his sermon. When

Early 1890 view of Cliff Street, across the street from where Bob Ford was killed. *Denver Public Library, Western Collection. Photo by E. E. Pascos*

Parson Uzzell was in Creede and someone stole his pants containing the collection, Soapy managed to have the trousers secretly returned—with a considerable addition to the original collection.

Major Wason was an outstanding Creede character; together with Mark Bidell he had come to Saguache (near Creede), arriving in the middle of a fiesta involving the usual gambling and horse racing. Later they acquired an interest in two mines, the Shenandoah and the Dives, which they sold to an English syndicate. Wason also built up a freight business running between Del Norte and the San Juan mines. In addition, he managed to lease as well about eighty miles of state lands, extending from his ranch, four miles below Creede, to the Lost Trail area near the Rio Grande River. His ranch comprised 2,000 acres, 1,200 head of cattle, and thousands of horses, no small accomplishment for one who had come to Creede virtually penniless. He later married the wife of an Episcopalian minister, adopting her children. Wason was a great spender and no

one was ever denied a meal or lodging at his ranch. When the Creede boom collapsed, he fed over 400 miners who otherwise would have gone hungry.

Wason built a toll road between his settlement of Wason and Willow Creek, which the settlers resented. After many lawsuits, the state paid him $10,000 for his rights, and discontinued the toll. In the process, Governor Routt (the territory's last and the state's first) had visited Creede, which went all out to make it a real state occasion. The governor was greeted by a large delegation of miners, led by the town spokesman—in a red flannel shirt and high miner's boots—who suggested that they all proceed to Soapy Smith's saloon and get down to business. On the way, the governor, a short man, found the snow too deep, and the miners had to precede him while tramping down the trail. Arriving at the saloon and standing on a beer keg, Routt delivered a short speech, concluding with "you fellows are getting into trouble following the advice of some jack-leg lawyers." That unsettled the crowd, and Routt lost his

Bob Ford's funeral at Creede. His grave still remains, but the body was removed to Missouri by his faithful common-law wife, Nell Watson. *John La Font*

Creede mill—Humphrey's Mining Company, 1901. *John La Font*

The picturesque Emperius Mine near Creede is remindful of an aerie in the Bavarian Alps. The ore bins can be seen in the foreground, as well as the portals above the cribbing on the steep slope at the left. Still in operation, the Emperius Mine produces lead and zinc primarily, with some silver, gold, and copper as by-products. *Bureau of Mines*

IDAHO'S SAWTOOTHS

Less romantic perhaps than Creede, Colorado, but important to the economy of Idaho, was new mining activity in the Sawtooth Mountains. The eastern side of Idaho's Sawtooth Mountains witnessed gold mining in 1876. Some mining had occurred in the area in the 1860s, but it was the discovery of the General Custer Mine during 1876 that created the bonanza.

These eastern Sawtooths had been used by the Bannock, Shoshoni, and Sheepeater Indians who prevented any mining intrusions along the Salmon River. Here, Levi Smiley had discovered gold as early as 1878, but the hostile Indians quickly forced him to leave, although he returned the following year to create the Sawtooth stampede.

balance, falling into the laps of the miners who then informed him that the "jack-leg lawyer" was the man in the red flannel shirt. Fortunately the governor's fall restored the crowd's good humor and brought ultimate success to his mission. With the onset of the silver crisis, Soapy Smith decided to return to Denver, and many of its 10,000 population soon vacated.

Solomon Mill about 1900, the only mill up East Willow, near Creede. The mill is basically a lead and zinc producer, with silver as a by-product. Other operations in Creede are the Bird Creek Mine, now operated by the Newpark Mining Company about twenty miles southwest of Creede; a new mining venture near the ghost town of Summitville; a joint venture of the Cleveland Cliffs Iron Company, Union Pacific Railroad, and W. S. Moore Company at the old Reynolds Mining Company mine. Creede may be slowly returning to life again to become an important mining center, drawing colorful characters as it did in its heyday. *Alfred E. Birdsey*

Dredge tailings on Yankee Fork. Bonanza is barely distinguishable on the extreme right. Two years after the discovery of the General Custer Mine, Bonanza City and Custer were founded, centers of the new Idaho boom, with Challis as a supply base. In 1880 a road was built from Challis to Bonanza, passing through Yankee Fork. The *Yankee Fork Herald* published the tolls: 1 wagon and 1 span of animals—$4.00, each additional span $1.00, Man on horseback—50¢, Pack animals—25¢, Loose animals other than sheep or hogs —25¢, Hogs 15¢, Sheep—10¢. Bonanza dredging operations were extensive, and the town was supported by 1,000 residents and twenty-eight business establishments, including two general merchandise stores, two hotels, three saloons, one restaurant, a furniture store, barbershop, tin shop and blacksmith shops, a bakery, clothing store, hardware store, livery stables, two doctors, and eight lawyers. Visitors can see the old Boot Hill Cemetery near the Bonanza Guard Station of Challis National Forest. *United States Forest Service*

Custer in the early 1880s. Anyone could get a lot in Custer if he would put up a building. By 1880 the town was supported by 3,500 residents and thirty-four business establishments, including a Wells Fargo office, a hotel, three rooming houses, two restaurants, three general merchandise stores, two barbershops, butcher, carpenter, and blacksmith shops, a livery stable, furniture store, dance hall, newspaper, two Chinese laundries, five saloons, a Chinese joss-house church, a post office, and a school. *United States Forest Service*

A 1937 view of the remains of the General Custer Mill in Challis National Forest. The mill ceased operations about 1904. The Custer Mill was constructed in 1880 and operated until 1904, serving the General Custer, Lucky Boy, Fourth of July, McFadden, Sunbeam, Charles Dickens, and Montana mines. *United States Forest Service*

CORBIN AND WICKES

About 100 miles west of Idaho, a year after the Sawtooths sprang into action, Wickes, Montana—named for George T. Wickes, a mining engineer who came here with his partner J. Corbin—was the site of two mining camps, Corbin and Wickes, about two miles apart. The Alta Mine was their most important producer, but good yields were also provided by the Gregory, Ninah, and Comet mines. In 1884, the Helena Mining and Reduction Company opened a lead-silver smelter at Wickes, the first smelter built in Montana. Two years and some 1,500 people later, Wickes was a merry town featuring five dance halls and twenty-two saloons. But most of the population left in the late 1890s, and fires in 1900 and 1902 destroyed what remained of the town. However, the Alta Mine, which produced $32 million in lead, gold, and silver, still operates.

Old mine building at the Vienna Mine in the Sawtooth Mountains, built around 1888. Levi Smiley returned with an exploring party to stake out a claim for the Vienna, shown here, as well as the Silver King, Columbia, Nellie, and Nellie Extension mines. It was the start of a stampede into the Sawtooths. Mines were also rapidly developed in Smiley's Canyon. In 1882 the Nellie Mine was the most developed and valuable, and other important mines were the Solace, Lion, Lucky Boy, Cambria, Atlanta, Wire Silver, and several others. In 1881 Sawtooth City had been founded—the Pilgrim Mine its principal producer—with the Goodwell and Beaver Extension mines running parallel. Nearby, the Silver King main vein was discovered, in 1882, all of which spurred the construction of a mill in Sawtooth City, which also processed ores of other Beaver Canyon mines. And Vienna built a rival mill in 1889 that quickly turned it into an important mining town. Unfortunately, a bitter rivalry sprang up between Sawtooth and Vienna, but the mining days of both towns were doomed to decline—spasmodic mining continued into the 1930s, but in 1938 the Sawtooth and Vienna mines, the last important survivors, closed, and only small individually owned mines and dredges were able to continue operations. *United States Forest Service*

MOLY

In Colorado, a new material was found that would take more than twenty years to identify and another fifteen or sixteen years before a use would be found.

Out of what began in 1879, two metallurgical giants merged on the last business day of 1957, to become American Metal Climax—a consolidation of American Metal and Climax Molybdenum. "Climax" and molybdenum are almost synonymous because, from its inception in 1918, the Climax Molybdenum Company developed into an almost unprecedented molybdenum monopoly. From a single mine, at Climax, Colorado, the largest underground mine in North America, if not the world, the company produced over half the world's output for nearly forty years.

Molybdenite on Bartlett Mountain, where the Climax Mine is located, was known to the early prospectors of the Colorado Rockies. However, they believed the material was galena, or graphite, because of their similar visual appearance. It all began with Charles J. Senter, a naval veteran of the Civil War and an Indian fighter with Custer's Avengers, when

Climax railroad station, located atop Fremont Pass, gave the mine its name. This photograph was taken in 1920—two years after Climax molybdenum mine went into production. J. H. White, mining superintendent, for whom the White (upper) Level of Climax mine was named, stands at far right. *American Metal Climax, Inc.*

he was mustered out of service in 1877. While working placer gold here, he sought out the "mother lode," which he found on Bartlett Mountain after two years, and named it the Gold Reef and Gold Reef No. 2. He could see that the mountain was heavily mineralized, but he did not know with what. Like any seat-of-the-pants miner, he must have felt that any mineral in large quantities must represent a valuable ore body. His ores were finally analyzed as molybdenite some twenty years later at the Colorado School of Mines. But, in those years, molybdenum interest was academic.

As interest in the deposits grew, from 1900 to 1916, claims and counterclaims jammed the local courts over competing claim rights. By the end of this period, however, word reached Max Schott, resident manager for American Metal Company (AMCO) in Denver who recommended purchasing the various claims. After hesitating, AMCO agreed to underwrite a minor share of development costs. But Schott quit to devote full time to developing the "mountain of molybdenum." (His zeal persuaded the officers of AMCO to make personal investments in the project.) Subsequently the Climax syndicate was formed (1917) with the major share held by Schott, Julius Loeb, and several others. AMCO held a small share while the balance was set aside for the owners of the claims.

Because of Schott's drive, his belief that molybdenum could be economically recovered and that it had a future as an alloying element, the syndicate purchased all the claims on Bartlett Mountain and, ultimately, Ceresco Ridge. It was this initial assembling that gave Climax the initiative to move forward and actively create markets for molybdenum where none had existed before.

The engineering staff of Climax poses in front of the original "general office" in 1917, during construction of Climax molybdenum mine. *American Metal Climax, Inc.*

In 1918, miners worked the Climax molybdenum ore deposit in Colorado by hand, using hand-held steel and single-jack hammers. *American Metal Climax, Inc.*

Raw slusher drift on Phillipson Level of Climax molybdenum mine in Colorado. The photograph was taken on August 12, 1937. In the picture, ore spills down a 45-degree angle from a "finger" behind miner at left into the drift, and is slushed down to an ore train. The miner wears carbide lamp. *American Metal Climax, Inc.*

Moly Mountain. On Sunday, October 2, 1955, 81,614 pounds of dynamite were detonated on the edge of a 700-foot arch that had formed abve the Phillipson Level in the center of the Climax Glory Hole. This shot succeeded in breaking the arch and releasing some 2,500,-000 tons of molybdenum ore. The Bartlett Mountain arch was becoming a hazard to miners before it was shot down. The drilling of holes and the placing of the dynamite was an extremely hazardous operation, but it was accomplished without a mishap. *American Metal Climax, Inc.*

View of the molybdenum mine at Climax, Colorado, the largest underground mine in the United States, producing more tonnage than any other mine of any kind. Climax is also the second largest producer of tungsten in the United States and is an important producer of tin, pyrite (valuable in the production of sulfuric acid), monazite (important for its rare earth content), and topaz. The by-product plant is being enlarged to extract even more such mineral by-products. By 1954, to meet the combined demands of the consuming markets, and of the stockpile, mine and mill capacity were increased from 15,000 tons of ore daily to 27,000 tons. From the time of its formation Climax was always closely associated with the American Metal Company. Their 1957 merger had a synergistic effect on both former companies, and today highly diversified American Metal Climax (AMAX) is one of the world's major metal and mineral producers. Its average daily ore production is approximately 44,000 tons against a work force of approximately 2,200 employees at the mine alone. In November, 1966, Climax inaugurated a chemical plant to recover molybdenum from oxidized ores, previously unrecoverable. Treatment in the complex plant provides an additional three million pounds of molybdenum per year to the world's supply. To further assure its continued supply, Climax began to develop the Urad Mine, near Empire, Colorado, in the early 1960s. This mine, which produces 7 million pounds of molybdenum annually, went on stream in 1967. The ore body is small, and total production will be only about 50 million pounds. In the course of developing the Urad, Climax geologists discovered a hitherto-unsuspected major molybdenum deposit located nearby, called the Henderson Project. The new deposit appears to equal the fabulous Climax in size, and the ore quality is high: proved (and probable) ore reserves equal 303 million tons at a grade of 0.49 percent molybdenum. Mine operation is scheduled for the mid-1970s, with an expected annual production rate of 50 million pounds. The Henderson Project should produce well into the twenty-first century. *American Metal Climax, Inc.*

NEW GOLD AT ASPEN

Coincidental with Colorado's molybdenum discovery was a new gold find in Aspen. It is only about thirty miles from Aspen to Leadville—with 14,418-foot Mount Massive lying between. Most of the desirable mining claims in the Leadville area had already been staked out, and gold seekers were looking to the west, to the other side of the virtually unknown Continental Divide. It took four days to cross it, via Independence Pass, at an elevation of some 12,000 feet. The few hardy souls who made it in three days found it a rugged and tiring experience.

In June, 1879, two groups, one under Charles E. Bennett, reached Aspen and Smuggler mountains, found traces of ore and staked out claims. They settled Ute City—between the two mountains—named after the Ute Indians whose land it was. But

Aspen in 1890. The photo by B. W. Kilburn of Little-ton, New Hampshire, became a popular subject for stereo viewers. In 1891 and 1892 Aspen was the world's largest silver camp, featuring several churches, three banks, six newspapers, an opera house, a large hotel, and a streetcar. Luxury abounded; a favorite recreation was the Bathing Train, which made daily runs every evening for a $2 round trip to Glenwood Springs, forty miles away. By their fifth year Aspen mines had pro-duced over $15 million, with no end in sight. A smelter, mills, reduction works, quarries, coal mines, and all facilities for mining were part of Aspen. *Colorado State Historical Society Library*

The Smuggler Mine at Aspen in the 1890s. Smuggler Mountain is in the background. *Colorado State His-torical Society Library*

the Indians were unimpressed. Rumors of an im-pending uprising frightened most of the prospectors back to Leadville. The uprising missed Ute City, but now everyone in Leadville knew about the strikes there. When the danger seemed past, the original prospectors, followed by hundreds of newcomers, rushed back. But with winter coming on and the threat of renewed Indian raids, many changed their minds and sold their claims, returning to Leadville. One newcomer, Henry Gillespie, already owned part of the Caribou Mine about ninety miles distant. Among several claims he now bought from departing prospectors were two on Aspen Mountain, for $25,000.

Gillespie was concerned about claim jumpers and called a meeting at which all agreed to respect each others claims, at least over the winter. Two men who remained, Hopkins and Bennett, were more cautious. After acquiring most of the vacated claims on Smuggler Mountain, they spent the winter in Denver, where they sold out. Back in Leadville, Gillespie was preparing for the difficult return trip over Independence Pass. He rounded up a number of

miners, mounted sleds on runners similar to modern skis, and ordered snowshoes for the men who would pull the sleds. Thus provided, they were able to catch and pass hundreds of miners who had started weeks before. Within a year, regular shipments of silver ore were riding toward Leadville, and new mines had opened up. With them came trials and battles. Each mine claimed the right to follow a vein in any direction, in accordance with established Colorado law. Amid constant court litigation, mining continued, and Aspen thrived as the telegraph and railroad came to town in the 1880s. Aspen's popula-tion exceeded 11,000 in 1893, the year of the silver panic, when the United States changed from silver to a gold standard. In one month nearly 2,000 miners were out of work, the banks closed, and the gold camps experienced a new rush, particularly Cripple Creek. As the silver panic continued, many mines went bankrupt. Once the mines were idle, the shafts filled with water, so high that even the pumps were engulfed. It was the beginning of the end of Aspen's mining days; some mining, above the water level, continued for a while. Over $100 million in silver had been taken out, almost equally divided be-tween Smuggler Mountain and Aspen Mountain. In 1894, it was the Smuggler Mine that held the title to the world's largest silver nugget (93 percent pure silver). It weighed over a ton. Because it was too large to bring up the shaft, it had to be cut into pieces, the largest weighing 1,840 pounds.

The over-2,000-pound nugget of native silver mined at the Smuggler Mine in 1894. The piece shown was part of it, weighing 1,840 pounds and producing 20,534 ounces of silver. At the price of 60¢ an ounce, it was worth $12,320. *Colorado Bureau of Mines*

Aspen was not quite dead. In 1936 it again came to life—as a ski resort. These old tramways on Aspen Mountain, once used for silver mining, have now been replaced with modern ski tows and gondolas and chair lifts. Today it is one of the most famous winter recreation areas in the country. *Colorado State Historical Society Library*

Hartville, Wyoming, circa 1900. More than 2 million pounds of copper were mined about this time. The Rambler Mine, Hartville's main copper producer, was originally opened as a gold mine around 1870. *Stimson Photo Collection, Wyoming State Archives and Historical Department*

The Office Saloon, Battle, probably in the 1890s. *Wyoming State Archives and Historical Department*

George Doane, an experienced miner who had worked in Leadville and Aspen, was interested in gold, not copper, and ignored the trenches and shallow shafts and two old cabins he took over on old copper-lead property, the Rambler Lode. So it remained for Ed Haggarty who had worked as a miner at Cripple Creek to make the most important copper discovery in Wyoming. In 1896, John Rumsey, Robert Deal, and George Ferris grubstaked Haggarty; a year later he staked his Rudefeha claim (the first two letters of each grubstaker's surname and his own). Haggarty continued prospecting around the Rudefeha claim, locating several adjoining properties. By 1889, with thousands of shares of stock on the market, the mine was known as the Ferris-Haggarty Mine. An aerial tramway from the Ferris-Haggarty Mine to a smelter was Wyoming's outstanding engineering achievement in early mining. Except for some mining in the Hartville district during World War II, Wyoming copper production remained low. Ferris-Haggarty was eventually indicted for fraudulent stock sales and the town of Encampment dropped from its population high of 2,000 to 200, mostly ranchers.

SILVER BECOMES KING

About this time, one of the world's major silver strikes, even greater than the Comstock, was opening up in the fabulously beautiful Coeur d'Alene area in the panhandle of Idaho, in the northern part of the state.

Beginning in 1882, the development of the silver and silver-lead mines converted the area into the state's most important mining district. It would even rival Colorado's gold. Of the Coeur d'Alene mines, two were world famous, the Bunker Hill and Sullivan Mine (the country's leading lead-silver producer for many years) and the Sunshine Mine (after 1930, the world's largest silver producer). Over 80 percent (nearly $2 billion in metal) of Idaho's total wealth in metal production derives from the Coeur d'Alene district.

In April, 1882, A. J. Prichard discovered placer gold deposits along the banks of Eagle and Prichard creeks. Prichard at first worked secretly, hoping to preserve his fortunate find for the benefit of the Liberal League, of which he was an active member.

On January 8, 1883, he wrote to "Friend Burk":

> Wishing to assist my infidel friends whenever opportunity offers, and to assist in throwing into our ranks all I can, I give you this information and hope you will assist in extending it to others throughout the [Liberal] Leagues, and if possible not outside of our brethren and sisters.

> As near as I can judge from what I have done there is enough to give employment to 15 or 20 thousand men, and I should like to see the Liberals get the lion's share, if possible.... If the Liberals will act promptly and not get excited and work together they can get a good slice of it and also build a city that they can control and have good laws and regulations.

Prichard succeeded in keeping his discoveries secret only until the fall. Within months the news had spread, and, on February 1, 1884, the Northern Pacific Railroad issued "Circular No. 6," extolling the virtues of the district in such glowing terms that

In 1901 and 1902, the Hercules and Hecla properties came into prominence in Idaho—both destined to be large mines. This photo was taken at the Hercules Silver Mine, near Burke, shortly after its discovery in 1901. The Hercules later merged into the Day Mines, which turned out to be Burke's richest. The Hecla Mining Company is in Burke. (Hecla has paid dividends for sixty years.) Its old mine is worked out, but its Star Mine is operated through the Hecla shaft. Another of the large early-day mines in Burke Canyon was Standard Mammoth, which once employed 700 men. *Idaho Bureau of Mines and Geology*

a major gold rush occurred—to the profit of the railroad, which carried most of the prospectors. But the circular's references were to gold, not silver, which would become the major metal. The railroad raved about "fields which are unequaled in richness and extent, the yield being practically inexhaustible, rendering impossible any overcrowding of the district by reason of too great an influx of prospectors or miners. There is more than enough for all who come.... A hundred dollars per man per day are being taken out of the rimrock of the gulches while in the gullies $25 to $50 per man per day are being panned out." And continuing in its praise of the district's virtues: "This ore assays from $28 to $196 per ton gold, the former being the smallest assay ever obtained, as high as $900 in gold per ton being not infrequent while certain specimens have assayed $10,000 per ton gold." The circular was signed by Charles S. Fee, General Passenger Agent.

One of the first mining towns to be established after the issuance of the circular was Murray, home base of "Molly b'Dam," ostensibly a cultured philanthropist but actually leader of an underworld gang. She was known to outswear any miner, hence her name. But Molly and Murray soon faded along with the diminishing claims as prospectors outnumbered the acreage. In three years, most operations had been converted from panning and rockers to hydraulic placers.

But in the second year, in May, the Tiger Mine had been discovered at Burke, a town made famous by Robert Ripley in his "Believe It or Not" cartoons. Burke is in a narrow canyon and was the only mining camp in the world to get a railroad before it got a wagon train. The railroad tracks ran up the center of the main street, and both the street and the railroad tracks ran over a creek; in fact, at one time the railroad ran through the Tiger Hotel, since torn down. Even today when the freight train comes through the town, cars must be moved from parking places on the tracks and awnings pulled in to let the train pass by. Ripley once said that the streets were paved with silver, not a complete misstatement since the streets were graveled from waste rock from the mines, in which a small amount of silver remained. Much of Burke was odd. It was even said that the butchers gave tough beef to families whose girls refused to dance with them.

A few days after the discovery of the Tiger Mine, W. R. Wallace and a group found the Poorman Mine lode at Ore-Or-No-Go. Wallace of course was the founder of the city of Wallace and Ore-Or-No-Go is self-evident. The Poorman Mine, which set off Idaho's silver rush, later became part of the Hecla Mining Company, also in Burke.

The Frisco mill in Burke Canyon, a shambles after the explosion that was followed immediately by the proclamation of martial law by the governor of Idaho. Federal troops were moved in and order was quickly restored. By the end of 1892 the mines and mills were again operating at capacity. *Idaho Bureau of Mines and Geology*

LEGAL PROBLEMS IN KELLOGG

Perhaps the most important discovery in the Coeur d'Alene district followed Prichard's by three years. Noah S. Kellogg, a carpenter who had worked through Murray's gold rush constructing homes, obtained a grubstake from John T. Cooper and Origin O. Peck, partners who operated the Cooper and Peck general merchandise store. They provided Kellogg with a burro and $18.75 worth of provisions, including fifteen pounds of flour, seven pounds of bacon, two pounds of coffee, eight pounds of beans, four pounds of dried apples, $1 worth of sugar, one pair of $2.75 shoes, and half a dozen printed location notices. Their arrangement was made on August 1, 1885, and, on the twenty-ninth of the month, Kellogg returned to Murray with samples of what proved to be ironstone. Cooper and Peck replenished his supplies and sent him searching for quartz rock along Big Creek. This simple grubstake would become important evidence in a major lawsuit. Kellogg would later claim in court that he had consumed Cooper and Peck's supplies and purchased others elsewhere.

This time Kellogg remained until September 12, when again his supplies were exhausted. He returned saying he had failed to discover any gold-bearing

quartz, but he did give Cooper and Peck copies of location notices for the "Mary A" and "Kellogg" claims to which he had added their names as owners. He returned their burro and subsequently insisted that this terminated their grubstaking and prospecting agreement.

Historians, and the testimony in the lawsuit that was to follow, show conflicting differences between these events and those that followed. Evidence exists that Kellogg, subsequent to terminating his agreement, showed ore samples to Phillip O'Rourke, an experienced miner from Leadville, and to Jacob Goetz, an adventurer known as "Dutch Jake." Goetz and his partner Harry Baer had a grubstake agreement with O'Rourke. If Kellogg's statement to Cooper and Peck that he had not found gold-bearing quartz was true, where did the ore samples come from? O'Rourke recognized the samples as possibly coming from the cap of a lead lode similar to ore that he had mined at Leadville. A deal was made for Goetz and his group to join Kellogg in staking the ground, after which Goetz turned over his horses and provisions to O'Rourke and Kellogg.

Some reports state that Kellogg and O'Rourke, with a Cornelius "Con" Sullivan and Alex Monk, then went searching for the gold, but other evidence indicates that only Kellogg and O'Rourke went down the South Fork of the Coeur d'Alene River to Milo Creek at the Bunker Hill outcrop. Exactly who discovered this outcrop is also subject to question but Goetz swore that O'Rourke was the discoverer. It was also claimed in court that Goetz and O'Rourke removed the original notice that Kellogg had placed on the stakes (the one designating Cooper and Peck as part owners), substituting a new location notice signed by Kellogg as the only locator. They named it Bunker Hill after the battle of the Revolution. While they continued their exploratory work they found a white burro that Cooper and Peck had given Kellogg as part of his grubstake. Their own horses had wandered off. Kellogg, upon reflection, thought that he had better not have his name appear on the claim as the sole locator since Copper and Peck might demand an interest because of the first grubstake. According to Goetz, they then threw away the current location notice and wrote a new one with O'Rourke as the locator and Kellogg as the witness. When they returned to Murray, Sullivan was taken into the deal. Meanwhile, Peck, who had heard about the new find, decided to search the site of the claim, and actually found the original location notice discarded by Kellogg. (Some historians state that this notice was found by Peck and Cooper's lawyers.) Peck also learned that his "lost" burro had been used by

Kellogg and O'Rourke who had staked a further claim, calling it the Sullivan Claim. Both claims were filed at Murray.

Peck and Cooper immediately hired two lawyers to represent them. On the basis of the slip of paper that was alleged to be the original location notice, the case was brought to trial.

Kellogg claimed that he had used up his original grubstake, returned to Murray, formed a new partnership, and then discovered the Bunker Hill lode. The jury found in favor of the defendants, but their decision was overruled by Judge Norman Buck who believed that Kellogg could not have used up his entire grubstake in such a short time. The case was appealed but Judge Buck's decision was upheld on the grounds that there was deliberate fraud.

Probably more is remembered about the lost burro than about the actual facts of the case. Jim Wardner in his autobiography presumably quotes Judge Buck's decision: "From the evidence of the witness, this Court is of the opinion that the Bunker Hill Mine was discovered by the jackass, Phil O'Rourke, and N. S. Kellogg; and as the jackass is the property of the plaintiffs Cooper and Peck, they are entitled to a half interest in the Bunker Hill and a quarter interest in the Sullivan claims." Actually, the text of Buck's decision shows the above statement to be completely incorrect. Whatever the true facts of the case were, none ultimately prospered from the find. Goetz moved to Spokane, where he became the proprietor of a successful hotel; Kellogg died a pauper; O'Rourke died in an institution in Vancouver, Washington; and Sullivan moved to Butte, Montana, using the money he made out of the Bunker Hill for other mining ventures, all unsuccessful. In 1901, Sullivan went to Alaska where pirates broke into his camp and murdered all but one, a man named Rooney who hid under a canoe and survived to tell the story. The burro went into happy retirement at a farm in Oregon.

Within sixty days of Kellogg's discovery, Wardner's population approached 4,000 while other mining camps developed around the area. The lead and silver discoveries soon made it the largest district in the United States.

By the end of 1886, the Bunker Hill and Sullivan properties were sold for $650,000 to Simeon G. Reed of Portland. In 1890, Reed resold them to a California–New York group headed by John Hayes Hammond, a mining engineer.

At this juncture, mining unions had been formed in most of the towns, and in 1891 they merged into one union. But in the interim, competition notwithstanding, the Northern Pacific Railroad (on the Helena smelter run) and the Union Pacific Railroad (on an Omaha smelter run) combined in 1890 into a smelter trust to raise freight rates. The mines responded by reducing wages, which set off bloody violence between the mine operators and the miners. The objectives of the union now were to obtain higher wages, to cut the monopoly of the company-owned stores and boardinghouses, to secure more safety measures, and to obtain the benefits common to union management today.

The consolidated union, as well as independent unions, had resisted wage cuts prior to 1892. Now with mine shutdowns, partly from the railroad rate increase and partly from declining lead and silver prices, the railroads were forced to rescind their rate increase within two months. But the Coeur d'Alene mines were still reluctant to reopen unless the miners would accept lower wages to match the declining metal prices. The miners refused, and as a counter-measure, in May, 1892, managements arranged to import nonunion help to resume partial production. To strengthen their efforts, they formed the Mine Owners' Protective Association, which in turn hired a Pinkerton detective, Charles A. Siringo, to spy for them. Siringo, or C. Leon Allison, his assumed name, joined the union, was employed in the Gem Mine, and worked his way up to secretary of the union. In July the miners discovered his secret, the Frisco Mill was dynamited, a fight followed, and five men were killed; but Siringo was not among them. He had managed to crawl underneath a boardwalk and escape. But the mill's nonunion crew were held captive, along with men at adjacent mines, and all the mines were quickly occupied by union miners. Before long, Burke Canyon was entirely cleared of nonunion miners, and when the union next seized three concentrators, at Wardner, all its nonunion men were dismissed to save the concentrators from destruction. Within three months after the outbreak of armed violence, the mines agreed to discharge all nonunion men, and, on that same day, July 12, President Harrison sent in federal troops to maintain martial law. The troops remained until mid-November.

Some 600 union miners had been arrested, but

Troop encampment at Wallace in July, 1892. The troops were sent here to prevent strike violence in the Coeur d'Alene District. *Idaho Historical Society*

Federal troops in the streets of Kellogg, called in to quell strike disorders in 1892. *Idaho Bureau of Mines and Geology*

United States troops camped outside the Bunker Hill Mine in Kellogg in June, 1892, during the strike violence. *Idaho Historical Society*

any convictions in federal court were dismissed on appeal. The confrontation had led to the formation of the Western Federation of Miners, comprising about 200 local unions, with 15,000 members.

The Coeur d'Alene district suffered along with all the others in the 1893 panic, but by this time the unions had gained control of all except the largest mine, the Bunker Hill and Sullivan. Although the company had agreed to raise wages to meet union scales, it refused to recognize the union or to discharge its nonunion help. The reaction of the union was predictable. A large union force seized a train, loaded it with explosives, and demolished the Bunker Hill and Sullivan concentrator. That was on April 29, 1899. The state government's response was swift and drastic. The United States Army was called in to restore order, and the union men were denied the privilege to work anywhere in the entire area. Hundreds of miners were confined in a hastily constructed enlarged bullpen, and protests were heard across the nation. Idaho instituted court action against the union on the grounds of conspiracy. The first was against Paul Corcoran, secretary of the Burke local. He was found guilty of conspiracy on July 28, 1899, and sentenced to seventeen years in prison. He was pardoned two years later. A federal suit was brought against thirty-two miners for interfering with the United States mail (in their use of a freight train to destroy the concentrator); ten of them were sentenced to two years in the penitentiary. On April 11, 1901, when the troops were withdrawn, the Western Federation was virtually out of business.

Two views of the Bunker Hill and Sullivan Concentrator destroyed by striking miners on April 28, 1899. *Idaho Historical Society*

The miners returned to work, but the bitter battles were not forgotten.

Governor Frank Steunenberg, who had backed the mines and called in the federal troops, was killed December 30, 1905, when he opened his dynamited front gate at home. Harry Orchard was arrested for the crime. Orchard had a lengthy criminal record ranging from perjury and kidnapping to arson and murder. He had belonged to the Western Federation and had also worked in Colorado as a spy for the mine owners' association. While in jail awaiting trial, he confessed to this crime, as well as to others dealing with the mines. With Orchard's testimony, the state cited the officials of the Western Federation of Miners for conspiracy to murder the governor. The principal defendants were Charles Moyer, the president of the union; William D. Haywood, the secretary and treasurer; and George Pettibone, allegedly the contact man for Orchard. The trial lasted from May 9 to July 28, 1907. William E. Borah was counsel for the prosecution, Clarence Darrow for the defense, and nationwide publicity settled on both. Haywood was tried separately and acquitted on grounds of insufficient testimony in support of

Orchard's statements. Pettibone's trial ended similarly, so the state decided not to try Moyer. Orchard, however, was sentenced to life imprisonment and served forty-six years until his death on April 13, 1954.

After the trials, the Coeur d'Alene mines prospered without interruption. The Bunker Hill and Sullivan Mining and Concentrating Company Inc., established in 1887, was in 1956 truncated to the Bunker Hill Company. Although initially involved in mining and the concentrating of lead-silver ore from the big Bunker Hill Mine, today it also has an interest in five other mines that produce lead, silver, and zinc, among them the Crescent Mine, which has been in continuous operation since 1885 producing silver six miles east of Kellogg. It is one of the nation's most important silver producers and is connected to the Bunker Hill Mine by a 17,000-foot tunnel 400 feet below sea level.

The Bunker Hill operation starts about 3,600 feet above sea level. At present there are over 100 miles of open workings extending to nearly 2,000 feet below sea level, or a vertical distance of over a

Early underground mining view in the famous Bunker Hill silver mine. Today miners wear hard hats, and use battery-powered lamps instead of candles for illuminating the work areas. *The Bunker Hill Company*

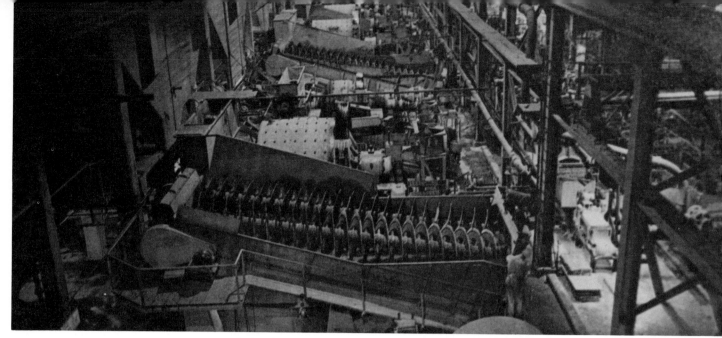

Following the initial crushing, ore is put through the second step of further grinding, concentrating, and classifying. *The Bunker Hill Company*

mile. Since its discovery, the mine produced some 27 million tons of ore, good for over 2 million tons of lead, 100 million ounces of silver, and 350,000 tons of zinc. Mine operations are among the most modern in the country, including concentrating facilities, smelting plants, and the former Sullivan Mining Company Zinc Plant, all in the Coeur d'Alene district.

THE BEER-BARREL STRIP

One of the strangest materials might never have been discovered had it not been for beer barrels! Few people have ever heard of a material called gilsonite, and perhaps even fewer of a town known simply as "The Strip."

In 1885 a lightweight, glossy black asphalt material was found in northeastern Utah, in the Uinta Basin. Originally called Uintaite, it was later changed to gilsonite after an S. H. Gilson of Salt Lake City who helped develop the mineral for commercial uses. Gilsonite not only makes fine lacquers, paints, and varnishes, but in the 1880s it was found to be an excellent sealing material for beer barrels. Adolphus Busch of the Anheuser-Busch Brewing Company of Saint Louis, Missouri, was interested in the black mineral to use as a sealer for his brewery's beer barrels. Most of the gilsonite was contained in a 700-acre triangular piece of land lying within the borders of the Ute Indian Reservation. Perhaps through the brewer's influence, Congress passed an act and made a treaty with the Utes to permit the gilsonite to be mined on this "island" within their reservation. The mine opened in 1887 and was called "The Saint Louis" after Busch's home town.

Since the land was within the borders of the Ute reservation, the territorial government could not enforce the law, nor could the police of Uinta County. Furthermore, the Indian agencies had no jurisdiction except in Indian country, and the triangular strip, which never received a formal name and thus evolved into "The Strip," was no longer in Indian country. The federal marshalls could only enforce violation of federal statutes, and these did not include gambling, liquor, and prostitution, which were amply provided, as well as two saloons, gambling houses, brothels, a hotel, general store, dance hall, livery stable, stage station, blacksmith shop, telegraph office, and barber shop. Without any law enforcement, The Strip attracted outlaws, gamblers, freighters, miners, Indians, and others, some interested in the gilsonite and some seeking immunity from arrest.

Murders were common and at least sixteen shooting deaths were officially recorded, not to mention the many that went unrecorded. The Strip soon became known as Utah's most lawless town. The mine was as much of a threat as the six-shooters. Twice it exploded, taking an unrecorded number of lives, the second blast killing all but one miner. Some bodies were never found.

After the discovery of other gilsonite properties in 1904, the mine closed. But the new discoveries could not equal The St. Louis, which has been held in reserve since then. In 1966 it reopened for limited production, which continues. Of The Strip, little remains but for a few charred odds and ends, including the foundation of the old general store.

278

JOHN L. LEWIS' IOWA

While towns boomed throughout the late nineteenth century, Coaltown, Iowa, renamed Angus, became the largest coal camp in the state in 1885, with a population of about 5,000. But it was short-lived. Angus' principal mine belonged to the Climax Coal Company, but eight or nine other companies had been operating out of Angus when a strike ended in a bloody riot in the first days of January, 1885. The miners had demanded a 12½-cent-per-ton wage increase.

Increasing violence now brought the militia to protect the town. When the militia was withdrawn, thirty strikebreakers were imported. On January 7, a mob of 250 rioters attacked them with clubs and stones. Several men were wounded and two killed. As a result, the Climax group closed the mines permanently, signaling the end of Angus.

Labor arrangements up to this period provided for an equal sharing from gross coal sales—the miners' half to be divided in proportion to the work done by each worker to give him a wage equal to three cents a bushel (eighty pounds). But when this system had been abandoned sometime earlier, a

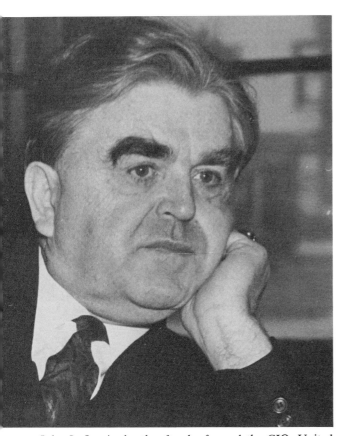

John L. Lewis shortly after he formed the CIO. United Mine Workers Journal

strike had resulted. To break that strike, Negro laborers were imported from Virginia and other southern states, and, with the cheap labor they provided, management put them on permanently; hiring practices included Negro help until a miners' union was established.

Miners were not selected for experience but purely on the basis of physical strength. They were assigned to work with a skilled miner until they learned their trade. In the early 1880s the Consolidation Company employed 500 men, 350 of them Negroes. Later the blacks numbered 1,500. For the protection of the blacks, "colonies" were established, with dues of a dollar a month for married men and fifty cents for single men, about 80 percent of the money going to medical services and the balance to a sinking fund. The colonies, or societies, were structured on the unincorporated town, actually no more than a miner's camp. They featured nonelected city officials and a court to hear disputes among the members. The courts provided no appeal to other civil branches. Offenders were fined and the money applied to the sinking fund. Refusal to pay meant expulsion from the society and loss of employment.

In its report for 1889, the Society of the Muchakinock Colony contained the following minutes:

> Pres. J. H. Lewis; The sick benefit was raised from $2.50 a month to $3.00; a grant of $25 was made to Mrs. Patterson who is obliged to leave a Company house; the burial of persons of color who are not members of the Colony is rescinded; Mr. Hammet and Mr. Fry were fined $5 for fighting and disorderly conduct; deceased member, Titus Cosley, death due to a fall down a shaft; total sick benefits paid out, $841; 3 funerals, $78.43; members suspended, L. A. Weeks and W. H. London.

Many of the Negroes were ex-slaves, and the wages seemed munificent. Negro social life was active—constant parties, feasts, and receptions, featuring Hobe Armstrong's Muchy Fair, an annual treat that lasted five days and nights and was attended by many whites. Harness races, foot races, gambling, and crap games were common, and southern fried chicken was the favorite dish. Although prohibition prevailed in most of Iowa, beer and hard liquor were openly sold at bars and bootleg joints. Street fights and barroom brawls were fairly common, with razors and beer mugs instead of guns or pistols as the principal weapons. But there were no murders, and a tranquil setting prevailed compared with the roaring gold camps of the forty-niners. Nevertheless, gamblers, prospectors, and bootleggers poured in each payday to syphon off as much of the miners' hard-earned wages as possible.

In 1891, the white Iowa Mine Workers Union tried to organize Consolidation's colored employees. About 300 union members in military order marched four abreast toward Eddyville, intending, as a start, to drive the black miners out of town. But the Negro workers were well prepared. A company of black miners had been equipped with arms and ammunition. When the marchers arrived in Muchakinock, or Muchy, they were amazed to find the streets patrolled by six-foot Negroes loaded with armament! It so unnerved the union workers that they decided to talk things over among themselves and, the following morning, instead of attempting to drive the Negroes out, sent in a committee to negotiate. Their talks failed, and the next day they reluctantly left for home rather than clash with the menacing blacks. Muchakinock was never unionized.

A principal concern of the union (since the miners shared in the production) was the size of the coal. Following a Whitebreast Coal Company strike in 1882, it had been agreed that coal that could pass through a wire-mesh of ¾-inch squares would be considered unmarketable. Although seemingly unimportant, the screen size was the major question dividing labor and the mine operators. Between 1880 and the early 1900s, a number of local unions had been formed, and each fought for what it deemed most important. Screen size, measurement by the ton rather than by the bushel, wages, coal prices, and living conditions, all were a part of the battle.

This was the environment of the young John Llewellyn Lewis. His father, Thomas, a Welsh miner, had immigrated to Iowa in the late 1870s. Thomas was a product of the misery and poverty indigenous to the Welsh coal mines, which drove so many Welsh miners and their families to the New World, seeking employment in the only work they knew. When John was two years old, his father was leading the bitter strike against Whitebreast that led to the importation of Negro strikebreakers from the South. Thomas was blacklisted and could find no employment in any Iowa mine. He took odd jobs; he was a night watchman and later a city jailer in Des Moines. In the meantime, John went to grade school, sold papers, played baseball, and fought the fistfights that prepared him for future battles. In 1897, after five years, the blacklists were abandoned and the Lewises returned to their home in Lucas. Thomas and his two sons went to work at the Big Hill Coal Company.

John soon became active in the unions, to which, after 1906, most of his time went. His presi-

THE WHITE HOUSE
WASHINGTON

May 5, 1949

Dear Senator:

I appreciated very much your letter of April twenty-ninth, suggesting John L. Lewis as Ambassador to Russia.

I've already appointed a good man to that post and for your information I wouldn't appoint John L. Lewis dogcatcher and, I think, you understand that is the case. I appreciate the good humor in your letter.

Sincerely yours,

Harry Truman

Honorable Neal D. Bishop
Senator First District
Denver, Colorado

President Harry Truman's letter of reply to Colorado State Senator Newl Bishop's suggestion that John L. Lewis be made ambassador to Russia. Bishop, a Denver Democrat, made the suggestion in jest, back in 1949. But not until October 4, 1950, did he make public Truman's reply. Lewis said on October 5 that he had written to Bishop, saying the President could ill afford to have more brains in the dog department than in the Department of State. *Wide World Photo*

dency of the United Mine Workers of America capped his rise through the ranks.

THE UMW

The UMW was formed thirty years earlier by a combination of the National Progressive Union and the mine locals under the Knights of Labor, which was affiliated with the American Federation of Labor (AFL). The UMW was a national organization covering all workers in coal mines, anthracite and bituminous, and constantly fought for continuity of employment, the reduction of occupational hazards, and against company-owned towns. Its weapons were strikes, and it attempted to improve conditions by collective bargaining. In 1894 the union fought for and won an eight-hour day, and by 1920 mine operators recognized the UMW as the official bargaining body for the miners.

OTHER COALTOWN UNREST

In the interim, Tennessee was having its problems with the coal operators. Trouble began in 1883 when the Tennessee Coal, Iron, and Railroad Company leased 1,300 convicts from the Tennessee Penitentiary upon the theory that labor unions would not strike if they knew that labor could be easily provided by the use of convicts.

In 1891 in Briceville, Tennessee, the Tennessee Coal Mine Company offered a contract that provided for "scrip" pay for miners, a no-strike pledge, and other terms that were rejected by the men. The company had the convicts tear down the miners' houses and build stockades in their place as a home for themselves. The miners attacked the stockades. There was no bloodshed but the militia was called in anyway, and the convicts remained entrenched in the stockades. A similar action was repeated the next day, resulting in labor demonstrations all over the state demanding repeal of the convict-lease law, but no action was taken.

On the night of October 31, 1891, the miners forcibly freed the convicts. They burned down the stockades of the Tennessee Coal Mine Company and two other companies, releasing about 500 convicts. By the turn of the year, the situation grew worse as insurrections broke out throughout Tennessee; more convicts were released and stockades burned, and a few troops were killed. But the convicts were again reinstated. However, a year later, under pressure of the demonstrations and public demand, the convict-lease system was abolished by the legislature.

RAILROADS HELP DISCOVER COAL

By 1888, railroads were serving mines in the Midwest, but transcontinental service was the desperate requirement. Profitable transcontinental railroad operation depended on a sufficient coal supply obtainable within reasonable shipping distances. The growth of the railroads thereby created incentive for locating and developing coal deposits. For example, the Burlington and Missouri River Railroad in 1888 was being constructed to connect with the Northern Pacific Railroad at Billings, Montana, but work had to be suspended until an adequate coal supply could be found. Construction companies sent out prospecting parties. One party discovered a six-and-a-half-foot seam in the Black Hills of South Dakota, in Little Oil Creek Canyon. After they got the mine operating, wives and families arrived and were housed in company-built homes. The settlement became known as the Antelope City section of Cambria, set on top of the canyon. A school was also constructed here. For those homes that were built in the canyon itself, the children had to climb 365 steps to Antelope City, so a new school was built in the canyon.

Cambria was a model town—no saloons, no gambling, and no crime. Its coal mine developed into one of the country's most modern, and a model for the entire industry. Every known type of automatic machine was installed to save labor, and the miners were provided with clean showers and locker rooms.

Strangely, gold was found in the coal and coke; assay tests sometimes reached $2.00 a ton in the coal

Workers at the Cambria Mine. At Cambria, where the mine was located, the population soared to 1,500— miners and their families brought in from all over the United States. About 550 were employed directly in the mine. *University of Wyoming, Robert L. Lang Collection*

Timbers cut for props being hauled to the Cambria Mine about 1899. To mine the coal, a water supply had to be developed and machinery hauled 170 miles by teams and wagons from Alliance, Nebraska. Machinery and supplies had to be lowered into the canyon, roads had to be built, and a 150-mile railroad spur completed. *University of Wyoming, Elizabeth Thorpe Collection*

The first use of compressed air in coal mines occurred when new compressors were installed in the Cambria Mine in October, 1900. The Cambria mines also utilized the first coal undercutting machines in the West, and were the first to use electricity for power and lighting. The Cambria Mine provided the only coal in the northwest that could produce coke, and 74 beehive coke-making ovens were built to supply the gold smelter at Deadwood. *University of Wyoming, Robert L. Lang Collection*

A shoring crew at work in the Cambria Mine. After being mined, the coal reached the tipple by a tail-rope system and a steam locomotive. It then was crushed and sized by revolving and shaking screens, and loaded into railroad cars by gravity. Water for the mine, the railroad, for Cambria and nearby New Castle, was piped through wire-bound wooden pipes from Sweetwater; by 1890 increasing needs required a deep well. The mine was free of explosive gasses and contained little water, two factors that held accidents and labor disturbances to a minimum. By 1928, 12 million tons of coal had been produced, but it was evident that the veins soon would be depleted. After an intensive but unsuccessful search for new veins, in March, 1928, the mine was forced to shut down. Some miners remained for about two years to dismantle the machinery. *University of Wyoming, Robert L. Lang Collection*

and $5.60 a ton in the coke, for which the Cambria Mine was paid a bonus. When the mine closed after some forty years, a memorial building with a museum was built, housing interesting exhibits loaned or given by the people of Cambria. Adequate maintenance funds were not provided, and although the structure still stands, it no longer contains exhibits of the interesting days of the Cambria Mine.

CRIPPLE CREEK BONANZA

Coal was also being mined in Colorado, and transportation helped open up one of the last and greatest of the Colorado gold rushes not far from Pikes Peak.

Most historians through legend or tradition attribute the name Cripple Creek to a very small stream running through ranchland pasture where cows customarily injured or broke a leg while crossing its rocky bed. Employed on one of these ranches was a cowboy, Robert Womack, who in 1878 found a small piece of gold containing rock assayed at $200 a ton. While continuing to work at the ranch, for some ten years Womack searched for the source of his solitary gold-bearing rock. In December, 1889, he secured a grubstake so that he could devote full time to his search. Ten months later his perseverance was rewarded when he staked a claim on Beacon Hill, the El Paso Lode.

Since only two years before Womack's discovery, a stampede of nearly 5,000 miners at Mount McIntyre (a few miles west of Cripple Creek) turned out to be following a completely false lead, not much attention was paid to Womack's discovery, and for over a year very little mining was done, though a few claims had been filed by local farmers. But when two years later a reputed German count living in Colorado Springs bought a claim, the sale aroused some interest, and Womack decided to sell the El Paso while there was a market, for the small sum of $300, and later sold another claim for $500. This was all the money Womack ever got out of the mining business, and he died in poverty.

The cattle ranch where Womack worked was owned by a real-estate firm, and, because of the slowly awakening interest in local mining, it decided to sell lots, plotting the town of Cripple Creek. The timing was perfect and the firm did extremely well. By the spring of 1892, miners were pouring in. By winter, Cripple Creek had grown to a full-fledged town of 5,000. Bennett and Myers, the real-estate firm, also built a number of inexpensive small cabins, which were rented by the month to transient miners and other newcomers.

The Portland and the nearby Independence Mine proved to be the greatest gold producers of the nineteenth century. The undated photo shows the operations of the Portland Gold Mining Company at Cripple Creek. *Colorado Division of State Archives and Public Records*

The Abe Lincoln Mine at Cripple Creek, about 1894. In the background, on the hill, are several other mines. *Colorado Division of State Archives and Public Records*

A cage scene in the Ajax Mine in the Cripple Creek district. *Colorado State Historical Society Library*

Cripple Creek lies in the shadow of Pikes Peak, and, although speculation and stories of gold finds in the Pikes Peak area had run rampant since the late 1850s, most attempts to search for gold in the area had been sidetracked by the finds in the Central City and Leadville areas, and others nearer Denver. Cripple Creek was one of the last and most important of Colorado's mining rushes; it reached its zenith in 1893 with the discovery of two great mines, the Independence and the Portland, both on Battle Mountain. Mines had been staked out and some even put into production throughout the entire Cripple Creek basin, but Battle Mountain, on the south side of the basin, proved to contain the greatest deposits.

Winfield Scott Stratton was a carpenter contractor and a keen mining student who, beginning in 1874, studied the area carefully, searching for gold when he could spare the time from his carpentry work. Grubstaked by fellow tradesman Leslie Popejoy, a plastering contractor, Stratton came to Cripple Creek in 1891 where he staked two claims, the Independence and the Washington. He decided in favor of developing the Independence, and Popejoy, having little faith in the prospect, sold all of his rights to Stratton for less than $300. Stratton tried to sell the entire claim for $115,000, but fortunately for him the deal fell through just before he found an exceptionally high assay vein. Fearing influxes of miners and prospectors should the news leak out, Stratton played it cautiously, limiting his production and concealing new lode discoveries for future use and development.

Meanwhile, in 1893, James Burns, James Doyle, and John Harnan found that their claim, also on Battle Mountain, contained rich gold veins, and like Stratton, also feared encroachments from surrounding claim owners. They, too, secretly removed the ore from their Portland Mine, working nights only.

The three Portland owners and Stratton pooled their resources in defense against increasing numbers of encroaching claims. Twenty-seven lawsuits were brought against the Portland Mine, but the new combination cleverly manipulated the legal battles by

Mining was very often done in extremely tight quarters.
This 1908 scene is from the Union Mining Company
operation. *Colorado Bureau of Mines*

Cripple Creek in 1892, the year the town's most productive mines, the Independence and the Portland, had their greatest success. The scene is Bennett Avenue looking east. *Denver Public Library Western Collection*

buying out the minor claims, using them to threaten countersuits against the larger contestants. By the time all the litigations were settled, Stratton, Burns, Doyle, and Harnan managed to corner all the property on Battle Mountain. The Portland Mine, now enlarged by the new acquisitions, was incorporated, with Stratton owning a slight majority of the stock, and Burns, Doyle, and Harnan, the balance.

As Colorado's silver mines continued to shut down in 1893 while the country went on the gold standard, many hard-luck miners flocked to Cripple Creek looking for gold instead of silver. Low wages, long hours, and high prices made it inevitable that labor problems would arise. Some mines, taking advantage of the large pool of available labor, increased the eight-hour workday to ten hours, at the same $3-a-day rate. Employees quickly formed a union, which amalgamated with the Western Federation of Miners. In January, 1894, when all mines in the district switched to a ten-hour day, a strike was

Cripple Creek on the Fourth of July, 1893, from a photo by J. G. Wilson. *Colorado State Historical Society Library*

called, principally against those mines in the Bull Hill and Battle Mountain areas that had sponsored the longer workday. The miners, led by John Calderwood, held out until March, when the mine owners secured an injunction against the union. The miners were headquartered at nearby Altman where a central feeding station had been set up for the workers. When the sheriffs tried to serve the injunction papers on the union officials at Altman, they were quickly run out of town. Calderwood then took more drastic steps to win the fight for the miners, establishing a picket line through which no one could pass except those authorized by the union. Governor David H. Waite sent the militia to quiet the uprising and the mine leaders were arrested. After the troops withdrew, they were acquitted and the picket lines were reestablished at Bull Hill.

It was not long before rioting again erupted; independent nonunion workers were beaten, and stores, saloons, and other establishments were wrecked. The mine owners hired a group of strike-breakers, many of them sheriffs and former policemen, and general warfare broke out.

First, the surface workings of the Strong Mine were blown up, and Calderwood, who had been visiting other mining areas, returned and attempted to quiet the action. Seven hundred miners were defending Bull Hill, and an army of 1,200 fighters were sworn in as deputies to oppose them. There was even an exchange of prisoners of war, and an attempt by the governor to arbitrate the ruckus at a

meeting held in Colorado Springs turned up an angry mob that broke up the meeting. All attempts to attack Bull Hill failed, until the state militia was again called in.

Finally the strike was settled, with all mines agreeing to pay a wage of $3 a day for eight hours work. It was further agreed that the deputies would disband, the miners would turn over all their arms, and the militia, stationed in Goldfield, Colorado, would remain until all operations were normal. Calderwood and about 300 miners also agreed to stand trial, but only two miners were convicted, both for blowing up the Strong Mine.

From the time of the strike settlement, Cripple Creek prospered, despite several major fires. Railroads were built and additional gold finds were uncovered at nearby Victor. By 1896 Cripple Creek had its own stock exchange, and two others had opened at Colorado Springs. Cripple Creek was

Troops quartered at Camp Goldfield during the Cripple Creek strikes in 1903. *Colorado State Historical Society Library*

The beginning of the holocaust on April 25, 1896, when about 10 percent of Cripple Creek was destroyed by fire caused by a lighted gasoline stove that tipped over. Four days later, a pot of grease in the kitchen of the Portland Hotel caught on fire, and the high winds soon carried flames to all parts of the town, destroying every building remaining except a few that were built of brick. The town was quickly rebuilt with a business district constructed entirely of brick. *Colorado State Historical Society Library*

filled with stockbrokers, saloons, gambling houses, and brothels, a condition that remained until the beginning of World War I. Most brothels were on Myers Avenue, and when Julian Street wrote an article that was published in *Collier's* magazine in 1940 describing the red light district, the town renamed Myers Avenue Julian Street.

Although murders and ordinary robberies were not as prevalent in Cripple Creek as they had been in some of the earlier mining towns, thefts of gold from the mines became a common practice. The low wages had induced the miners to steal whatever and whenever they could, by secreting pieces of gold in everything from sandwiches to shoes. The habit of stealing high-grade ore became so common that it was practiced by everyone, from the lowest laborer to some mine owners themselves. It is estimated that of the more than $410 million in gold produced at Cripple Creek, at least 5 percent was stolen.

Stratton became the town's leading millionaire. By the turn of the century, more than thirty millionaires had acquired their fortunes from Cripple Creek gold, but none exceeded Stratton's, who finally sold his mine to an English group for $10 million. Stratton had probably sold out just in time, for during the next fifteen years, less than $20 million in ore was removed. The English finally sold the mine for $325,000. During this time Stratton died, and believing that they had been cheated, the English interests sued Stratton's estate for misrepresentation; the suit failed in court. Stratton established a home for orphans and elderly people near Colorado Springs that is still in operation.

After World War I, Cripple Creek's decline was rapid, until the 1930s when some production was revived and the mines began producing about $5 million a year in gold. This soon died out, and today, although some mining still persists, Cripple Creek is no longer a major mining center.

DIATOMITE

Far to the west of Colorado and Pikes Peak, a strange new material was discovered in 1890. We all know that plankton are small plants, or animals, that live in the sea and furnish food for whales and other marine species. But few know that diatomite, in a sense, is the plankton of from 5 to 20 million years ago. Upon the death of these microscopic, single-celled diatomaceous water plants, their shells settled to the bottom to form siliceous sedimentary deposits called diatomite.

Such diatomite was used for brick by the Romans in A.D. 532, and Alfred Nobel used it to absorb liquid nitroglycerine in 1886. It was identified as being similar to German deposits, called "kieselguhr," widely used in the German brewing industry. After the Lompoc, California, discovery in 1890, it was used for insulation and for filtering material.

Diatomite has qualities that make it a superb filter medium and offers ideal applications as an industrial filler for thermal and acoustical insulation,

286

including also miscellaneous uses such as abrasives, polishes, absorbents, glazers, paints, insecticides, fungicides, and other applications. About 500 million tons a year are produced in the United States, mostly from the Lompoc area, which at one time was probably an archipelago of low-lying islands where the sediments were slowly but surely deposited.

Mining of diatomaceous silica was more or less a family affair until about 1902. Most operations were on ranches, but with the formation in California of the Magne Silica Company in 1904, the first mill was built, and in 1906 put into operation. Ten years later the company name was changed to Celite Products Company, later to the Celite Company, which continued in operation until 1928, when the Johns-Manville Corporation acquired the company. Today, modern methods of stripping, mining, and material handling have built the diatomaceous earth business to more than $25 million annually.

Diatomite is mined in a simple surface-mining operation, with use of standard excavating equipment. *Eagle-Picher Industries, Inc.*

Cutting large blocks of crude diatomite from quarry, Lompoc, California, 1915. *Johns-Manville Corporation*

Microscopic diatoms, shells of tiny sea animals, typical of more than three hundred varieties found near Lompoc, California. These are widely used as filter aids for water, beverages, and chemicals, and as fillers and extenders in the plastics, paper, and paint industries. *Johns-Manville Corporation*

Horse-and-wagon transport, 1925, Lompoc. The diatomite was cut in easily handled pieces, and stored in open fields for shipment. *Johns-Manville Corporation*

OTHER SIGNIFICANT HISTORICAL EVENTS

The Field Broadens

Arizona

1870s: Fairbank established as a major supply point for mines around Tombstone.

Contention City established to process silver.

1882: Pima—Copper in district first developed at Emperor Copper Mining Company.

1898–
1914: Azurite Copper and Gold, Mineral Hill Consolidated Copper Company, Twin Buttes Mining and Smelting, Senator Morgan, Copper Glance, Copper Queen, Copper King mines all flourished.

1950: Pima Mining Company, Cypress Mines Corporation, Union Oil, Utah Construction Company began open-pit mining of a new large copper-ore body.

1955: Duval Sulphur and Potash Company began strip mining.

1958: American Smelting and Refining began underground development.

South Dakota

1876: Rochford founded with gold discovery; Standby Mine most important.

1876: Rockerville founded with gold discovery; major operations were by the Black Hills Placer Mining Company.

1876: Galena founded with discovery of silver veins; Florence and Sitting Bull claims staked.

1880: Perry founded with gold find on Elk Creek, followed by Uncle Sam Mine, which filled with water and closed.

1889: Uncle Sam Mine bought by Frenchman who renamed it Perry Roubiax.

1930s: Anaconda took over Uncle Sam Mine for brief period.

Idaho

1863: Bay Horse mining district located.

1880s: Town of Bay Horse founded.

Colorado

1880: Comprise Mine opened, one of the world's largest ore bodies.

Wyoming

1870: Rambler Mine in Medicine Bow Mountains opened as gold mine, but in 1880s it mined copper.

1901: Boston and Wyoming Smelt Power and Light Company began, and consolidated with Ferris-Haggarty to become North American Copper Company.

1906: Penn-Wyoming Company bought out above.

1909: United Smelters Railway and Copper Company bought out the above and soon went bankrupt.

Idaho

1884: Sunshine Mine founded with discovery of Polaris (now owned by Hecla Mining Company) and Yankee Lode (the nucleus of Sunshine Mining Company).

1899: Lucky Friday located, now part of Hecla.

early
1900s: Galena Mine began producing; today managed by ASRCO.

1958: Polaris and Hecla merged. Hecla operates the Star Mine in Burke, the deepest zinc-ore body in the United States (6,900 feet down).

Utah

1904: Barber Asphalt Company made new gilsonite discoveries.

1957: Barber's successor, American Gilsonite, developed The Strip.

Iowa

1881: Whitehead Coal and Mining Company became a major producer—until 1891 when it closed; the Cleveland Mine continued operations with new discoveries.

Wisconsin

1962: Montreal Mine abandoned, once largest in state.

1965: Last iron ore mined in state at Cary Mine in Hurley, in operation since 1885.

California

1969: Most of the country's diatomite comes from this state; smaller quantities are from Nevada, Washington; lesser amounts from Arizona, Maryland, Oregon. Johns-Manville, Great Lakes Carbon Corporation, Eagle-Pitcher Company, Airox Company supply 93 percent.

North to the Klondike

In 1897 no one was worrying particularly about diatomite or gold or silver or copper. Things were running smoothly; no great discoveries appeared to be in the offing; the nation had weathered the silver panic satisfactorily; some mines had been depleted and others were slowly reaching their maximum production; labor was consolidating its few victories and preparing for new battles. Then suddenly it happened again, in a region gold seekers had been prospecting for thirty-five years—Canada and Alaska (in the Klondike and the Yukon). Earlier events were behind this Alaskan gold rush.

GEORGE WASHINGTON CARMACK

In 1885, influenced by his father who prospected (unsuccessfully), in the California gold rush in 1849, George Washington Carmack came to the Klondike. There he married an Indian. Carmack enjoyed the rugged life, including hunting and fishing, and though he had come to look for gold, he had almost forgotten his original purpose—until one day while hunting along Rabbit Creek he reached down and picked up a gold nugget. Panning the

Alaskan miner, typical of those who searched for gold along the river edges of the inland waters in the early mining days. *University of Washington, Audio-Visual Production Services*

area, he extracted additional gold and staked his claim, not at all hesitant about relating his discovery to everyone he met. In no time, the nearby town of Fortymile was deserted while within two weeks Bonanza was completely staked. However, the prospectors soon discovered that to reach the gold deposits, they had to dig deep, to bedrock. What they had found on the surface was simply evidence that gold might lie below. Sinking shafts, the miners were forced to dig drifts from the shaft bottoms, hoping to find and follow the gold lode. Soon a local gold rush was in full swing. Although prospectors from Alaska and British Columbia poured in, they were only a dribble compared to the torrent that arrived after the news reached Washington, Oregon, and California.

THE RACE IS ON

Toward the end of July, 1897, two ships carrying Alaskan gold arrived at Pacific Coast ports. One, the *Excelsior,* landed at San Francisco on July 15 with a score of prospectors and about a thousand pounds of gold, then worth $17 an ounce. At first, the arrival of the *Excelsior* created little excitement, but rumors grew rapidly that an even larger shipment of gold would arrive at Seattle a few days later. Like most rumors, the news had spread quickly; nearly 5,000 people jammed the dock the morning of July 17 when the *Portland* tied up at Seattle. The waiting crowds had their expectations fulfilled. More than two tons of gold were aboard, and everyone soon knew that vast treasures were to be found along the Klondike, a tributary of the Yukon River.

Talk of Klondike gold had been heard for six months before the arrival of the *Portland*, with few believers, despite the gold carried back by the few prospectors who had made the arduous trip. However, a detailed report of the new finds was published in the Seattle *Post-Intelligencer,* and suddenly the *Portland* was booked to capacity for the return trip. Within a few hours everyone rushed to obtain passage, a condition reminiscent of the 1848–1849 exodus from San Francisco. The streets of Seattle became so crowded as to be impassable. Everyone was quitting his job, hoping to get to Alaska. Lack of passage forced the creation of groups, each sending a representative north to stake a claim. By the time the *Portland* sailed for Alaska, on July 22, the price of tickets had risen from $200 to $1,000, with speculators reselling tickets for $1,500.

Scraping every dollar together, men left their families and rushed north in hopes of striking it rich. The race was on, the fantastic Klondike-Yukon gold rush.

There were only two ways to reach the interior of Alaska and Canada's Yukon Territory on its eastern border. One was by the water passage via the Pacific Ocean and the Bering Sea, a trip of over 2,100 miles; the other was by a shorter route via the eastern inland passage to Alaska's Skagway and Dyea, lying on the Yukon's underbelly. The objec-

tive was Dawson, a hop over the Alaskan border, the Canadian takeoff point for the nearby goldfields. But nobody knew how far along the Yukon River Dawson was. The hazardous problems of autumn, the winter freezes on the waterways, and the dangers of being frozen in were genuine perils, and most gold seekers, anxious for speed, and playing it safe, naturally took the shorter route. Soon every kind of vessel that could float was making the trip, loaded with prospectors who at first rushed to Dyea, nine miles west of Skagway. Unloading ships was difficult at both towns, but docks soon were built at Skagway, making it the gateway to the Klondike.

The first boat landed in Skagway in July, 1897. Within three months, it was a bustling community

This odd-looking group fording the Dyea River en route to the Klondike was not prospectors, nurses, potential cooks, or workers, but a group of actresses who found performing more profitable than panning. *New York Public Library Picture Collection*

The Dawson red-light district, known as "White Chapel," set up by authorities at the edge of town. The photo, obviously posed, reveals a group of five women in the left background watching the proceedings. Perhaps business was bad and the ladies needed wood to keep warm. *University of Washington, Audio-Visual Production Services*

Dawson in 1898. *New York Public Library Picture Collection*

of around 20,000 people, with streets, hotels, saloons, gambling houses, dance halls, and stores—as wild and rough a town as any in North America. Supplies, food, whiskey, clothing, and mining equipment were in fantastic demand; horses became almost unobtainable, and the cost of sled dogs was literally their weight in gold.

SKAGWAY AND SOAPY

The Northwest Mounted Police called Skagway "A little better than a Hell on earth." From Creede, Colorado, Soapy Smith turned up in Skagway in 1897 to add his little bit. He opened a saloon and soon became the leader of the rowdies and the lawless. He had been in town barely one day when the opportunity to take over presented itself. A crowd was about to lynch a local saloon owner, John E. Fay, for the murders of Andy McGarth and a United States deputy marshall. Smith gathered a bunch of town toughs, stopped the lynching, and persuaded the crowd to ship the guilty man to Sitka for trial. He also collected several thousand dollars for the two widows of the murdered men. Soapy and his new-found gang immediately took over, instituting a system of 50 percent commission for all illegal ventures in return for guaranteed protection. His gang numbered nearly 300 men, and he became a virtual dictator. His modus operandi sponsored theft and murder of incoming and outgoing prospectors but prohibited robbing local permanent residents. Anyone returning to Skagway from the goldfields with gold in his possession had little chance of getting it out.

Smith met his Waterloo in J. D. Stewart, a Canadian miner who returned to Skagway with nearly $3,000 in gold. He soon was robbed, but Stewart, generally a mild-mannered individual, formed a vigilante committee that demanded that Smith return the gold. A district court judge handed Smith an ultimatum to return the money by four o'clock that afternoon. At the deadline, Smith refused, and was killed after shooting a guard. The vigilantes ran wild. They tore down the saloons and the dives, routed the remnants of Smith's gang, and captured forty prisoners, intent on a mass lynching party. Fortunately, they were persuaded to ship them to the United States instead, and Skagway's lawless days passed into history.

As the rush to the north continued, ships cluttered the crowded ports; others disappeared, and some ran aground. Still the crowds continued to pour north, and the price for passage became even more prohibitive.

Construction on the Salmon Dam near Juneau, well under way in 1914. When built, the dam was the largest construction job ever attempted in Alaska. The Alaska Juneau Mill dominated the harbor; perched on the side of a mountain, the mill was a major engineering job. *A. J. Industries, Inc.*

The Alaska Juneau Mill, built in 1915. *A. J. Industries, Inc.*

Juneau, founded in 1880 when Joe Juneau and Dick Harris, exploring by canoe, made a rich gold strike that was followed by a minor stampede, was the last major stop before Skagway and Dyea, and was the shipping base for supplies. When these supplies reached Dyea and Skagway, there were mad scrambles to unload them.

DYEA AND THE CHILKOOT TRAIL

Dyea before the gold strike was an Indian village with a few hundred Indians and half a dozen whites, but by the fall of 1897 it was swollen with perhaps more than 10,000 people, living in or around Dyea in tents, hotels, log cabins, saloons, lean-tos, in fact, in any structure that could afford shelter, no matter how flimsy. Everyone had the same purpose—to beat the crowd north to the Chilkoot Trail, an Indian trial that had been used by a handful of miners for nineteen years. At first it was the Indians who struck gold, reaping fortunes by

Prospectors camping en route to the Yukon goldfields. Some idea of the amount of supplies the miners had to carry can be seen from the piles in the photograph. *New York Public Library Picture Collection*

This human chain ascends the summit of Chilkoot Pass en route to Dawson. The few stragglers stopping to rest often had to wait hours to get back into line. Local Indians made fortunes charging fifty cents a pound to tote supplies to the Canadian border at the top of the pass. William S. Greever, in his superb book *The Bonanza West,* wrote that the statistics on the number of people coming to Dawson "even though not precise, are impressive." He continues: "Perhaps 100,000 people set out for Dawson; 30,000 to 40,000 got there, 15,000 to 20,000 prospected, 4,000 found some gold, 15,000 people out of the year's rush remained in the Klondike when winter closed in, and another 5,000 departed before the spring came. They spent somewhere between $30 to $60 million for transportation and supplies, yet the yield of gold from the Klondike in 1898 was hardly more than $10 million." Although the fantastic Klondike-Yukon gold rush did not begin until the latter half of 1897, gold was first discovered in 1861 on the Stikine River, where very little prospecting was done at the time. The Yukon River displayed gold coloring in 1866, and prospecting began in the area around 1873; the first known prospectors on the Alaska Yukon were Arthur Harper and Leroy McQuesten. *University of Washington Libraries. Photo by E. A. Hegg*

charging as much as fifty cents a pound to haul a miner's supplies up the trail. Male Indians would carry a 100- to 150-pound load up the trail, wives and squaws, seventy-five pounds, and children, from fifteen to sixty pounds, depending upon their age, while their dogs were able to carry fifteen pounds. All worked to reap the harvest while it lasted. Innocently abetting them, the Canadian government permitted no one to cross its territory without a year's supply of food and clothing, the equivalent of more than a ton per person. At fifty cents a pound this was more than most gold seekers could afford, and many were forced to move their supplies up the trail themselves, in relays.

Wily local residents, also eager to extract money from the stampeding hordes, used any and every method they could dream up. Toll bridges were built, wayside stands sold high-priced whiskey and food at outlandish prices, and expensive blacksmith shops sprouted. Avid for gold, the men continued to pour in.

About twenty-five miles up Chilkoot Trail was Sheep Camp, a tiny community of tents, a few frame buildings, a log cabin, and a hotel with a single large room. *Harper's Weekly* described the hotel as "crowded with a wild, dirty, wet, unkempt crew from Chilkoot . . . where beans, tea and bacon are thrown into them at seventy-five cents each, payable strictly in advance. When supper is over the floor is open for guests. All who have blankets unroll them and spread them on the floor, take off their socks and shoes and hang them on the rafters, place a coat under their heads and turn in."

But Sheep Camp was just the beginning of the

Sheep Camp at Chilkoot Pass, April, 1898. *University of Washington Libraries. Photo by E. A. Hegg*

difficult struggle; four miles beyond was Chilkoot Pass, at an elevation of over 3,500 feet, impassable for horses; pulling sleds up the incline was virtually impossible. Consequently, most supplies had to be carried on the prospectors' backs. The last mile (The Scales) was the toughest, averaging nearly thirty degrees steep and rising more than 1,200 feet.

Near the summit, the Canadian customs officials had set up headquarters to inspect the supplies, ensuring that only those with a year's supply could go through. The miners tramped between Sheep Camp and The Scales, assembling their gear just below the steep climb over the pass, near the customs officials' headquarters. Taking a look at The Scales —1,200 to 1,500 steps notched into the frozen snow by the boots of preceding climbers—many quit, and prospectors who were short of equipment were able to purchase abandoned supplies at bargain prices— ten cents on the dollar. Hopefuls waiting to climb The Scales extended for miles, and anyone foolish enough to get out of line had to wait hours to get back. Canadian officials claimed that over 40,000 people had climbed through the Chilkoot during the gold rush.

Despite all the difficulties, there were few ac-

Near the summit of the Chilkoot Pass was the customs station manned by the Northwest Mounted Police, who checked all prospectors to see that they had a year's provisions before permitting them into Canadian territory. This station established a disputed boundary between the United States and Canada. *University of Washington, Audio-Visual Production Services*

Beyond the summit of the Chilkoot Pass, hundreds of miners rigged up sails on their sleds to travel the ice-covered rivers and lakes to Dawson. This photo shows such a group crossing Crater Lake. *University of Washington, Audio-Visual Production Services*

cidents. However, one especially bad avalanche in April, 1898, covered the trail with thirty feet of snow, burying hundreds of gold seekers. Though most scrambled out and others were rescued, sixty-three men were killed.

Once the summit was reached, it was a long downhill trail all the way north to Dawson, about 375 miles over rivers, lakes, and ice fields.

WHITE PASS TRAIL

But soon another trail, paralleling the Chilkoot, became the popular route to Dawson and the Yukon —the White Pass Trail, which, although rugged, was a lot easier than the Chilkoot, having none of its impossibly steep climbs.

The White Pass Trail continued north to Lake Bennett, with the forty-odd miles to the lake often taking a month to travel. Here a little town sprouted, catering to the needs of the miners. Portions of the trail to the lake had such insecure footing that more than 3,000 pack horses died, many falling off the

treacherous path—into a rocky pit nicknamed Dead Horse Gulch—while Dead Horse Trail was littered with abandoned supplies and sleds. (Today Lake Bennett is a popular tourist spot, still reached by the White Pass and Yukon Railroad, or by guided trips on horseback along the old trail.) Beyond Lake Bennett another small town soon flourished, Whitehorse, a tent city where travelers from both the Chilkoot and White Pass trails converged, and which was about 360 miles from the present Dawson City, the center of the Klondike gold strike. By 1899 more than 40,000 people lived here, mostly sourdoughs, all hoping to strike gold in this strange American community administered by Canada.

In July, 1898, the White Pass and Yukon Railroad started to lay tracks. Over 2,000 men rushed to assist. It was impossible to transport construction machinery over this rocky, rugged land, and though every stone had to be removed by hand, by the summer of 1899 track was laid as far as Lake Bennett.

This Hegg photo shows the first passenger train to travel over the White Pass and Yukon Route to the summit, on February 20, 1899. *University of Washington, Audio-Visual Production Services*

This Hegg photo was taken on May 30, 1898, one day after the ice broke on Lake Bennett, where the miners converged after going through the Chilkoot Pass. The shores of the lake are lined with boat builders, and more than 1,000 boats left for Dawson from this point. Many of them can be seen on the water. *University of Washington, Audio-Visual Production Services*

Building the White Pass and Yukon Route was not only a problem of cutting away rock and blasting footholds on the cliffsides, but also clearing the tracks after heavy snows. This Hegg photo shows such activity after a snowstorm on the summit of the route on March 20, 1899. *University of Washington, Audio-Visual Production Services*

ON TO DAWSON

An original White Pass passenger train crosses the Slippery Rock grade, descending gradually to Skagway at the head of Lynn Canal. Slippery Rock presented one of the most difficult engineering obstacles during the construction of the White Pass and Yukon Route. Men were slung by ropes down the mountainside to drill blast holes. *White Pass and Yukon Route*

Dawson City, 1900, center of the Klondike gold rush. Founded in 1896, it soon had a population of over 30,000; but by 1901, it had dwindled to 9,100, and in the 1950s, fewer than 1,000 people lived there. *William Culp Darrah Stereo Collection*

Near Dawson during the Alaska gold rush, dogs were sometimes used to pull small mine carts in the drifts. This Saint Bernard appears to be wearing earrings, but they are probably connections to his harness. *University of Washington, Audio-Visual Production Services*

Once beyond the Chilkoot and the White Pass trails, the best way to get to Dawson City was by boat, especially in the spring when the ice had thawed. The boats had to shoot the difficult White-horse Rapids, but most prospectors still made the attempt, even while the water was full of ice. Getting a boat was not easy. They had to be constructed by the prospectors themselves or bought from enterprising boat builders who appeared seemingly from nowhere at this juncture. Boats, of course, had to be sturdy and strong to withstand the pressures of the rapids and the ice forming in the waterways leading through the lakes to the Yukon River, via the Lewes River South.

The major problem in the Klondike was food. Dawson's growth had far exceeded its ability to supply food for the hordes of newcomers. During the summer, veteran suppliers had managed to move in 800 tons of food and general merchandise. Based on the Canadian customs regulations—a ton per person—this was clearly inadequate to feed the 40,000 who ultimately reached Dawson.

Newcomers were warned that food was not sufficient in Dawson to last the winter, and the Northwest Mounted Police tried to get the sourdoughs to move to Fort Yukon in Alaska. But the miners remained, fearful their claims would be jumped or declared forfeit if they left. Fortunately, only 200 accepted the Canadian government's free transportation to Fort Yukon; the food supply there was barely enough to serve the 200. At this point the United States intervened, issuing a seven-month

Rugged Alaskan weather required sturdy construction at the mining camps in 1899 and 1900. *William Culp Darrah Stereo Collection*

supply on credit while guaranteeing the local merchants against loss, and also buying 540 reindeer in Norway. By the time the deer arrived in Seattle, the animals' food supply was exhausted. The deer, at first freed to pasture in a Seattle city park, were shipped to Dyea where the United States Army fed them alfalfa, an unnatural diet for reindeer, which caused the death of many. The fewer than 200 that survived were turned loose at Circle City to forage for themselves. When food supplies finally arrived in Dawson, prices fell drastically; eggs, for example, dropped from $1.50 each to $3.00 a dozen.

The Klondike gold rush spurred some unusual projects, one of which was the exportation of 4,000

A well-kept miner's home in Alaska about 1899. *William Culp Darrah Stereo Collection*

Working Faulkner's claim at Gold Hill in the Klondike in 1900. *William Culp Darrah Stereo Collection*

New England spinsters as potential wives for the miners, the inspiration for a TV series. Unique inventions were created, such as an electric-powered steam-heated sleigh, chemical food tablets that could be carried in a pocketbook, and an X-ray machine that would detect gold deposits. Sadly, none worked.

BONANZA FOR AUTHORS

The gold rush was a bonanza for many authors, who through their writings on the subject achieved fame and world-wide renown. Robert W. Service, an Englishman, although never participating in the gold rush himself, was inspired by it. He wrote such poems as "The Shooting of Dan McGrew," and "The Cremation of Sam McGee," and also a number of books: *Songs of a Sourdough, Spell of the Yukon, Ballads of a Cheechako,* and his first novel, *The Trail of '98.* Rex Beach actually started for the Klondike but only reached Fort Yukon, though later he went to Nome. Jack London traveled the Chilkoot Pass in 1897. Though he did not reach Dawson, he spent the winter on the trail and gathered material for many stories and novels. *Burning Daylight, The Call of the Wild,* and others are based upon his experiences in the Yukon or upon characters he met in Alaska. Joaquin Miller hiked the Chilkoot Pass to Dawson. Afterward he toured the United States, reaping his bonanza through speaking engagements and vaudeville appearances based upon his and others' experiences in the Klondike.

STAMPEDE TO NOME

As rumors of new strikes continued to spread, disappointed prospectors rushed from one new area to another. Miners flocked to Fairbanks and the hundreds of spots accessible by the easy river travel. The Yukon tributaries and other streams and rivers were overrun with those who found placer mining an easy task after the terrors of Dyea and Chilkoot passes. But now Nome was to become the "Promised Land," the principal target of thousands of disappointed men.

Though it was over 1,100 miles from Dawson to Nome on Alaska's west coast, travel down the Yukon was comparatively easy for those who could get on a boat. Reports that gold strikes had been found on Anvil Creek precipitated a second stampede, toward Nome. Disappointed prospectors from Dawson rushed west, while newcomers from Seattle pushed north. As Nome grew, it became a mixture of tents and huts. Suddenly attention was diverted from the mining activities at Anvil Creek and Snake River

Anvil Creek, a rich gold strike less than five miles from Nome, Alaska, 1898. *Carrie M. McLain (from the University of Washington)*

Nome beach where miners camped. All the rockers and machinery were improvisations to separate the gold from the sands (Hegg photo). *University of Washington, Audio-Visual Production Services*

"Sluicing the dump," a means of washing gold residue from the huge pile of dump material or "tailings" in the background. Dumps from previous workings often contain rich residues of gold that can be reclaimed by improved methods. This early 1900 photo was taken at the Flat Creek Mining Company in Alaska. *Carrie M. McLain*

It was impossible for the ships to dock at the shallow beaches and amid the heavy surf at Nome, and passengers were carried on scows from the ships, which can be seen lying a mile or so off the beach. *University of Washington, Audio-Visual Production Services*

to the beaches of Norton Sound and the Bering Sea. This was the kind of gold mining that appealed to all—no hills to climb, no shafts to dig, just a nice sandy beach where one could pan for gold comfortably.

Unfortunately, Nome had no port. Ships, unable to approach the shallow beach, had to anchor miles off; even landing barges were impractical, making it often necessary to wade ashore. This made it almost impossible to bring supplies into Nome, which had grown so suddenly that its facilities were completely inadequate. Soon typhoid and malaria were rampant, and to add to the woes of the sourdoughs, there just wasn't enough beach.

It was not legal to stake a claim in tidewaters, and by common agreement one could pan only as far as his shovel could reach. Long-handled shovels were in great demand.

To settle the legal problems of beach claims and of the properties of Anvil Creek and the Snake River, Federal Judge Arthur Noyes was sent to Nome. Noyes, however, was in league with the claim jumpers, and, as a receiver for the mines, he appointed a friend, Alexander McKenzie, who took over their entire production. But the mine owners, appealing to the circuit courts in San Francisco, obtained writs, which Noyes refused to honor. Meanwhile, McKenzie had tried to remove the gold dust from the banks, but the mine owners held him off at gunpoint. Finally, the United States deputy marshalls from San Francisco restored all gold and titles to their proper owners, McKenzie was sent to jail, and Judge Noyes, found guilty of contempt, was fined.

According to Nome historian Carrie M. McLain, beach mining in Alaska extended along the beach for thirty miles, with 8,000 prospectors' tents dotting the area. In 1899 and 1900, $2 million in beach gold was extracted from the black sands.

But it had turned the Nome countryside into a mass of pans, rockers, sluices, and dredges. The dredges could not be operated successfully on the beaches, but as new finds were made inland, channels were dug and the dredges began to turn the gold-bearing soils topsy-turvy.

Front Street, the main street of Nome, always crowded and busy. At times, especially on Sundays and holidays, it was impossible to pass through. It was on Front Street that Wyatt Earp owned the Second Class Saloon, "the only second-class saloon in Alaska." *University of Washington, Audio-Visual Production Services*

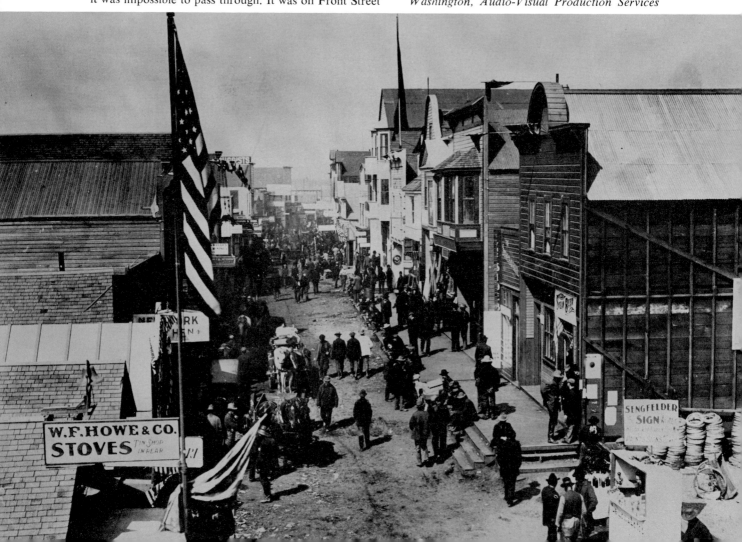

By the very early 1900's the business district of Nome had spread along River Street on the Snake River. The building at the extreme right is the Riverside Saloon, with the ladies' entrance directly behind the man tipping his hat. Beyond the grocery store is an attorney's office. Note the boardwalk sidewalks (Hegg photo). *University of Washington, Audio-Visual Production Services*

One of Nome's most valuable commodities was lumber, seen piled high along the waterfront. Lumber was vital for construction of all kinds, especially for flumes for carrying water to the gold deposits. *University of Washington, Audio-Visual Production Services*

Soon after this photograph was taken, there was hardly room to pitch a tent along the beaches at Nome. *Carrie M. McLain*

A few miners managed to build some semipermanent structures along the beach at Cape Nome. *Carrie M. McLain*

Cape Nome beaches were lined with rockers. One man could handle from one to two cubic yards of dirt per day with a rocker. *Carrie M. McLain*

Away from the Nome beaches, the gold-bearing dirt was carried in long sluices rigged with baffles called "Hungarian riffles." *University of Washington, Audio-Visual Production Services*

Dexter Creek, 1899, a rich, shallow creek ten miles north of Nome. *Carrie M. McLain*

The Bessie Mine, Nome, 1906. *University of Alaska Museum, Mackay Collection*

An interesting 50-foot hydraulic lift at Glacier Creek, a rich find discovered shortly after the famous Anvil Creek strike. *Carrie M. McLain*

"There's always something doing." Two men on a windlass with a bucket raised from the shaft. Nome, 1906. *University of Alaska Museum, Mackay Collection*

The *Wisconsin,* a bucket dredge with an endless chain and 28-foot ladder. It was built in Seattle, Washington, in 1898, and towed by tugboat to Nome where it was stranded by a storm in 1902. The mortgagee sold it for $1,800 in 1907, although it had cost $60,000 to build. After it was sold, it went back to work on the Snake River, near Nome. *Carrie M. McLain*

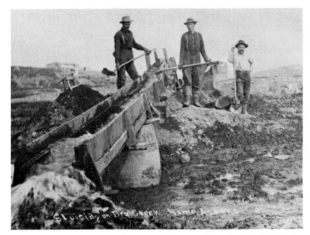

Sluicing on Dry Creek, near Nome. *Carrie M. McLain*

"Rocking" on Taylor Creek. *Carrie M. McLain*

Little Creek dump, Nome, 1906. Out of such beginnings since the first gold strike, nearly $2 billion worth of minerals has been unearthed in Alaska. And it still continues to produce. Copper, oil, natural gas, and coal are abundant. In coal alone, about 800,000 tons are being mined yearly. Lead, silver, and zinc are abundant, and platinum is commonly dredged on the Salmon River. In 1968, huge oil deposits were discovered that were said to have greater oil reserves than now exist in the entire continental United States. The story of mining in Alaska is far from finished; in fact, many think it has just begun. *University of Alaska Museum, Mackay Collection*

Into the Space Age

Gold, silver, copper, lead, zinc, and coal were the principal mined products of the nation at the dawn of the twentieth century. True, such elements as molybdenum, among others, were being produced, but new methods of production, exploration, and refining were rapidly under development and a host of newer materials were still to be discovered.

LITHIUM

Lithium was first found in the United States while all eyes were on Alaska, and the discovery almost went unnoticed. The metal was first found abroad in 1817, but in the United States it was first isolated in 1898 at the Etta Mine in the Black Hills of South Dakota, when thirty tons of spodumene were recovered. Spodumene from pegmatite and lithium-sodium-phosphate taken from brines are the raw materials from which lithium is recovered. Spodumene, by an acid or alkali method of recovery, is converted to lithium compounds, used for alloying in nuclear energy work and in ceramics. Lithium is the lightest of all metals. It also has various applications in greases, batteries, welding, ceramics, air conditioning, and bleaching. Spodumene and most lithium minerals are mined by open-pit and underground methods, usually as a by-product or co-product of feldspar, mica, quartz, or other mineral mining. In 1938 Searles Lake, California, began producing lithium from brines, and in 1953 spodumene was commercially rendered at Kings Mountain, North Carolina.

Foote Mineral Company lithium operation, Kings Mountain, North Carolina. *Foote Mineral Company*

TUNGSTEN

Beginning in 1900, mines in California, Nevada, Colorado, North Carolina, Montana, and Idaho began producing tungsten (or "heavy stone"), which formerly was imported from China and elsewhere. Tungsten, also called wolfram from the ore wolframite, originally was discovered by a Swedish chemist, Karl Wilhelm Scheele, in 1781. He called it tungstic acid.

Tungsten metals are generally found in quartz veins but occasionally in placer deposits. Both underground and open-cut mining methods are used. Before the nuclear and space programs became such an important part of our industrial economy, tungsten metal was used for lighting and electrical applications, and tungsten carbides were extensively employed in metal-shaping tools, drilling bits, and other applications that required resistance to wear. Shortly

Placer mining for tungsten near Nederland, Colorado. *Standard Oil Company of New Jersey*

Shoveling waste into bucket in a tungsten mine on outskirts of Nederland. It will then be hoisted to the top. *Standard Oil Company of New Jersey*

Miners prepare rail line in a new level of the Climax Mine at Climax. *American Metal Climax, Inc.*

before the opening of the nuclear and space ages, tungsten reached fruition: the element has the highest melting point of all known metals. Tungsten was classified as a critical material during the Korean War and stockpiled by the United States government. About half or more of our production comes from five out of nearly 700 producers.

In the late 1940s considerable research evolved a process for the recovery of the minute tungsten content, 0.025 percent, or a half pound per ton, in Climax Molybdenum's ores. A by-product recovery plant was completed, which enabled the company to

recover several valuable minerals associated with the molybdenum in the ore body.

The name molybdenum occurs in Pliny's writings but denoted substances containing lead. Molybdenum was isolated in 1790, and is never found free in nature but always chemically combined with other elements.

STONE

Stone quarrying or mining began strictly as a local development by the early settlers who utilized any stone material close at hand for elementary construction work and other minor uses. It was rare indeed for anyone to "prospect" for stone in the early days and most discoveries sprang from a search for local sources. It was only after heavy industrialization of the railroads that stone was shipped any great distance, and even today high freight rates generally preclude long-distance shipments.

Before 1900 almost all stone (dimension stone, slate, and crushed or broken stone) was used indiscriminately for construction purposes. Since then dimension stone has been the primary construction material, competing with many other structural materials—brick, for example. It is also a decorative and ornamental material and has other uses, such as

Engraving of a limestone quarry in 1874 (from *Harper's Weekly*). *Kansas State Historical Society*

Two three-inch quarry bars carrying jackhammers for drilling holes in Tennessee marble for the Thrasher Marble Company, Knoxville. *Tennessee State Library and Archives*

Entrance to Rutland Marble Company's north quarry, Vermont, circa 1880s. *William Culp Darrah Stereo Collection*

Working out the granite at the Mohegan Quarry, Peekskill, source of granite for the Cathedral of St. John the Divine in New York City. *New York State Museum of Science*

Turntable at Diamond Hill Granite quarries, Rhode Island, circa 1800s. *William Culp Darrah Stereo Collection*

In 1916, marble was cut into blocks directly from the quarry face, and removed for further cutting at the Colorado Marble Company. *United States Forest Service*

Gang saw cutting oilstones in Hoosier National Forest. *United States Forest Service*

in curbing, gravestones, and so forth. The principal varieties of stone used for these purposes are marble, granite, limestone, and sandstone.

Quarrying dimension stone usually involves cutting stone from quarry faces into large blocks with channeling machines or wire saws that undercut the stone at the floor level. The material is then broken by wedging, after which the mass is cut into blocks of the required size. Blasting is rarely practiced in quarries since the explosive force damages the stone.

Various types of dimension stone are found in

After the block in the previous picture was cut, it was broken off at the bottom with wedges and then toppled on its side. Unless the blocks are to be used for special purposes, they are cut into smaller blocks for shipment to the nearby mills, where they are cut into slabs and converted into finished stone. *Indiana Limestone Institute*

Grainless Indiana limestone is easily split in any direction. The stone is cut by electrically driven wire saws, often into pieces weighing considerably more than 100 tons. The block on which the man is standing (to the left of the ladder) has already been cut. The 1900s saw a boom in building and industrial construction that turned many small quarry operations into major ones, particularly in the use of limestone as a dimensional building material. Between Bloomington and Bedford, Indiana, a 23-mile belt of limestone supports more than 100 quarries that have produced limestone for some of the most famous structures in the United States. This remarkable limestone strata supplied the facing for New York's 102-story Empire State Building, Rockefeller Center, and United Nations headquarters. Among dozens of magnificent Washington, D.C., structures built with this Indiana limestone are the Pentagon Building, the Justice, Labor, Commerce, and Post Office buildings, and the National Cathedral. Some of the world's largest office buildings, such as the Merchandise Mart in Chicago, have utilized this limestone, as well as more than 200 county courthouses, more than 10 state capitals, and dozens of college campuses. The heart of the Indiana limestone district is the town of Oolitic, named for the type of limestone found in the belt. Most of the limestone is finished at mills near the quarries, and it is not unusual to form single columns out of pieces weighing more than 100 tons. *Indiana Limestone Institute*

different areas of the United States. From Maine and Vermont to Georgia and Alabama, granite and marble are the principal products; between the Appalachian and Rocky mountains, most of the mined material is limestone and sandstone (the most famous limestone quarried in the United States comes from Indiana); some granite is found in Minnesota, South Dakota, Wisconsin, Missouri, Oklahoma, and Texas; the western states have huge deposits of sandstone and some metamorphic deposits of limestone and marble.

As for slates, these are sedimentary rocks that can readily be split into thin plates; for this reason its principal uses are for roofing, veneer materials, electric panels, billiard-table tops, blackboards, and grave vaults.

Slate is usually mined from open quarries with different forms of mining sometimes required, ac-

cording to the dip or angle at which the slate is found. In some places it is even mined in shafts. Its natural cleavage makes the material easy to split into thin sheets, and its softness enables it to be cut easily with circular saws. Slate is generally found in the northern counties of Pennsylvania, and in Maine, New York, Vermont, and Virginia. Minor quantities are produced in Arizona, Arkansas, California, Georgia, Michigan, Tennessee, and Utah.

Fifty years before dimension stone became a primary construction material, Eli Whitney Blake had invented the mechanical stone crusher that revolutionized the market for crushed stone. About three quarters of all crushed and broken stone is derived from limestone. By far the largest dollar volume of stone mining is in the crushed stone, about $1 billion a year. Its basic uses are in the construction, chemical, and metallurgical raw material fields. Highways and industrial construction projects consume the bulk of the material, and the balance is absorbed in cement manufacture, steel mills, and in chemical, metallurgical, and agricultural uses.

Crushed stone is mined in every state. Mining, where practical, is done from surface quarries, but some of the largest operations, particularly in limestone, are underground mines, usually worked by leaving about 25 percent of the rock as supporting pillars for mine roofs.

After limestone is cut into mill-size blocks, it is piled at the edge of the quarry, where it is ultimately loaded into freight cars for shipment to the mill. *Indiana Limestone Institute*

Bowden Limestone Quarry. The limestone seam underlies four mountains, and offers cover ranging from 1,000 feet upward. *West Virginia Department of Archives and History*

Limestone operation at Maginey Quarry, Lewiston, Pennsylvania. *Indiana Limestone Institute*

Granite quarry, Barre, Vermont. *Felix A. Peckham*

Marble quarry, Proctor, Vermont. *Felix A. Peckham*

A wooden derrick and an old-style steam channeler can be seen at the left of this photograph of the Alexander King Quarry and its working force in Stinesville, Indiana. The photograph was taken in the summer of 1927. *Indiana Geological Survey*

Beginning around 1870, large limestone deposits were developed for quarrying in the Rockland, Maine, area. The limestone was exposed to the surface, and easily quarried. The ease of transporting the quarried limestone by boat along the coast developed the limestone industry extensively from 1870 to 1880. *Maine Historical Society*

During the same period, large deposits of slate were quarried near Mayfield, Maine. The slate was easily scaled and was removed by ox team for shipment down the coast. *Maine Historical Society*

OLD HAT DISTRICT

Number 3A and 3B San Manuel shaft areas in 1955. In the center foreground are the shaft and hoist house and in the center the mine-to-plant railroad for hauling ore. At the top left in the distance is the plant site. The famous mining towns included San Manuel in Old Hat District, Arizona. Some older areas came to life with the turn of the century. The history of the Old Hat Mining District, for instance, relates wholly to the San Manuel Copper Corporation located at the new town of San Manuel, about forty miles northeast of Tucson. Some prospecting had been done in the area before the Civil War, but there was very little production. The San Manuel group of claims, located in 1906, have been held continuously to the present time. Not until 1917 were some exploratory holes drilled, but they did not indicate sufficient copper content to encourage further exploration. However, in the 1940s, test drilling confirmed the existence of important copper deposits, and in 1944 the Magma Copper Company purchased the property and some adjacent claims. The San Manuel Copper Corporation started in 1945, when the Magma Copper Company deeded the property in the district to the new corporation, and since then the company has become an important copper producer. A surface plant, including a concentrator and a smelter, railroads, complete housing facilities, and the town were constructed. The town, built for the San Manuel employees, contains more than 1,000 homes, shopping facilities, and a hospital, and is owned by the Magma Copper Company. *San Manuel Copper Corporation*

TITANIUM—TWENTIETH CENTURY

A "traveling lake" near Starke, Florida, where ilmenite, a black sandy ore, is mined as the raw material for titanium dioxide, the whitest white pigment known. The floating dredge digs the sand and pumps it to the "wet mill" in the background, where the black ilmenite is separated from the sand. Both the dredge and the separators float in the lake that was dug out of the sandy soil. After separation, the sand is poured out behind the "wet mill," and thus the lake and the full rig travel in the direction of the work. Titanium comes from two ore minerals, rutile and ilmenite. Ilmenite is more abundant than rutile, but rutile, which is found in sand deposits mined by dredging, contains more titanium, and commands a higher price. Ilmenite is found in rock deposits mined by open-pit methods, and occasionally in dredged sand deposits. Titanium's principal use is in the manufacture of titanium dioxide, a white pigment widely used in paints, lacquers, plastics, paper, floor coverings, rubber, coated fabrics, textiles, and other products. (Rutile is used principally for welding, rod coatings, and for making titanium metal.) In its metal form, titanium has many uses, especially in the aircraft industry for airframes and power plants. It also serves the missile and space-component industry, which absorbs about one-third of the total production. *Du Pont de Nemours*

THE MAN WHO DUG THROUGH A MOUNTAIN

The opening years of the 1900s produced no stranger story than that of Burro Schmidt, who drove a 2,100-foot tunnel completely through the granite of the El Paso Mountains in the upper Mojave Desert. Schmidt, who spent thirty-two years of hard, solitary labor on his project, worked only with a four-pound hammer, without using power tools of any kind. As a one-man venture, it is undoubtedly without parallel, especially since he knew nothing of mining when he started. Nevertheless, he was able to excavate a stable tunnel, five feet wide and seven feet high, through a hard rock mountain to an exit exactly where he had planned it. Originally, all he had wanted was to find an easy way to transport ore from his mine to the smelters; his claims were surrounded by rugged mountains requiring miles of road building.

William Henry Schmidt was known as Burro because for twenty-five years his only close companions were two burros. His story begins with his first visit to California, where he hoped to cure his tuberculosis. He stayed a year, returned East, and then came back to the Mojave Desert in 1900. Early mining activities farther north—at Cerro Gordo, Coso, Darwin, and Panamint—had ceased, and prospectors now were milling around the El Pasos. Nearby was the sensational Yellow Aster Gold Mine, and Schmidt, hoping to be one of the "lucky ones,"

had located several claims, leasing some for possible development. For years they had lain idle because of the lack of roads, until Schmidt, still believing they had possibilities, in 1906 decided to try to tunnel through the mountain.

Only at the tunnel entrance and exit did Schmidt do any timbering. At first he used lanterns for light, but to economize he settled on candles, at three for five cents. In his economies, he violated common-sense safety rules, using the shortest possible fuses for the small blasts he set off to loosen the rock, and consequently had several narrow escapes from death. Fifty or sixty feet into the mountain, he struck the only commercial mineral possibilities in the entire tunnel—gold, silver, copper, iron, and other ores—but he made no attempt to develop this discovery, probably by now imbued with the sole purpose of completing his tunnel. Ultimately he obtained an ore car, laid tracks to help remove the accumulated rock, pushed the car out by hand, dumped the ore, and then pushed the car back in again. The longer the tunnel grew, the longer the trip, until a round trip was nearly a mile. In the beginning he sometimes worked on vegetable farms in the summer to earn money for his tunnel work, but he finally sold some claims, obtaining enough capital to continue his mine work year round. His stupendous achievement was finished in 1938. It received a great deal of national publicity and was featured by Ripley in his "Believe It or Not" column.

The entrance to Burro Schmidt's tunnel. In 1906 he began a task here that would take the greater part of his lifetime—hand-digging a tunnel through a granite mountain. The only timbering in the entire tunnel is at the entrance and exit. *George F. Jackson*

At the exit of the tunnel, completed in 1938—high above the desert floor—a boy and his dog look into the dark interior with awe. *George F. Jackson*

Schmidt was eighty-three years old when he died in 1962, but his tunnel remains, and probably will for half a million years—if it is not blasted away.

The shack that served as Schmidt's home is a sort of museum, containing some of his clothing, his cookstove, and other materials. Mrs. Tony Seger, who now owns the property, permits visitors to walk through the tunnel at no charge, furnishes lanterns for the walk, and is extremely gracious about showing the cabin and its relics. Though the old railroad tracks now shine, polished by the shoes of visitors, the mine itself remains just as it was when it was finished. It can be reached by Last Chance Canyon from the Red Rock Randsburg Road, by Mesquite Canyon from the Garlock Road, or from Harts Place and California State Route 14, thirty-five miles north of Mojave.

ASHES OF WOOD

As early as 1911, rumblings of impending war brought action by Congress to ensure a domestic supply for needed materials. One of these was potassium, because potassium had been completely controlled by a German cartel, and United States production was virtually nonexistent.

In 1911, Congress provided funds to research domestic potassium sources and to develop processes for extraction. The need was so acute that by war's end nearly 130 plants were producing potassium compounds from sources including wood ashes, kelp, brines, beet-sugar waste, and others. Southeastern California's American Potash and Chemical Corporation in 1916 had recovered potassium salts and other chemicals from the brine of Searles Lake's salt mass. But with the armistice, abundant supplies again were available, and almost all domestic operations ceased.

Potash mine near Moab, Utah, begun in 1961 and opened in 1966. Modern structures of the aboveground facilities were designed to harmonize with the natural beauty of the red canyonlands along the picturesque Colorado River. *Texas Gulf Sulphur Company*

In 1924 a law was enacted "authorizing investigation by the United States Geological Survey to determine the location and extent of potash deposits in the United States." The survey team, together with the Bureau of Mines, drilled twenty-four holes in Texas, New Mexico, and Utah, while oil-well drillers were alerted to watch for the material. Many deposits were located between 1926 and 1931, and a National Potash Reserve was set up about fourteen miles northeast of Carlsbad, New Mexico.

Potassium mining is usually by room-and-pillar

Southwest Potash Corporation's modern equipment at its potash mine at Carlsbad, New Mexico. Between 1929 and 1940, United States Borax and Chemical Corporation, the Potash Company of America, International Minerals and Chemical Corporation, and the Union Potash Company provided all United States production. Others went into production in the 1950s:

Duval Corporation, the Southwest Potash Corporation, and the National Potash Company. And in 1964, the Kermac Potash Company, owned jointly by National Potash and the Kerr-McGee Oil Industries, Inc., developed a mine in Carlsbad. *American Metal Climax, Inc.*

Loader in the Cane Creek potash mine near Moab, Utah. *Texas Gulf Sulphur Company*

method, underground, and by pumping from brine reservoirs. Ninety-four percent of all potassium compounds are used by the agricultural industry, with the balance consumed by the chemical industry for manufacturing detergents, soaps, glass, ceramics, textiles, dyes, and drugs.

Before the development of potassium deposits, wood ashes were put in iron pots and boiled until the liquid evaporated, leaving a deposit, leached from the solution, called "pot ashes"—or potash. In general, it is used today to mean potassium or potassium compounds. The ore from which potassium is now extracted is sylvinite.

COLORADO STRIKES OF A NEW KIND

While new technologies were revolutionizing the metals industries, coal operators took a giant step backward. On September 23, 1913, 9,000 southern Colorado miners went on strike in the midst of a blizzard. In anticipation, the coal companies had brought in armed guards and strikebreakers from the East, and from Texas and New Mexico. Before long, violence broke out—five deputies machine-gunned a group of strikers at the Trinidad Mine in Forbes, wounding one fifteen-year-old boy and killing a miner.

Aboveground facilities of the Cane Creek mine. From the 179-foot headframe of the mine shaft (above), ore is conveyed to the mill for processing and stored in two warehouses, each with a capacity of 125,000 tons. View below is from the rail loading station. *Texas Gulf Sulphur Company*

311

At the miners' camp in Ludlow, following threats by guards, 1,200 miners and their families—comprised of foreigners and Americans—were protected by a few miners armed with rifles and shotguns. In an attempt to break up their meetings, the strikers were fired upon, picket lines attacked, strikers arrested, and union leaders physically removed from the state. The National Guard was sent in, but it was impossible to restore full order, and fighting continued for six months.

Thousands of workers were brought in from the East to become strikebreakers, although they had been assured that there was no strike. Many objected, but the militia would not permit them to leave, although hundreds escaped. By April, 1914, there were still three companies of militia protecting the mine-owners' interests.

On the day after their elaborate Easter celebration, the Ludlow miners' colony, almost entirely a tent city, was attacked by 400 fully armed guards, detectives, and strikebreakers armed with machine guns and explosive bullets. Women, children, and miners were attacked indiscriminately. Fighting continued all day, and another force of militiamen arrived late that afternoon, bringing two additional machine guns to supplement those that had been firing unceasingly into the tent colony. That evening, in the encroaching darkness, the tents were set on fire by the militiamen who continued to pour their deadly bullets into the fleeing refugees.

The next morning the *New York Times* carried the headline:

45 DEAD, 20 HURT, SCORES MISSING,
IN STRIKE WAR
Women and Children Roasted in Pits of Tent Colony
as Flames Destroy It

The *Times* reported that two thirds of the dead were women and children, and that the "Ludlow camp is a mass of charred debris, and buried beneath it is a story of horror, unparalleled in the history of industrial warfare. In the holes which had been dug for their protection from the rifles' fire, the women and children died like trapped rats when the flames swept over them. One pit, uncovered this afternoon, disclosed the bodies of ten children and two women."

The exact number of wounded will never be known, but more than 100 were treated. The battle continued the next day, and on April 24 a truce was declared, after five days of fighting that destroyed more than $1 million of property and resulted in over sixty deaths. Spasmodic fighting continued for another five days until federal troops arrived to end the strife. It did not end the strike, however, which continued until the fall, a more than fifteen-month struggle that ended with the workers forced to accept a company union.

Soon after, John D. Rockefeller, Jr., a director of the Colorado Fuel and Iron Company, was questioned by the House Committee on Mines and Mining that inquired into the Colorado coal strike. He was firm on his insistence that miners should have the right to work wherever they pleased, and opposed recognition of any union other than a company union, while demanding an open shop. The company union remained in existence until 1933, when the United Mine Workers was finally recognized. The National Recovery Act helped to eliminate the wars and riots that formerly accompanied almost all major strikes.

THE RADIOACTIVE ELEMENTS

Contrary to popular conception, the search for uranium-radium sources occurred long before the development of the atomic bomb. (Radium is a natural product derived from the radioactive decay of uranium 238 and has had application in X-ray and other medical uses, especially cancer therapy. Actually, over 150 uranium minerals have been identified.) Carnotite, which, together with pitchblende and coffinite, is uranium's chief source, was known to exist in quantity in southwestern Colorado and southeastern Utah; Colorado became a major uranium (named for the planet Uranus) ore producer about 1911, exporting carnotite to France a year later. However, the first mining of uranium minerals could have been at the Ruggles Mine in Grafton, New Hampshire, where small amounts of uranium minerals, gummite and autunite, were found in 1803 or 1804. But this was never followed up. Pitchblende's properties remained unknown until Henri Becquerel discovered radioactivity in uranium salts. Two years later, G. C. Schmidt and Madame Curie found similar properties in thorium and discovered the highly radioactive elements polonium and radium. Soon other radioactive elements were isolated, and the theory of radioactive disintegration was propounded in 1902. From 1914 to 1916, with the cooperation of the United States Bureau of Mines and the National Radium Institute, a plant was built in Denver to recover radium, but with the discovery of rich deposits around 1923 in the Belgian Congo, the domestic industry almost vanished. In 1930, pitchblende, originally discovered in 1789 by Klaproth, the German chemist, was found at Great Bear Lake in Canada. At the time, uranium had few uses beyond being a coloring agent in ceramics and glass products, and it was used in photography.

In 1939, with the approach of war in Europe, German scientists Otto Hahn and Fritz Strassman split the uranium atom, while shortly thereafter, United States laboratories duplicated the experiment. Scientists immediately were alerted to the fact that tremendous amounts of energy could be released in a chain reaction and, if sufficient ore could be obtained, that uranium could easily supply the world demand for energy to replace gas, oil, and coal should those sources become exhausted.

On August 2, 1939, Albert Einstein proposed to President Roosevelt the possibility of an atomic bomb, and a full-scale research program began. On December 2, 1942, Enrico Fermi created a self-sustaining chain reaction, initiating the "atomic age." Fortunately, about 1,200 tons of pitchblende ore had been imported from the Belgian Congo in 1939 and 1940, which, combined with additional ore flown in from the Eldorado Mine and the ore that was produced as a by-product of vanadium (at Naturita, Colorado), supplied the material for the Manhattan Project.

URANIUM FROM VANADIUM—AND VICE VERSA

Vanadium, from which we get a steel-white metal, was extensively mined on the Colorado Plateau during World War I and in the year following, but during World War II, the vanadium-mining companies, working closely with the Manhattan Project, redesigned their plants to permit extraction of uranium. Conversely, vanadium today is not mined but recovered as a by-product of uranium mining.

In 1946, only about fifteen Colorado mines produced any uranium, and total production was negligible. Two years later the Atomic Energy Commission instituted a program that provided for a guaranteed minimum price for all domestic ore, a bonus for discovery and production, a mine-development allowance, premiums for higher-than-average grade ore, and allowances for haulage. The results were beyond expectation—huge deposits were rapidly uncovered on the Colorado Plateau and in Wyoming. A "uranium rush" brought varied prospectors to the Plateau—ranchers, oilmen, laborers, storekeepers, businessmen, clerks, professional geologists, and adventurers all rushed in, sure of finding uranium. Most failed, but some struck it rich. They traveled by foot, jeep, truck, and airplane, as well as by mule, burro, and horse, not unlike the old-time prospectors. But their principal tool was the Geiger counter, which picked up signals from uranium-ore rays. By 1954, 900 western mines were producing uranium ore. Their discoveries enabled the building

of power reactors to produce energy for peaceful uses, and by the early 1960s production surpassed requirements for both military and peacetime use. At times, as many as 1,000 mines were producing. In 1963, only 730 mines, operating in fourteen states, produced nearly 6 million tons. However, many of the mines were small and produced only a few tons; fewer than 100 produced over 12,000 tons a year, fewer still over 200,000 tons.

The Geiger counter plays an important part in uranium discovery. Despite the success of the initial uranium search program, the hunt for mineral deposits continues. The major difference is that individual prospectors rarely do the hunting. Instead the larger successful companies are continuing the explorations. And Colorado is no longer the leading uranium producer, taking third place after Wyoming and New Mexico, followed by Utah, South Dakota, and Texas. A few of the important companies that mine or mill uranium are the Federal Resources Corporation, American Nuclear Corporation, Federal-American Partners, Kerr-McGee Corporation, Utah Construction and Mining Company, Anaconda Corporation, United Nuclear Corporation, American Metal Climax, Susquehanna Corporation, Union Carbide Company, Western Nuclear Corporation, and Homestake-Sapin Partners, whose new mill can process 3,000 tons of uranium daily. A number of oil and gas companies are also involved in the uranium industry, including Gulf Oil Company, Continental Oil Company, Humble Oil and Refining Company, Getty Oil Company, and Atlantic-Richfield. Headquarters of many uranium mining companies are located at Grand Junction, Colorado, which, because of the Atomic Energy Commission's Operations Office, became the nerve center of uranium operations. Grand Junction is halfway between Denver and Salt Lake City, and at one time was among the largest peach-growing centers in the country. Estimated reserves of domestic uranium are very large; the United States is surpassed in its uranium resources only by Canada, while together they hold nearly 60 percent of the world's uranium supply.
Union Carbide Corporation

The horizontal formations of sandstone on the walls of the mesas are likely spots for uranium discoveries. The sandstone was laid down ages ago by vast inland seas. *Union Carbide Corporation*

The search for uranium deposits is more complicated than generally realized. The Geiger counter may be a most useful tool in its detection of electric-current pulsations produced by radioactivity, but satisfactory application requires a proper knowledge of how to read the result; every radioactive pulse does not necessarily indicate the presence of uranium. Use varies from tests of individual specimens to systematic radiometric ground (and sometimes air) surveys. There are also chemical methods for finding uranium deposits, but ultimately, because some deposits lie deep underground, exploratory mining or drilling is required. At Ambrosia Lake, New Mexico, for example, ores are found anywhere from 300 feet to 1,500 feet down.

Claims are staked like any other valuable metal. Land is surveyed and corner posts locate claim boundaries. Claims cannot exceed an area of 600 feet by 1,500 feet, and a notice must be posted along the center line announcing the discoverer's rights to the minerals within the stakeout. Drilling is then necessary to determine whether there is sufficient ore to warrant mining. Once it has been determined that

Ore is stored in bins like this one until it is hauled to the processing mill. Processing uranium ore is highly technical, involving a mill-concentrating method of hydrometallurgical leaching. The ore is dumped into receiving bins, and crushed and screened into small pieces. Chemical reagents, such as salt and acid, separate the mineral from the other solids. Settling tanks are carefully combed for any metal that remains after the leaching process. The end product is a solution of uranium compounds that runs into long filter presses where the liquid is squeezed out, leaving a material of clay-like consistency called "yellow cake." This is dried and packed in drums for delivery to the Atomic Energy Commission. *Union Carbide Corporation*

The large companies dominate the field either by developing their own mines and mills or by buying up hundreds of claims or purchasing the entire outputs of small mines. This photograph is of Union Carbide's Uravan mill operations in the San Miguel valley (Colorado). The company operates nearly fifty mines in this state alone, and has extensive workings in Wyoming as well as three mines in Utah. The name Uravan is derived from uranium-vanadium. Originally the United States Vanadium Company produced vanadium here. Now Union Carbide operates the mill to serve its mines. Uravan is largely a company town, and all community property buildings except the school are owned by Union Carbide. New and attractive homes abound, a far cry from the old company-owned towns of the 1800s and early 1900s. *Union Carbide Corporation*

mining is a worthwhile project, it is necessary to drill or blast through the waste rock to get to the ore. If the ore is deep, the standard mining procedures of stoping, room-and-pillar mining, or other techniques are employed, depending upon the size and direction of the ore bodies. In small mines, the old pick and shovel come in handy, but air compressors, jackhammers, and jackleg drills are preferred. In large mines, giant drills or diesel-powered loading and hauling machines are employed. If the ore is sufficiently close to the surface, electric shovels can strip the overburden and remove the ore by open-cut methods.

From the mines, the ore is carried by trucks to buying stations or to nearby processing mills. More than twenty-five such mills are in operation on the Colorado Plateau.

Of course, there are health problems. Radioactive gas (radon, derived from the disintegration of the radium) is a major hazard. Inhaled and retained small particles found in dust also can be dangerous. Federal agencies require thorough mechanical ventilation to reduce radon atmospheric concentrations to a safe level.

Apart from its obvious military uses, uranium is invaluable for the production of radioisotopes, used in medicine, agriculture, industry, and research. Radioisotopes are radioactive and must be handled by remote control. Ingenious equipment can select isotopes from storage racks, move bottles, uncap them, and measure out exact amounts into shipping bottles that are then sealed. Radioisotopes in minute quantities are injected into living matter, leaving a radiation trail to reveal their paths. Radioactivity often is used to irradiate other metals, such as cobalt, cesium, and gold, for use in attacking cancerous tissue. Iodine is radioactivated for diagnosing thyroid conditions. In industry, radioisotopes are used to measure thicknesses and monitor the manufacture of such products as paper, metals, plastics, rubber, and textiles. Radioactivity is also used in food preservation and in the investigation of plant growth, nutrition, and plant-breeding experiments.

Anaconda Company's famous Jackpile Mine, located on Laguna Indian Reservation and recognized as the largest open-pit uranium mine in the world. Anaconda operates a mine at Haystack Mesa, fifteen miles northwest of Grants, New Mexico, on land belonging to the Atchison, Topeka and Santa Fe Railway. The company built the Bluewater Mill to process the ores from Haystack Mesa and from a substantial deposit of uranium ore on the Laguna Indian Reservation, about thirty-five miles east of Grants. Here are the Jackpile and Paguate pits, two large open-pit uranium mines that employ mostly Indians. *Chamber of Commerce, Grants, New Mexico*

The Day Loma open-pit uranium mine of Western Nuclear, Inc., in the Gas Hills area of central Wyoming. This photo, taken in 1964, is a striking example of uranium pit mining. Western Nuclear, Inc., was founded in March, 1955. For approximately two years no mining or milling operations were carried out, but some unexplored property was acquired and investigated. In 1956 the company received a contract from the Atomic Energy Commission to construct a plant for processing uranium ore and for purchasing about three million pounds of uranium oxide. From this beginning Western has become an important factor in the uranium business, operating mills and mines. *Western Nuclear, Inc.*

Pushing a car full of waste from a uranium mine near Monogram, Colorado. *Standard Oil Company*

Aerial view of Section 30 mine headframe, one of Kerr-McGee's five underground shaft mines in the Ambrosia Lake area of New Mexico. These shafts, 8 feet by 18 feet, are sunk to the ore-bearing formations at depths of approximately 800 feet. From the shafts, drifts and stopes are developed to reach the ore bodies. The uranium ore is processed at their mill, one of the nation's largest uranium production units. *Kerr-McGee Corporation*

Uranium mine and camp on south slope of Paradox Valley, near Naturita, Colorado. The valley is seen in upper center. *Standard Oil Company*

MAGNESIUM—THE OLD-NEW METAL

War had created a demand also for magnesium. Production of magnesia from dolomite (a calcium magnesium carbonate, which includes much of the common white marble) began in Pennsylvania in 1913, but when foreign sources of necessary magnesia were cut off during World War I, a search was made for domestic sources. By 1917 magnesite deposits were being mined in California and Washington, and in 1929 magnesium began to be recovered from brucite in Nevada. But in the last ten years production here has ceased. Magnesite, as well as olivine (chrysolite), is mined by standard open-pit methods. The world's first quantity, very small, was obtained in 1808 by Sir Humphry Davy, an English chemist and physicist also responsible for isolating potassium, sodium, calcium, barium, boron, and strontium. A. A. B. Bussy prepared magnesite in larger amounts in 1831.

In general, magnesium refers to magnesium metal, and magnesium compounds refer to a host of chemical minerals. Most magnesium compounds, of which magnesia is the principal product, are obtained from magnesite, usually combined with dolomite. Magnesium metal, however, is extracted by electrolytic processes from seawater and brines, and from thermal reduction of dolomite and its associated deposits such as brucite, olivine, cornallite, and others.

In the mid-1950s, the development of the electrolytic method of recovery from brine waters was expanded, and this is now an important source of magnesium. About 80 percent of magnesium metal is used in the aircraft and space industry for jet engines and guided missiles, as well as for automotive and transportation equipment, and as a reducing agent for titanium, zirconium, uranium, and other metals. Magnesium compounds are widely used in commercial products.

After World War I, came a period of industrial development that seemed to be confined to expanding existing workings and developing more modern methods rather than searching for new bonanzas. Veteran prospectors, however, still live in hope of finding a bonanza, and a few small operators still searched for gold and other valuable metals, many using the old, proven methods, regardless of the problems.

Many old uranium mines are now used for the questionable purpose of permitting arthritic victims to sit in them and receive the "benefits" of radiation. *Western Ways Photo*

Huge settling tanks in which magnesium hydroxide is precipitated from sea water. Currently magnesium is produced in many states, principally Washington, North Carolina, New Jersey, Mississippi, Alabama, California, Florida, Texas, Michigan, and Illinois. Several other states produce minor amounts. *Dow Chemical Company*

This bank of electrolytic cells reduces magnesium chloride to primary magnesium and chlorine gas. *Dow Chemical Company*

Molten magnesium transported from the electrolytic cells flows from this trough into an ingot-casting machine. *Dow Chemical Company*

HIGH-ELEVATION PROSPECTING

Often gold-yielding land was not only highly inaccessible but found at great elevations, creating weather conditions as bad as Alaska's. Prime examples are the old-time rich hillside placer mines near the top of the Pennsylvania Mountain in Colorado, at elevations ranging from 11,000 to 14,000 feet above sea level. At such elevations, the land is perpetually frozen, a permafrost zone, where only minor thawing at the surface of the ground occurs during the summer. Attempts at mining at these elevations are similar to small-scale attacks on Mount Everest, requiring base camps and logistic support.

In 1938, H. W. C. Prommel and a group of thirteen men leased property on Pennsylvania Mountain for sampling, with the hope of possibly opening large-scale operations. At an elevation of 12,250 feet, the party came upon an old wind- and storm-blown shack built by an ambitious early timer. Prommel's party used this shack as a base, adding a bunkhouse, office, kitchen, and dining room.

To get supplies to the mountaintop, an auto trailer was transformed into a two-wheel horsecart, which laboriously hauled up building supplies for the bunkhouse, including wire, powder, winter clothes for the men, and other necessary materials.

Sampling pits had to be dug deep into the permafrost and protected from the weather, since the snow would fill them up at night. Each pit was covered with a tent for protection from the wind that would blow in snow, ice, and dirt, creating hazardous and extremely uncomfortable conditions for those working in the pits.

Finally, after two seasons, because of the difficult and costly working conditions, the project was abandoned.

The old cabin on Combination Placer found by H. W. C. Prommel and his associates in 1938, which was used as the party's headquarters. A large nugget was found in the open cut to the left of the cabin. Mosquito Gulch, 1,250 feet deep, separates the mountains in the right background from Pennsylvania Mountain in the foreground. The cabin is at an elevation of 12,250 feet. *H. W. C. Prommel*

Prommel's auto trailer transformed into a two-wheel horse cart to transport loads from Halfway Camp to the mining site. *H. W. C. Prommel*

Pit Number 9, 28½ feet deep, photographed in an October, 1938, blizzard. From 50 to 100 buckets of water had to be hoisted out of this pit every morning before the men could get down. *H. W. C. Prommel*

On October 12, 1938, during the height of the blizzard, the temperature was five degrees above zero. The supply sent on the right was formerly occupied by Prommel and part of the crew, and a snowdrift is covering it up. The tent on the left was occupied by four men, and the bulging of the tents is caused by the strong winds and the drifting snow. *H. W. C. Prommel*

PERLITE

At about the time Prommel's party was prospecting in high altitudes, Lee Boyer was operating an assay office in Superior, Arizona, experimenting with an old furnace in the hope of finding a new insulating material. By chance, he tossed some perlite, a lava material he had found on nearby Picket Post Mountain, into the furnace. To his amazement, the heated perlite started to pop and expand like popcorn. His superficial examination led him to believe that perlite might prove to be a lightweight, heat-resistant material. Analysis by the Arizona Department of Mineral Resources confirmed Boyer's hope and showed that the perlite contained up to 5 percent water sealed in its pores. When heated, the expanding steam caused the explosive popping. Perlite also turned out to be fireproof, as well as lightweight, and of excellent insulating quality.

Boyer set up an experimental plant, mixing the perlite with gypsum. It was the first of a number of major commercial operations starting in 1946 near Superior, Arizona, and Beatty, Nevada.

Perlite in its natural state is extremely sharp, and capable of cutting shoes or boots to pieces. Now widely used in combination with gypsum, it is usually crushed and screened at the open-pit mines from which it is taken. Although nearly 300,000 tons are mined in the United States annually, it remains known mostly to industry, where it is widely used as a retardant in the conduction of heat and sound and as an aggregate in concrete, and, of course, building plaster. These uses, and those of the construction industry, account for about 60 percent of the perlite consumption. It is also employed as a filter aid for the petroleum industry. Its principal advantage, in addition to its thermal retardation properties, is its light weight, an important factor in the construction industry.

Perlite mine, North Agua, New Mexico. *Johns-Manville Corporation*

BAUXITE

Anyone who has ever dug in a garden has handled bauxite, one of the commonest of minerals and the principal source of aluminum. Most bauxite is mined by the open-pit method. The first bauxite was mined in this country in 1941 by the Reynolds Mining Corporation in Arkansas, whose rich deposits account for over half the United States production. Bauxite occurs widely and comprises about 15 percent of the earth's surface. From bauxite we get alumina, from which aluminum is made. Nobody mines aluminum, since it does not occur free in nature. It is a constituent of many minerals, including clay, mica, feldspar, and others.

Aluminum compounds had been widely used abroad for many years preceding the discovery in 1886 of a method of manufacture. C. M. Hall, an Oberlin College student, received the credit. Simultaneously, Paul Heroult, a French metallurgist, made the same discovery. The name bauxite derives from his laboratory at Baux.

The largest walking dragline ever built for bauxite mining takes 25-cubic-yard bites of Arkansas earth at the Reynolds Mining Corporation mines near the town of Bauxite. The 1,600-ton dragline towers 17 stories high, and dwarfs the regular pickup truck alongside. The four major companies in the business are integrated —all the way from mining through the production of semifabricated aluminum. Two of them, the Aluminum Company of America and Reynolds, process domestic and foreign bauxite; others import their bauxite, either from their own foreign mines or by foreign purchase. *Reynolds Metals Company*

OIL FROM ROCKS

In 1945 the Bureau of Mines and the United States Department of Interior built the Anvil Points Oil Shale Research Center, near Rifle, Colorado, which for about eleven years operated as an experimental research center. The research program concentrates on gas-combustion retorting, a method of extracting the oil from the shale under extreme heat. Possibilities exist of recovering a trillion barrels of oil from 1,600 square miles of oil shale.

Oil shale had been known as an energy source long before the white man arrived. The Colorado Indians used the "burning rock" for fires, and even the gold miners of the mid-1800s chipped off chunks of shale to use for heating and cooking. The material is actually a sedimentary rock called marlstone, and a three-and-one-half-inch cube yields about six ounces of oil. It is found mainly in Colorado, but other deposits exist in Utah and Wyoming.

Cottonwood Point—Bureau of Mines Oil Shale Demonstration Plant, Garfield County, Rifle, Colorado, 1945. *Bureau of Mines*

Anvil Points Oil Shale Research Center on the western slope of the Rocky Mountains, about seven miles west of Rifle, Colorado. Shale formations are visible near the tops of the mountains in the background. *Colorado School of Mines Research Foundation, Inc.*

This rig is used in room-and-pillar mining at Anvil Points. The odd overhead configurations are plates used to strengthen the roof. *Colorado School of Mines Research Foundation, Inc.*

Drilling bed No. 30 on Allen Point, at the Bureau of Mines Oil Shale Demonstration Plant, Garfield County, Rifle, Colorado, 1945. *Bureau of Mines*

THE ROCK THAT WILL NOT BURN

Prior to 1963, the only large asbestos production in the United States came from Vermont deposits, actually extensions of deposits in Canada. The United States, which consumes about one quarter of the world's production, produces only about 2 percent. In 1963, California began production that now equals Vermont's. Some small mines operate in Arizona, and Montana and Wyoming have deposits, too, but production is minimal. After Canada, Russia has the most important deposits.

Asbestos, a naturally fibrous material, is found

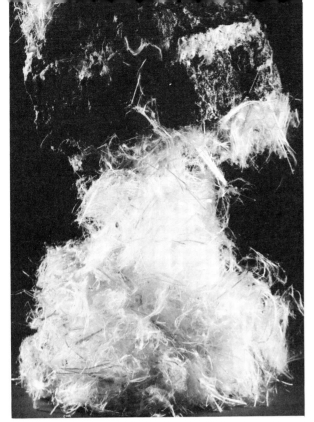

Fine, silky fibers of asbestos, drawn from crushed ore. They are often as strong as steel wire, and will not burn. *Johns-Manville Corporation*

in veins called chrysotile. Its fibers are separated from rock that is mined by open-air or an underground method, known as block caving. This consists of undermining a large block of ore in such a way that the entire block breaks down from its own weight. These blocks are about 200 feet square and extend about 400 feet; each block weighs about 1.5 million tons.

Through this ore body, shafts are sunk and tunnels are extended. Crosscut tunnels are then driven at 220-foot intervals—with drifts called slusher drifts extending from these. From the slusher drifts, draw points (funnel-like openings) are excavated upward to extract the ore, each 12.5 tons good for about two tons of asbestos fibers, the remainder being waste rock.

The asbestos is graded according to fiber length—the longer the better. Long-fiber asbestos is used for making cloth, clutch facing, safety clothing, and so on. Short-fiber asbestos is used for roofing shingles, magnesia block, pipe insulation, and asbestos paper, among other applications. The largest asbestos company in the United States is Johns-Manville Corporation.

Actually, asbestos' virtues were known to Plutarch when he referred to the "perpetual" lamp-wicks of the Vestal Virgins, and shrouds of woven asbestos appear to have been used in ancient times for cremations. In Greek, asbestos means "unquenched."

Asbestos mining (and all its stages of processing and packaging) presents a serious health problem. Extensive filtering and ventilation is only one solution, but the occupational exposure to asbestos continues to cause *pulmonary asbestosis* and *neoplasia,* and the development of cancer.

GOLD FROM DIRT

America's newest and possibly greatest gold strike is the Carlin Gold Mine in Nevada. Here there are no deep shafts or underground tunnels; nor is there any visible gold in strata of rock because Carlin gold is invisible except under a microscope.

The federal government through the United States Geological Survey, constantly on the search for new sources for such metals as gold and uranium, had reported an unusual fault structure in Nevada which prompted the Newmont Mining Corporation of New York to investigate. The fault had a lower layer of rock exposed by the erosion of the upper layers, and the survey team, believing that the lower layer might contain some minerals, had suggested as much in their 1960 report of the region.

Newmont sent their geologists to the site in the Tuscarora Mountains, and tests showed some evidences of gold. Newmont filed claims for six miles of mining rights and began testing in earnest in 1962. The tests revealed that the rock contained minute flecks of gold, invisible to the naked eye, even if examined under a magnifying glass. But microscopic analysis proved that the rock was saturated with infinitesimally small gold morsels.

Now the new Carlin Mine, twenty miles northwest of the little town of Carlin, is a beehive of activity. Here gold is mined in open pits and processed by unique space-age technology, making it possible to extract the gold profitably, despite the fixed $35-an-ounce price.

Newmont's first task in developing its claims was to remove millions of tons of overburden from the gold-bearing rock and to provide an adequate water supply, accomplished by drilling wells. This work was started in 1962, as well as construction of a vast extraction plant. By May, 1965, the mill produced its first gold brick. The pit, similar to the vast pits of open copper mining, is served by power shovels that bite out ten-ton chunks of blasted rock, which are loaded on trucks capable of carrying up to sixty-five tons. The ore is rushed to the crushers and grinders where it is pulverized into fine grains, soaked, filtered, and dissolved with cyanide, a process developed in 1887 in Scotland. The mud-thick

A photo of Carlin's open-pit mine. Although in operation for only a few years, the pit is a mile and a half long and several hundred feet deep. *Carlin Gold Mining Company*

solution is continually analyzed by gamma rays and assayed by an atomic process. After the sludgy solution has been placed in settling tanks, it passes through clarifiers and is mixed with zinc dust, which causes the gold to fall out of the solution. The sludge is then passed through filters into a furnace, which produces pieces of slag containing buttons of gold. These are further refined to increase the purity of the metal.

In a short space of time, Carlin has become the second largest gold mine in the United States, second to Homestake in South Dakota.

Open pit and streamlined plant (cyanide vats are shown in center) of the Carlin Gold Mining.Company, Eureka County, Nevada. This wholly owned subsidiary of the Newmont Mining Corporation was opened in May, 1966, following an investment of $10,000,000. It is now the second largest gold producer in the United States. Discovery of the ore body resulted from a geologic study made under a cooperative program between the United States Geological Survey and the Nevada Bureau of Mines. Profitable recovery of the low-grade ore (.32 ounce per ton) is possible today because of massive modern machinery and improved technology. *Mackay School of Mines, University of Nevada*

THE 1968 OIL BOOM

Nineteen sixty-eight marked one of the most remarkable oil finds in northern Alaska where the Atlantic-Richfield Company and the Humble Oil and Refining Company jointly struck oil near Prudhoe Bay, about 150 miles southeast of Point Barrow. The oilfield has been described as one of the largest petroleum accumulations in the world, and its reserves have already been estimated at between 100 and 300 billion barrels of oil, more than the oil reserves in all of North America.

The discovery touched off a rush by all oil companies to find other deposits in Alaska. Phillips Petroleum and Mobil Oil Corporation hold acreage in the area, and the British Petroleum Corporation has about 100,000 acres. Sinclair Oil, Shell Oil, Texaco, Standard Oil of Indiana, Union Oil of California, and Gulf Oil Company all have acquired holdings, and are rapidly developing wells.

WORLD'S GREATEST AUCTION SALE

In September, 1969, the State of Alaska received a bonus of over $900 million from an auction sale of oil land leases on the North Slope of Prudhoe Bay. If ever there was a bonanza in the mining business, it must be this sale of 179 oil leases that brought in nearly a billion dollars. Most of the world's largest oil companies were bidding, and one bid for 2,560 acres was ten times the $7.2 million the United States paid to Russia for the entire territory of Alaska.

Shipping from Alaska is difficult, and the severe winters make operations hazardous. Tank shipments move along the West Coast when arctic navigation is open, about eight weeks a year, and plans are afoot

Helicopters, under varying situations, provide vital transportation to remote locations. The unit above has helped extend the search for petroleum far into the rugged wilderness of Alaska. *Humble Oil and Refining Company*

to develop new-style icebreakers. At about the time of the auction, the *S.S. Manhattan,* rebuilt by Humble Oil at a cost of millions of dollars, began its trip to forge a northwest passage through the ice to the oil fields, and some weeks later successfully reached its destination. Opening this waterway will enable oil to be brought to eastern American ports at costs somewhat comparable to other eastern deliveries.

Two pipelines are contemplated, one running 600 miles across the Brooks Mountain Range and another 1,700 miles from Prudhoe Bay to the McKenzie River, across the Northwest Territory and Alberta, Canada, and then connecting to the Canadian oil pipelines stretching about 1,600 miles to the Great Lakes for a grand total length of about 3,250 miles.

While Anchorage is far from the oilfields, it is the nearest jumping-off point and has again become a boom town, which may yet far surpass the Alaskan mining camps of the 1890s. Several airlines supply service, bringing in men from all over the world to work the fields.

THE FUTURE

The romantic era of mining, has it really ended? Have those fabulous days of the Forty-Niners, of Cripple Creek and the Comstock Lode, gone forever? Have most of the world's important mineral deposits already been discovered or could we be on the threshold of new finds, more exciting, more fantastic than any prospector could have even imagined in the early days of mining? Though negative answers might sadden the hearts of old-timers, they certainly would raise the eyebrows of modern businessmen, for new discoveries occur almost daily, and prospecting for the riches of our earth goes on and on. Who would have thought, for example, that the Carlin Gold Mines, unheard of less than eight years ago, would so quickly become America's second largest producer? Who would have believed that in Alaska more oil reserves could have been found in one or two years than previously existed in the entire continental United States? What about the advances in oceanography, a comparatively new science dealing with more than seven-eighths of the earth's surface, all under water, that may open the door to new metallurgical possibilities? Will it become possible to extract more minerals and elements from the oceans themselves, where one puny, insignificant cubic mile contains, in suspension, more gold than mankind has recovered in the entire history of mining?

Today, nothing seems impossible or even improbable. Only 250,000 miles away is the moon, where meteorites very likely have deposited millions of tons of prized minerals. The first sixty pounds of rock brought back by our astronauts cost more than a third of a billion dollars a pound. Most likely man will be recovering minerals and metals from the sea long before he can economically mine on the moon. In fact, the scientists studying these moon rocks have concluded that they contain a lot of silicon, a mineral in which our earth is hardly deficient. Surprisingly, early studies of the moon rock material revealed that the rocks contain unusually large percentages of elements that melt at extremely

The Apollo 11's approach to the moon's surface reveals the relatively smooth area of the landing site at the top center of the moonscape. Later exploration of more mountainous terrain may reveal greater concentrations of metallic elements. *National Aeronautics and Space Administration*

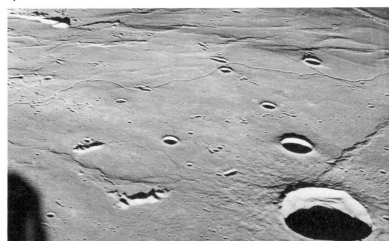

The surface of the moon in the vicinity of where the lunar module Eagle touched down. The photo was taken from the right-hand window of the LM. *National Aeronautics and Space Administration*

Photograph taken by Astronaut Neil A. Armstrong of Astronaut Edwin E. Aldrin, Jr., near the LM. Aldrin was inspecting the site to determine what rocks and moon material might be taken to earth for study and analysis. *National Aeronautics and Space Administration*

high temperatures. These elements are sparsely found in earth rocks and consist of zirconium, strontium, barium, yttrium, and titanium. Titanium in particular, was found in greater percentages than the richest such ores on earth, and the ratio of uranium to potassium in the lunar material was four times greater than typical earth samples. Whether these analyses are peculiar only to the material found thus far or are typical of all lunar material, awaits the findings from other moon trips. However, had spacemen from another world landed on the Sahara desert, apparently a likely landing place as seen from space, they would have been sadly misled about the earth's minerals. Our astronauts have yet to reach hilly or mountainous areas of the moon, whose upheavals might reveal fabulous metal deposits.

Questions abound. Are there materials existing on the moon not found on the earth? In another century, another age, could they have economic capabilities? Or, if useful minerals are found on the moon, would lack of gravity make it feasible to mine more economically than on earth? And, looking ahead to still another century, two hundred or three hundred years from now, might the rich bonanzas of the future turn up on Mars or Venus? The search seems only to have just begun.

OTHER SIGNIFICANT HISTORICAL EVENTS

Into the Space Age

1960s: Silver Peak, Nevada, became an important lithium producing area. Foote Mineral Company, American Potash and Chemical Corporation, Lithium Corporation of America produce and process most United States lithium.

1964: Together with the Colorado School of Mines Research Foundation, Socony Mobil Oil, Humble Oil and Refining, Sinclair Research Inc., Phillips Petroleum, Pan-American Petroleum, and Continental Oil are all developers of oil-shale processing technology.

Astronaut Aldrin, photographed by Astronaut Armstrong as Aldrin completes deploying the seismic-experiments package. Previously the laser retroreflector had been placed in position, and a contingency supply of "moon dirt" had been gathered. Additional rock samples were collected following this photograph. *National Aeronautics and Space Administration*

324

Bibliography

Adney, Tappan, *The Klondike Stampede,* New York, 1899.

Ajo Chamber of Commerce (miscellaneous pamphlets), Ajo, Ariz., 1952.

Alinsky, Saul, *John L. Lewis,* Putnam's Sons, New York, 1949.

Allen, W. W., and R. B. Avery, *California Gold Book,* Donohue and Henneberry, San Francisco, 1893.

Amax Journal, Vol. 6, No. 1, American Metal Climax, Inc., 1968.

Angel, Myran, *History of Nevada,* Thompson and West (1881).

Annals of Iowa, April, 1896; April, 1902; October, 1912; April, 1936; Historical Memorial and Art Department of Iowa.

Annual Report of the Smithsonian Institution for year ending June 30, 1903.

Appel, Benjamin, *We Were There in the Klondike Gold Rush,* Grosset and Dunlap, New York, 1956.

Arizona, Museum of Northern, *Museum Notes,* Vol. 7, No. 10, April, 1935.

Arizona Mining Association, various publications.

Asbestos the Magic Mineral, Johns-Manville Corp., 1958.

Averill, Harry B., and John M. Henderson and William S. Shiach, *An Illustrated History of North Idaho,* 1903.

Baker, James H., and LeRoy R. Hafen, *History of Colorado,* 5 vols., Denver, 1927.

Bancroft, Caroline, *Gulch of Gold, A History of Central City, Colorado,* Sage Books, Denver, Col., 1958.

————, *Silver Queen, The Fabulous Story of Baby Doe Tabor,* Johnson Publishing Company, Boulder, Col., 1950, 1955.

————, *Tabor's Matchless Mine and Lusty Leadville,* Johnson Publishing Company, Boulder, Col., 1953, 1960.

————, *The Unsinkable Mrs. Brown,* Johnson Publishing Company, Boulder, Col., 1963.

Bancroft, Hubert H., *History of Nevada, Colorado, and Wyoming, 1540–1888,* San Francisco, 1890.

Bartlett, Katharine, "Prehistoric Mining in the Southwest," from *Museum Notes,* Museum of Northern Arizona, Northern Arizona Society of Science and Art, Inc., April, 1935.

Bayley, William S., *Iron Mines and Mining in New Jersey,* Geological Survey of New Jersey, Vol. 7, 1910.

Beal, Merrill D., and Merle W. Wells, *History of Idaho,* 3 vols., Lewis Historical Publishing Co., Inc., New York, 1959.

Berton, Pierre, *The Klondike Fever,* Alfred A. Knopf, New York, 1958.

Bimba, Anthony, *The Molly Maguires,* New York, 1931.

Bining, Arthur Cecil, *Pennsylvania Iron Manufacture in the Eighteenth Century,* Pennsylvania Historical Commission, Vol. IV, 1938.

Birdsey, Alfred E., County Treasurer, Mineral County, Creede, Colorado, personal correspondence, 1968.

Bohakel, Charles A., *A History of the Empire Mine at Grass Valley,* Nevada County Historical Society, Nevada City, Calif. (n.d.).

Boucher, Jack E., *Of Batsto and Bog Iron,* The Batsto Citizen Advisory Committee, 1964.

Broehl, Wayne G., Jr., *The Molly Maguires,* Harvard University Press, Cambridge, Mass., 1964.

Brown, E. J. Ross, "A Peep at Washoe," from *Crusoe's Island, California and Washoe,* Harper & Brothers, New York, 1864.

————, "Washoe Revisited," from *The Apache Country: A Tour through Arizona and Sonora,* Harper & Brothers, New York, 1869.

Browne, J. Ross, *Illustrated Mining Adventures: California and Nevada, 1863–1865,* Horace Parker, ed., Balboa Island, Calif., 1961.

Bryson, Herman J., *Gold Deposits of North Carolina,* North Carolina Department of Conservation and Development, Bulletin No. 38, 1936.

The Bunker Hill Company, booklet published by Bunker Hill Company, Kellogg, Idaho.

California's Historical Monuments, Pacific Gas and Electric Company (n.d.).

Caugaty, John W., *Gold Is the Cornerstone,* Berkeley, University of California Press, 1948.

Celite, The Story of Diatomite, Johns-Manville Corp., 1964.

Chapman, Thomas G., *Treating Gold Ores,* University of Arizona Bulletin: Arizona Bureau of Mines, Metallurgical Series No. 4, Bulletin #138, Tucson, Ariz., 1935.

Clark, Badger, *Custer State Park, Black Hills of South Dakota,* pamphlet published by South Dakota Game, Fish and Parks Commission.

Cleland, Robert Glass, *A History of Phelps Dodge 1834–1950,* Alfred A. Knopf, New York, 1952.

Coeur d'Alene Mining District in 1963, The (pamphlet 133), Idaho Bureau of Mines and Geology.

Coleman, J. Walter, *The Molly Maguire Riots,* Richmond, Va., 1936.

Collier, William R., and Edwin V. Westrate, *The Reign of Soapy Smith,* Doubleday & Co., Garden City, 1935.

"Comstock Lode," *The Overland Monthly,* Vol. 10, No. 6, June, 1873.

Cooper, Ray H., "Early History of San Juan County," *Colorado Magazine,* Vol. XXII, 1945.

Copper Camp, Montana Writers' Program, Hastings House, New York, 1944.

Corlsen, Carl, *Buried Black Treasure, The Story of Pennsylvania Anthracite,* published by the author, Hazleton, Pa., 1954 (out of print).

Coulter, E. Merton, *Auraria,* University of Georgia Press, Athens, 1956.

Cruts, E. K. (Red), *Mining in the State of New Jersey* (n.d.).

De Quille, Dan (William Wright), *The Big Bonanza,* American Publishing Company, Hartford, Conn., 1877.

———, *A History of the Comstock Silver Lodes and Mines,* Virginia City, Nev., 1889.

Defenbach, Byron, *Idaho: The Place and Its People,* 3 volumes, Chicago, 1933.

Dewees, Francis P., *The Molly Maguires,* Philadelphia, 1876.

Dimsdale, Thomas J., *The Vigilantes of Montana,* University of Oklahoma Press, Norman, 1953.

Donaldson, Thomas, *Idaho of Yesterday,* Caldwell, Idaho, 1941.

Drier, Roy Ward, and Octave Joseph Du Temple, *Prehistoric Copper Mining in the Lake Superior Region,* published privately 1961; reprinted 1965.

Dunning, Charles H., and E. H. Peplow, Jr., *Rock to Riches: The Story of American Min-*

ing, Past, Present, and Future, as Reflected in the Colorful History of Mining in Arizona, the Nation's Greatest Bonanza, Southwest Publishing Company, Phoenix, Ariz., 1959.

Egenhoff, Elisabeth L., *The Cornish Pump* (in two parts), appearing in Vol. 20, No. 6, June, 1967, and Vol. 20, No. 8, August, 1967, of the Mineral Information Service published by the California Division of Mines and Geology.

———, *The Elephant as They Saw It,* "A Collection of Contemporary Pictures and Statements on Gold Mining in California," published as a supplement to the *California Journal of Mines and Geology,* October, 1949.

Ely, Sims, *The Lost Dutchman Mine: The Fabulous Story of the Seven-Decade Search for the Hidden Treasure in the Superstition Mountains of Arizona,* Morrow Press, New York, 1953.

File, Lucien, and Stuart A. Northrop, *County, Township, and Range Location of New Mexico's Mining Districts,* Circular 84 of the State Bureau of Mines and Mineral Resources, New Mexico Institute of Mining and Technology, 1966.

Freeporter, 50th Anniversary Issue (Vol. 9, No. 9), Freeport Sulphur Company, July, 1962.

French, Hiram T., *History of Idaho,* 3 vols., Chicago, 1914.

Gandy, Lewis C., *The Tabors: A Footnote of Western History,* New York, 1934.

"Georgia Mineral Newsletter," Vol. VI, No. 4, *Georgia Geological Survey,* Winter, 1953.

———, Vol. 10, No. 2, *Georgia Geological Survey,* 1957.

Glasscock, C. B., *The Big Bonanza; The Story of the Comstock Lode, Indianapolis,* 1931.

———, *The War of the Copper Kings,* New York, 1935.

Golden Sulfur, Texas Gulf Sulphur Company.

Goodwin, Victor O., and John A. Hussey, *Sawtooth Mountain Area Study—Idaho History,* United States Forest Service and National Park Service, 1965.

Greenough, W. Earl, *First 100 Years of the Coeur d'Alene Mining Region,* Mullan, 1947.

Greever, William S., *The Bonanza West—The Story of the Western Mining Rushes, 1848–1900,* University of Oklahoma Press, Norman, 1963.

Griffin, James B., *A Discussion of Prehistoric Similarities and Connections Between the Arctic and Temperate Zones of North America,* reprinted from the Arctic Institute of North America Technical Paper No. 11, 1962.

———, *A Non-Neolithic Copper Industry in North America,* reprinted by Museum of Anthropology, University of Michigan, from XXXVI, Congreso Internacional de Americanistas, 1966.

Griswold, Don L. and Jean H., *The Carbonate Camp Called Leadville,* Denver, 1951.

Hagar, Ivan D., "The Story of MacIntyre Development," from *Tahawus Cloudsplitter,* Vol. XVIII, published by National Lead Company.

Half an Hour in Eldorado, pamphlet of Wells Fargo Bank, 1955.

Halliday, William R., *Depths of the Earth,* Harper & Row, New York, 1966.

Harper's New Monthly Magazine, various editions.

Harrington, M. R., "Ancient Salt Mines of the Indians," *Scientific American,* August, 1926.

———, "Ancient Salt Mine Near St. Thomas, Nevada," Indian Notes, Vol. 2, No. 3, Museum of the American Indian, 1925.

Haskell, William B., *Two Years in the Klondike and Alaskan Gold-Fields,* Hartford, 1898.

Hawley, James H., *History of Idaho, the Gem of the Mountains,* 4 vols., Chicago, 1920.

Hearst, Vernon J., and Lewis H. Larson, Jr., "On the Source of Copper at the Etowah Site, Georgia," *American Antiquity,* October, 1938.

Henderson, Charles W., *Mining in Colorado: History of Discovery, Development and Production,* United States Geological Survey, Professional Paper No. 138, Washington, 1926.

Hewitt, Honorable Abram S., *A Century of Mining and Metallurgy in the United States.*

History of the Empire Mine, Nevada County Historical Society, 1968.

History of Mining in Arizona, Arizona Department of Mineral Resources, Phoenix, Ariz., 1963.

History of the Salmon River, Clayton Ranger District, Challis National Forest (mimeographed).

History of Washington, Idaho, and Montana, 1845-1889, San Francisco, 1890.

Hochschild, Harold K., *The MacIntyre Mine—From Failure to Fortune,* The Adirondack Museum, Blue Mountain Lake, New York, 1962.

Hollister, Ovando J., *The Mines of Colorado,* Samuel Bowles and Company, 1867.

Holmes, W. H., *Traces of Aboriginal Operations in an Iron Mine near Leslie, Missouri,* from the Annual Report of the Smithsonian Institution for year ending June 30, 1903.

Holmquist, June Drenning, and Jean A. Brookins, *Minnesota's Major Historic Sites—A Guide,* Minnesota Historical Society, 1963.

Homestake Story, The, Homestake Mining Company, 1st ed., June, 1939; 6th ed., September, 1966.

Horan, James D., *The Pinkertons: The Detective Dynasty That Made History,* Crown Publishers, Inc., New York, 1967.

Horner, John W., *Silver Town,* Caxton Printers, Caldwell, Idaho, 1950.

Hungerford, Edward, *Wells Fargo—Advancing the American Frontier,* Bonanza Books, New York, 1949.

Illustrated History of California's Gold Rush, An, Wells Fargo Bank.

Ingersoll, Ernest, *Goldfields of the Klondike,* Edgewood Publishing Company, 1897.

Iron Ore Mining in Michigan, Past and Present, Michigan Historical Commission, 1958.

Jerome—America's Largest Ghost City, pamphlet published by Jerome (Arizona) Historical Society.

Jerome—A Story of Mine, Men, and Money, Southwestern Monuments Association, Globe, Arizona.

John L. Lewis and the International Union, United Mine Workers of America—1917 to 1952, United Mine Workers of America.

Journeys of Observations, San Francisco, 1907.

Kelly, A. R., and Lewis H. Larson, Jr., "Explorations at Etowah, Georgia, 1954-1956," from *Archaeology,* Vol. 10, No. 1, 1957.

Kingsbury, Joseph L., "The Pike's Peak Rush, 1859," *Colorado Magazine,* Vol. IV, 1927.

Koschmann, A. H., and M. H. Bergendahl, *Principal Gold Producing Districts of the United States,* United States Geological Survey, Professional Paper 610, 1968.

Kurjack, Dennis C., *Hopewell Village National Historic Site, Pennsylvania,* National Park Service Historical Handbook Series #8, 1954.

La Font, John, Creede, Colorado, *personal correspondence,* 1968.

Lakes, Arthur, *Prospecting for Gold and Silver in North America,* Scranton, Pa., 1896.

Larson, Lewis H., Jr., "A Mississippian Headdress from Etowah, Georgia," *American Antiquity,* July, 1959.

Ledyard, Edgar M., *Early Mining and Smelting South of Salt Lake City.*

Lincoln, Francis Church, *Mining Districts and Mineral Resources of Nevada (1923),* Nevada Newsletter Publishing Company.

Lord, Eliot, *Comstock Mining and Miners,* monographs of the United States Geological Survey, Vol. IV, Washington, 1883.

MacKnight, James A., *Mines of Montana,* Helena, 1892.

McLain, Carrie M., *Gold Rush Nome, An Illustrated Historical Chronicle,* Nome, Alaska, 1969.

Mangam, William D., *The Clarks: An American Phenomenon,* Silver Bow Press, New York, 1941.

Marcosson, Isaac F., *Anaconda,* Dodd, Mead & Co., New York, 1957.

Marshall, John B., and Temple H. Cornelius, *Golden Treasures of the San Juan,* Sage Books, Denver, 1961.

Masten, Arthur H., *Story of Adirondac,* The Adirondack Museum, Syracuse University Press, 1968 ed.

Mazzulla, Fred and Jo, *Al Packer—A Colorado Cannibal,* privately printed, Denver, 1968.

Medical Survey of the Bituminous Coal Industry, Report of the Coal Mines Administration, Department of the Interior, Washington, 1947 (out of print).

Meltzer, Milton, *Bread—And Roses, The Struggle of American Labor, 1865-1915,* Alfred E. Knopf, New York, 1967.

Mineral Resources of Colorado, Colorado Mineral Resources Board, 1947.

Mineral Resources of Colorado,

First Sequel, Colorado Mineral Resources Board, 1960.

Mining in Idaho, Idaho Historical Society.

Mohr, Charles E., and Howard N. Sloane, *Celebrated American Caves,* Rutgers University Press, New Brunswick, N.J.,

Montana, Contributions to the Historical Society of.

Montana: A State Guide Book, Works Projects Administration, New York, 1939.

Montana Magazine of History, miscellaneous articles.

Morris, Earl H., *An Aboriginal Salt Mine at Camp Verde, Arizona,* American Museum of Natural History, Anthropological Papers, Vol. 30, 1928.

Mother Lode of California, The. Automobile Club of Southern California, Los Angeles, 1963.

Mumey, Nolie, *Creede: History of a Colorado Silver Mining Town,* Denver, 1949.

Murdoch, Angus, *Boom Copper (The Story of the First U.S. Mining Boom),* The Macmillan Company, New York, 1943.

Murray, Morgan, *One Man's Gold Rush* (photographs by E. A. Hegg), University of Washington Press, 1967.

Nevada's No. One Basic Industry—The Story of Nevada Mining, Nevada Bureau of Mines.

Newton, Harry J., *Yellow Gold of Cripple Creek,* Denver, 1928.

Ogilvie, William, *Early Days on the Yukon and the Story of Its Gold Finds,* New York, 1913.

Olin, Dr. Hubert L., et al., *Coal Mining in Iowa,* State Mining Board, Iowa Department of Mines and Minerals, 1965.

Olsen, Mary Ann, *The Silverton Story,* 1962.

Our Rock Riches, Michigan Geological Survey, Bulletin 1, 1964.

Outline of Nevada Mining History, Nevada Bureau of Mines Report Number 7, Mackay School of Mines, University of Nevada.

Page from the History of the Empire Mine, A, California Division of Mines and Geology, Mineral Information Service, September, 1963.

Paul, Rodman W., *California Gold: The Beginning of Mining in the Far West,* Peter Smith, Magnolia, Mass., 1947.

———, *Mining Frontiers of the Far West, 1848–1880,* Holt, Rinehart, and Winston, New York, 1963.

Pearse, John Bernard, *A Concise History of the Iron Manufacturers of the American Colonies up to the Revolution and of Pennsylvania Until the Present Time,* Allen, Lane and Scott, Philadelphia, 1876.

Perry, Clay, *Underground Empire,* Stephen Daye Press, New York, 1948.

Peterson, Magnus F. (Malapai Mike), *Reel History and Hysterical Events of Nevada,* Central Nevada Newspapers.

Petrified River, The Story of Uranium, Union Carbide Corporation, 1967.

Pierce, Arthur D., *Family Empire in Jersey Iron,* Rutgers University Press, New Brunswick, N.J., 1964.

———, *Iron in the Pines,* Rutgers University Press, New Brunswick, N.J., 1957.

Pinkerton, Allan, *The Molly Maguires and the Detectives,* New York, 1878.

Place, Marion T., *The Copper Kings of Montana,* Random House, New York, 1961.

Plumas, Eureka State Park and literature on Jamison City and Johnsville, California Department of Parks and Recreation Pamphlet.

Prommel, H. W. C., Denver, Colorado, *personal correspondence,* 1968.

Quiett, Glenn C., *Paydirt: A Panorama of American Gold Rushes,* New York, 1936.

Rakestraw, Lawrence, *Historic Mining on Isle Royale,* Isle Royale Natural History Association and National Park Service.

Rand, John R., *Maine Metal Mines and Prospects,* Department of Economic Development, Augusta, Me., Mineral Resources Index #3, 1958.

Ransom, James M., *Vanishing Ironworks of the Ramapos,* Rutgers University Press, New Brunswick, N.J., 1966.

Rickard, T. A., *The Bunker Hill Enterprise,* Mining and Scientific Press, San Francisco, 1921.

———, *A History of American Mining,* McGraw-Hill, New York, 1932.

———, *Through the Yukon and Alaska,* San Francisco, 1909.

Rocky Mountain Pack Burro Championship Race, Leadville to Fairplay, Race Program by Burro Race Committee, Leadville and Fairplay, Colo.

Romig, Robert Lawrence, *The South Boise Quartz Mines 1863–1892.*

Ronan, Peter, "Discovery of Alder Gulch," *Contributions to the Historical Society of Montana,* Vol. III, 1900.

Ross, Clyde P., *Mining History of South Central Idaho* (Pamphlet 131), Idaho Bureau of Mines and Geology.

Rydell, Raymond A., *Cape Horn to the Pacific: The Rise and Decline of an Ocean Highway,* University of California Press, Berkeley, 1952.

Saga of the Comstock Lode: Boom Days in Virginia City, New York, 1934.

Schlegel, Dorothy M., *Gemstones of the United States,* United States Geological Survey Bulletin 1042 G.

Sharp Bits, XIV (June, 1963), publication of the Homestake Mining Company.

Sherlock, Peter, "Active Mining Operations at Atlantic and

South Pass Recall the Gold Rush Days When Men Made Millions," *Wyoming State Journal*, April 11, 1935.

Short History of American Metal Climax, Inc., A, American Metal Climax, Inc., 1962.

Smith, Grant H., *History of the Comstock Lode, 1850–1920*, Nevada Bureau of Mines, Mackay School of Mines, University of Nevada, 1966 ed.

Smith, Robert W., *The Coeur d'Alene Mining War of 1892: A Case Study of an Industrial Dispute*, Corvallis, Oregon, 1961.

Sprague, Marshall, *Money Mountain: The Story of Cripple Creek*, Little, Brown and Co., Boston, 1953.

Stampede to Timberline: The Ghost Towns and Mining Camps of Colorado, Boulder, 1949.

State Mine Inspector's Reports, 1910, 1912, and 1914, printed by order of the Iowa General Assembly.

Story of Borax, The, United States Borax and Chemical Corporation, 1965.

Story of Cherry, The, American Red Cross, 1911.

Story of the Pacific Coast Borax Company, Borax Consolidated, Ltd., 1951.

Sweetwater Miner, "History of Gold in Sweetwater District," March 24, 1869.

Texas Gulf Story, Part I, The Years of Development, 1909–1929, Texas Gulf Sulphur Company, 1930.

Twain, Mark (Samuel L. Clemens), *Roughing It*, New York, 1904.

United States Department of the Interior, Bureau of Mines, *Mineral Facts and Problems*, Bulletin No. 630, 1965 ed.

———, *Mining and Mineral Operation in the United States —A Visitor's Guide*, 1967.

———, *Natural Resources of Alaska*, 1966.

———, *Natural Resources of Arizona*, 1963.

———, *Natural Resources of California*, 1965.

———, *Natural Resources of Colorado*, 1963.

———, *Natural Resources of Idaho*, 1965.

———, *Natural Resources of Massachusetts*, 1964.

———, *Natural Resources of Nevada*, 1964.

———, *Natural Resources of New Mexico*, 1964.

———, *Natural Resources of Ohio*, 1963.

———, *Natural Resources of Oregon*, 1964.

———, *Natural Resources of South Dakota*, 1966.

———, *Natural Resources of Texas*, 1965.

———, *Natural Resources of Utah*, 1965.

———, *Natural Resources of Washington*, 1963.

———, *Natural Resources of West Virginia*, 1964.

———, *Natural Resources of Wyoming*, 1966.

———, *Placer Mining in Alaska*, Information Circular 7926, 1959.

———, *Prospector, Cowhand, and Sodbuster*, 1967.

———, *Surface Mining and Our Environment*, 1967.

United States Department of the Interior, National Park Service, *Isle Royale National Park, Michigan*, 1964.

———, *Pipestone National Monument*, 1965.

United States Forest Service, *Boise National Forest*, descriptive pamphlet.

———, *Challis National Forest*, descriptive pamphlet.

———, *Salmon National Forest*, descriptive pamphlet.

———, *Sawtooth National Forest*, descriptive pamphlet.

Uranium Mining and Processing, Kerr-McGee Corporation.

Utah—Treasure House of the Nation, Century of Mining 1863 to 1963, edited by Everett L. Cooley for the Utah State Historical Society.

Van Nostrand's Eclectic Engineering Magazine, October, 1876.

Waters, Frank, *Midas of the Rockies: The Story of Stratton and Cripple Creek*, New York, 1937.

Wells, Merle W., *Gold Camps and Silver Cities*, Idaho Bureau of Mines and Geology, Bulletin #22, 1963.

———, *Rush to Idaho*, Idaho Bureau of Mines and Geology, Bulletin #19, 1963.

Wells Fargo, Pamphlet of Wells Fargo Bank, 1955.

West, George A., *Exceptional Prehistoric Copper Implements*, Bulletin of the Public Museum of the City of Milwaukee, Vol. 10, No. 4, March 4, 1932.

Williamson, Harold F., and Arnold R. Daum, *The American Petroleum Industry, The Age of Illumination, 1859–1899*, Northwestern University Press, Evanston, Ill., 1959.

Winslow, Cathryn, *Big Pan-Out*, W. W. Norton and Company, New York, 1951.

Wolle, Muriel S., "Adventure into the Past, A Search for Colorado's Mining Camps," *Colorado Magazine*, Vol. XXVII, 1950.

———, *The Bonanza Trail— Ghost Towns and Mining Camps of the West*, Indiana University Press, Bloomington, 1953.

Wormington, H. M., *Ancient Man in North America*, Denver Museum of Natural History, rev. ed.

Wright, William, *see* De Quille, Dan.

Young, Otis E., Jr., *How They Dug the Gold*, Arizona Pioneers' Historical Society, Tucson, Ariz., 1967 (limited edition).

Zinc—A Mine to Market Outline, 1967, American Zinc Institute, Inc.

Index

(Italicized numbers indicate photographs or their captions.)

330